NeeNee the Dolphin who thought and thought…

Wisdom from a 5 year-old.

By Anisa Banian

Inspired by real life stories with a little help from Mummy & Daddy.

Edited by Charles Levoir
Illustrations by Rita Halalau

Acknowledgements

With thanks to our beloved Bébé,
Umey, Ubey & Mum.

We love you!

"We are all innocent but for our thinking and we all do the best we can as parents and teachers. Thank you to all my teachers for pointing me back to the wisdom which lies within each and every one of us. Words are not enough to truly express my gratitude." **Anisa's Mummy**

Hello.

This is NeeNee the dolphin.

She is five years old.

NeeNee and her family live deep in the ocean in a little water town called Pebbleford. They have a lovely home and wonderful neighbours.

NeeNee loves discovering all about the world around her and learning new things.

She enjoys:-

- Going to school
- Meeting friends and cousins for playdates
- Doing somersaults
- Exploring new places
- Eating ice cream

She also really loves to read books.

Curiosity

NeeNee always has a lot of questions to ask about everything.

She wants to know:

Why?

What?

How?

Who?

When?

She is very curious!

One day NeeNee's mummy asked her where all these questions were coming from.

NeeNee didn't know.

She began to wonder…

She soon realised that it was all coming from her.

"I just want to know more", NeeNee told her mummy and daddy at dinner that evening.

"That's good", said mummy. "It is how we all learn and it is fun to want to know more."

"It feels nice", said NeeNee.

"There is always more to discover", said daddy with a smile.

Sadness

The next day NeeNee was playing with her best friend, Tartor. NeeNee started to feel '**sad**' because her friend kept telling her what to do.

She told her mummy Tartor was being bossy and she felt sad. Mummy said that it was normal to feel sad from time to time.

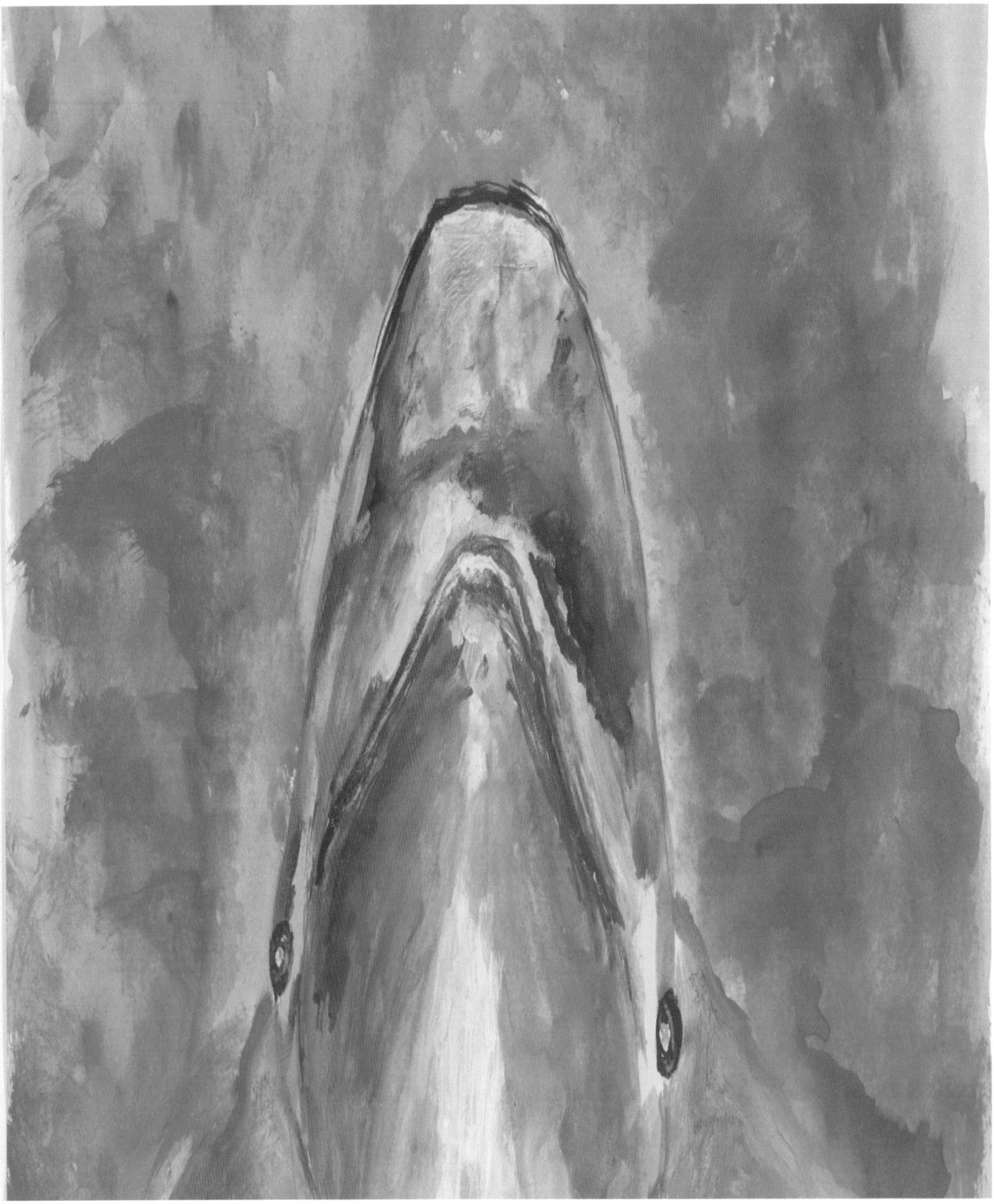

Mummy asked NeeNee if it was Tartor making her sad or whether it was her thinking about Tartor which made her sad. After all, they had played together many times and this had never happened before.

"You will only feel what you think", said mummy. "It only lasts as long as it is in your mind. Another thought will soon come along and replace this one."

NeeNee started to wonder again.

Jealousy

That weekend, NeeNee and Tartor were playing hide and seek in the coral park. They were having lots of fun!

All of a sudden Tartor saw her neighbour Sandy and went off to play with her instead. NeeNee started to feel **'jealous'** of Sandy.

NeeNee swam off in a huff. Her mummy told her: "It's ok to feel this way. It's just your thinking in this moment."

"Next time, maybe you could all play together and enjoy more play time?" she said, giving NeeNee a little squeeze.

Nervousness

The next day at school, NeeNee was asked to read her work to the class. She became very shy and didn't want to read to everyone. She started to feel **'nervous'**.

Her teacher asked her friend Vitan to read her work instead and NeeNee immediately felt better.

After school NeeNee hung her bag on the coat stand and told her mummy what had happened.

"It's ok to feel nervous", said mummy. "Was it the other children who made you nervous? Or was it what you thought would happen if you read the story?"

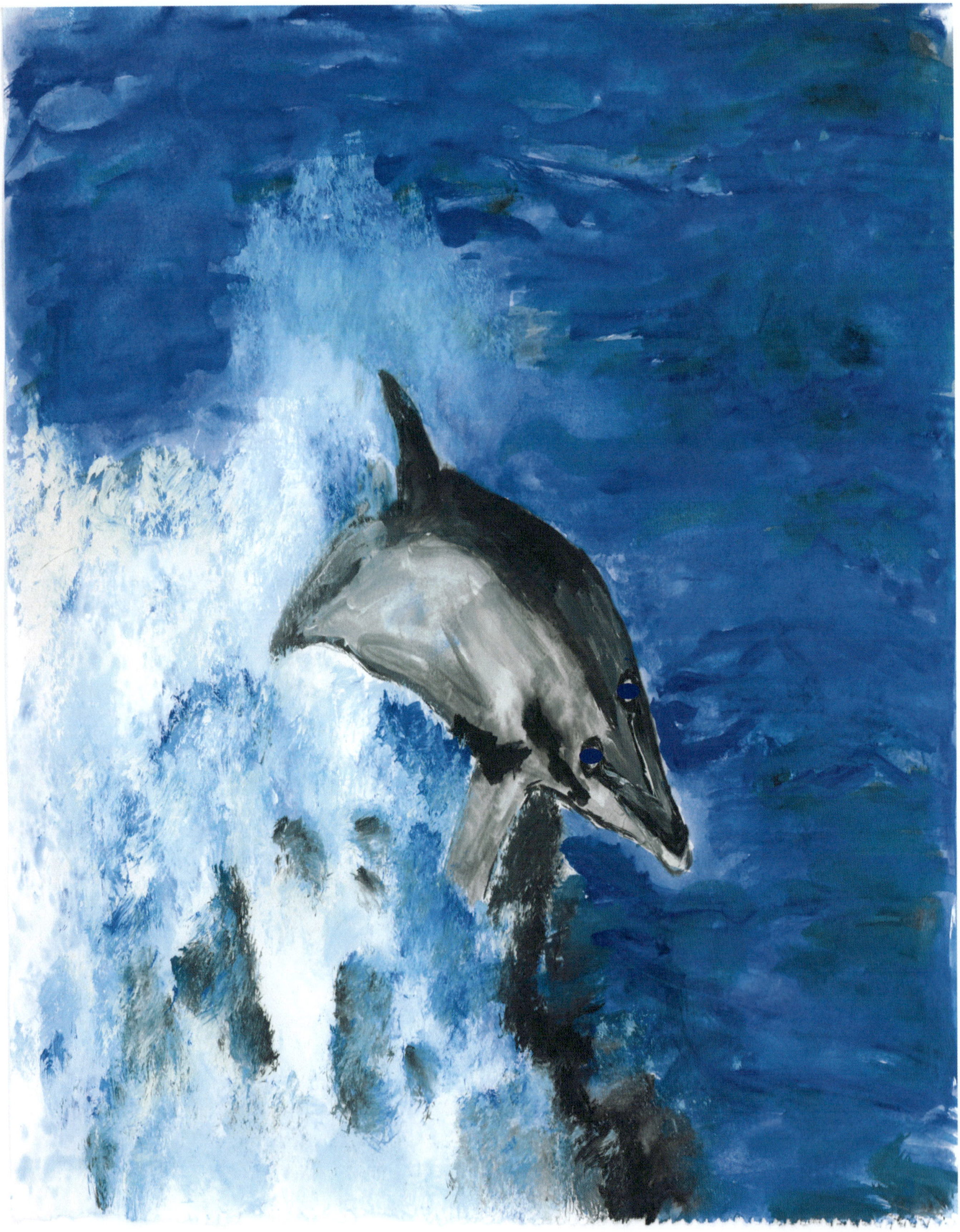

NeeNee thought the children would all laugh at her if she read her story. But then she wondered if it was just her thinking and maybe it would have been different if she had read.

"What if they didn't laugh?" wondered NeeNee.

She decided that next time she would read her story out loud. After all, she didn't know what would happen and the class did like her story when it was read by Vitan.

Fear

One evening after being tucked into bed, NeeNee remembered something. When she was playing in her garden that day a big shark had swum over her head. She remembered how dark it looked when the shark was above her and how afraid she had been. She started to cry.

Mummy came in and NeeNee explained about the shark. Mummy asked her to look around to see if there was a shark in the room. They looked under the bed and in all the cupboards.

"There is no shark", said NeeNee. "But it feels like there is".

"I know", said mummy. "It's just your thinking which makes it feel like there is. But there is nothing here."

Mummy tucked her back in bed and told her everything was fine and that she was safe.

She kissed her goodnight and NeeNee fell fast asleep.

Loneliness

NeeNee was in the school playground one day and realised no one wanted to play with her. Tartor wanted to play tag and the other dolphins wanted to go on a jellyfish hunt.

She began to feel **'lonely'**. Then she remembered what her parents had said. She remembered that feeling lonely was just a thought. So she started to play by herself. She had so much fun playing alone and was quite happy.

At the next break, NeeNee felt better about playing alone. As she played, her friend Shelly decided to join her and they had fun together.

Anger

One afternoon at school, NeeNee was playing with building blocks as a treat for doing some good writing. As she was about to finish her sea-house, Delilah snatched the last block and NeeNee started to feel '**angry**'.

NeeNee started to cry and got very upset. Soon after, when she stopped thinking about the blocks she was calm again and carried on playing.

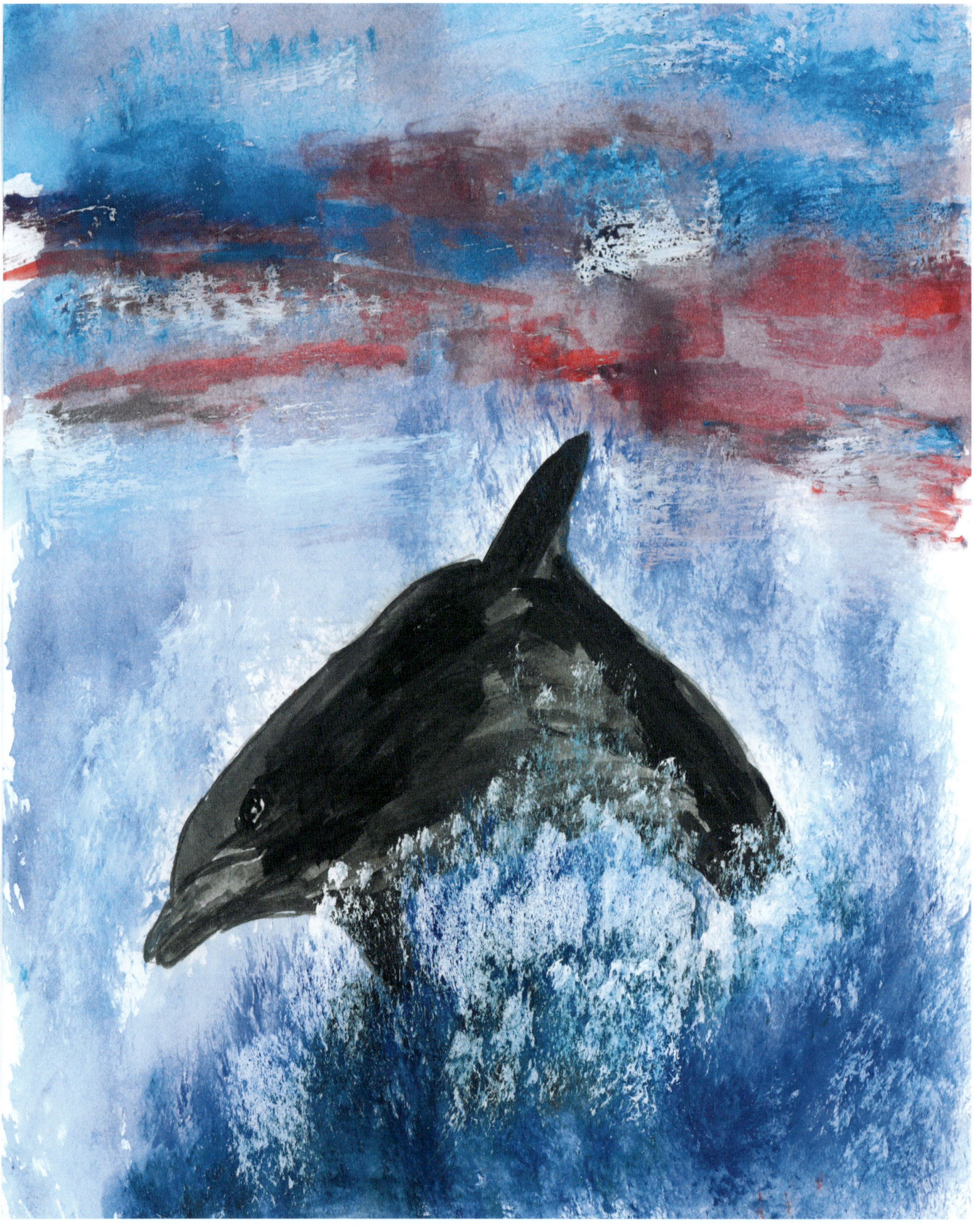

Later on the way home from school, NeeNee told her daddy what had happened.

"It is ok to feel angry", said daddy. "Did you feel angry because she took the last block?" asked daddy. "You could have just waited until she had finished playing with it and then finished your sea-house".

NeeNee was lost in another thought. She had been upset but now she saw a glittery seashell and was back to feeling '**Curious**' again. Daddy smiled.

Bravery

On Saturday morning as NeeNee was brushing her teeth, she realised that the things she liked to do were the things she knew she could do.

She felt happy when she was:-

- ❧ Painting and drawing
- ❧ Wheeling about on her fun sealies
- ❧ Sharing her toys with her friends
- ❧ Helping others with their work in class.

She found those things easy.

But when she thought she couldn't do something, she didn't feel good because she didn't think she could do it well and it was hard work.

NeeNee thought: "I am not very good at dancing and I don't want people to watch me. But what if it doesn't matter what people think? I might enjoy it. I will try to dance when I go to Bella's birthday party tomorrow."

Her daddy took her to the party and they played musical chairs. She listened to the music and began to wiggle her bum. As she did so she started to feel good. And then as she moved her fins and her head she had an amazing time.

That night while daddy was putting NeeNee to bed, she told him that she could dance and how she really enjoyed it!

Daddy told NeeNee that she could do whatever she wanted to do and the more she did something the better she would be.

"Learning to be ok with your thoughts and allowing them to float away like a balloon helps you to do more", said daddy. "That's how I became good at chess. And I still lose sometimes because there is always more to learn."

"Can I learn to be kinder?" asked NeeNee. "We can all learn to be kinder", said daddy.

Activity : Draw a picture of NeeNee dancing while playing musical chairs

Where do thoughts come from?

One day NeeNee asked: "Mummy? Where do thoughts come from? I know that I feel what I think. Is it all in my head?"

Mummy explained that thoughts just come and go. She said: "Our thoughts allow us to remember things from the past and to think about what may happen in future. But we don't know what is actually going to happen so we can only really enjoy this moment."

"So, we don't know where thoughts come from and it is OK not to know. What is important is that our thoughts don't stop us from doing what we really want to do and learning something new."

"I know you love to draw, NeeNee. So when you draw, where do your thoughts come from?" asked mummy.

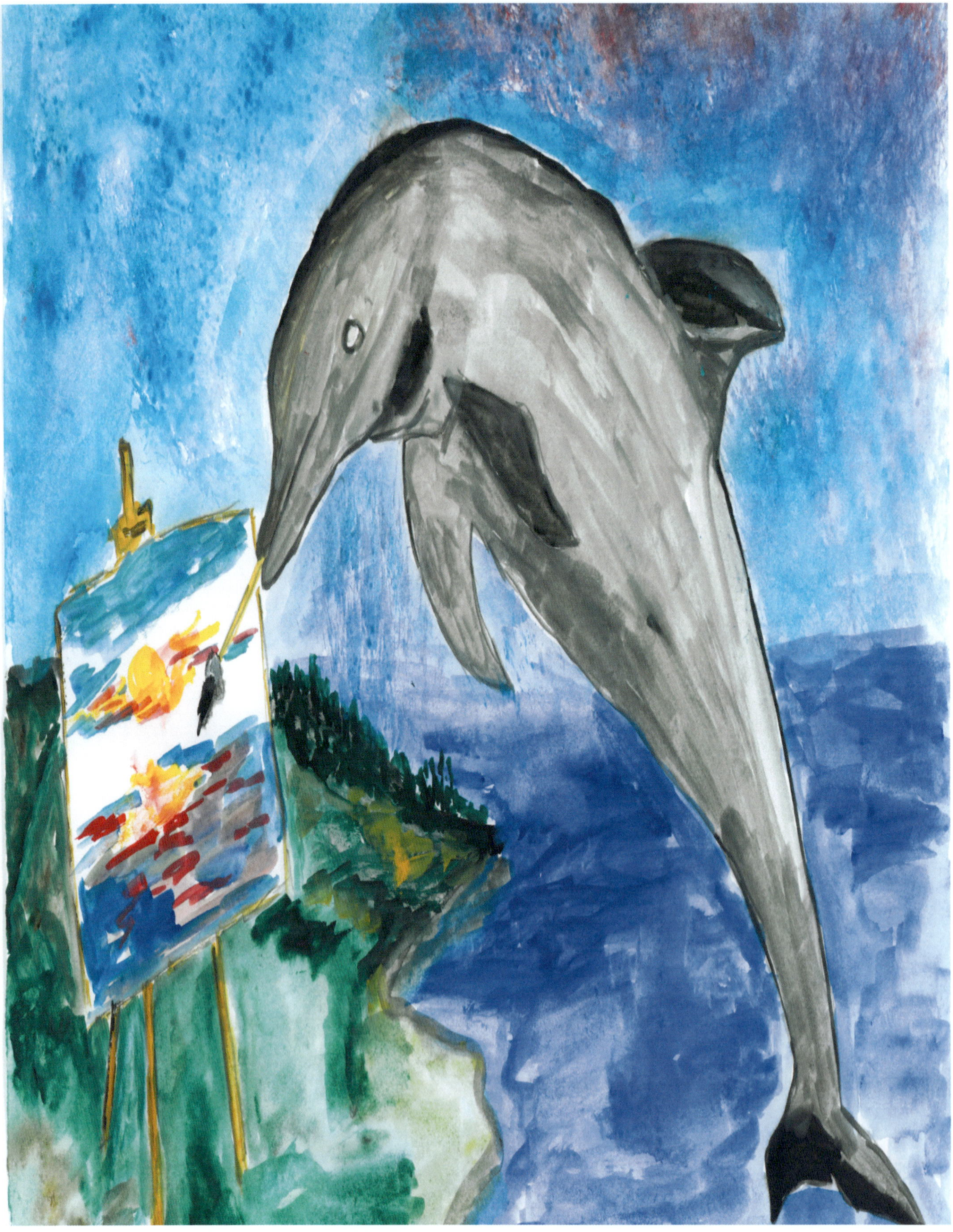

"I don't know", said NeeNee. "I just draw whatever I want. And then if I think it's bad and I don't like it, I feel bad. I'm rubbish."

"Is that always true?" asked mummy.
"No", replied NeeNee. "Sometimes I do good drawings too."

"And your feelings come from your thoughts?" asked mummy.
"Yes", replied NeeNee.

Mummy said: "You may not like what you do but it is only your thought at that moment. It changes. If you think your picture isn't good it doesn't mean that you're not good."

Peace

Later the next afternoon as they swam to the shops, mummy said that the water they were swimming in was holding them and that they were always safe. "We all get lost in our thoughts now and again and we can easily forget."

"It is OK to be Happy. Or Sad. Or Angry. Or Anxious. Or Jealous. Or Scared. Or Lonely. Or Excited. Or Peaceful. Or Calm. Or Curious."

"These feelings come and go as quickly as thoughts come and go. The moment we accept them, they simply disappear."

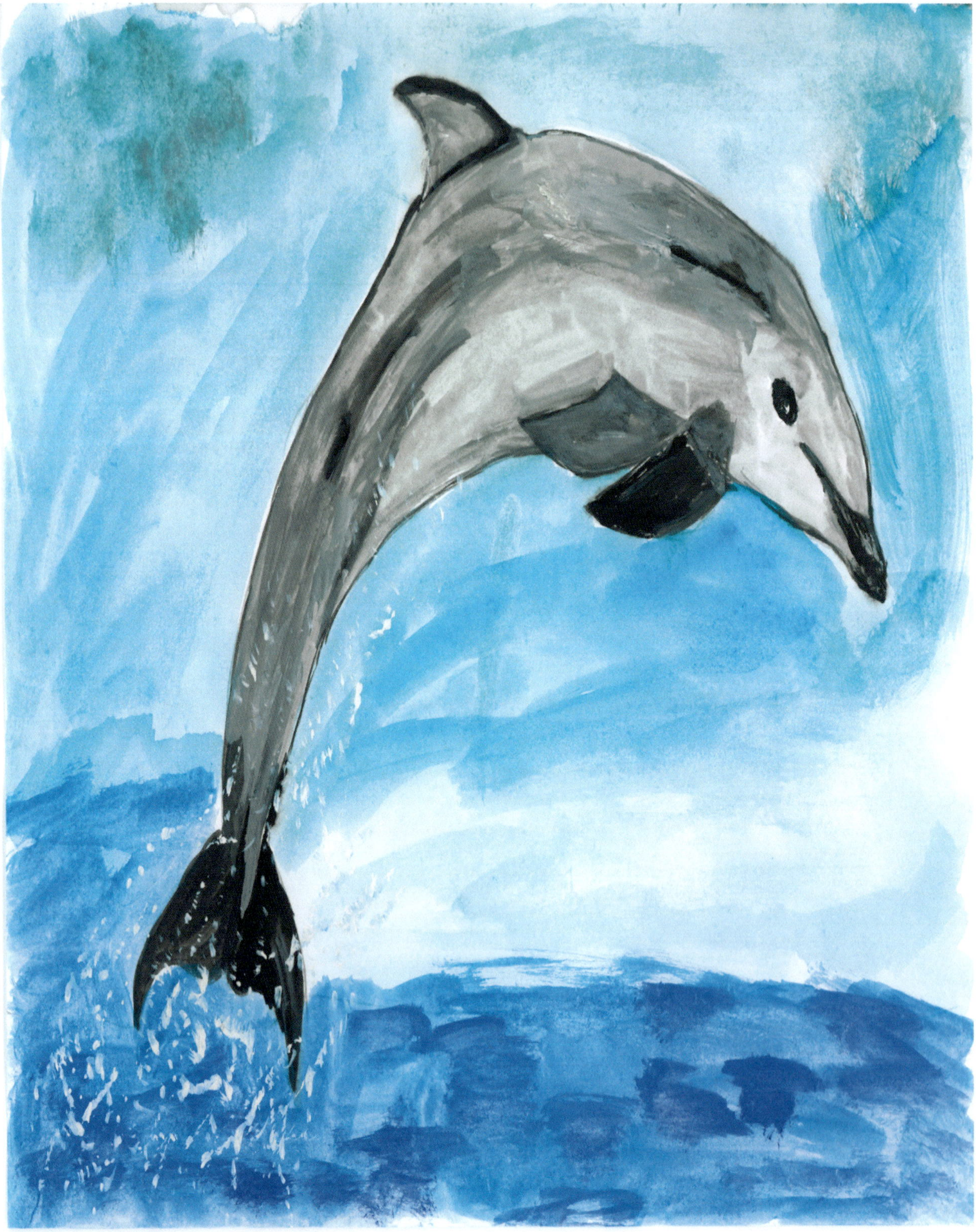

"Feelings aren't good or bad" said mummy, "they are just there". "I do like the nice feelings, mummy" said NeeNee. "I know" said mummy. "We all do."

In that moment, they smiled at each other and cuddled up as they watched the sun set over the ocean.

NeeNee felt peaceful and calm.
She felt like she could do anything!

NeeNee then noticed all the colours shining at the bottom of the ocean.

They were reflected from the sun in a kaleidoscope of colours.

And in that moment she felt like the happiest dolphin in the world.

★　　★　　★　　★

Activity : Use coloured pencils or crayons
to draw a kaleidoscope of colours

Exploratory Suggestions For Parents and Teachers

1. What do your children enjoy about the worlds in which they are in? What do they enjoy discovering? Ask them to share a couple of stories about something they have discovered recently? (Page 3)

2. How does it feel to wonder and to be curious? What does it look, sound, feel or even smell and taste like? (Page 6)

3. When did they have a moment of bravery? Did they have any new ideas? (Page 32)

4. How can they be kinder? (Page 33)

5. Explore with the children how each of the emotions feel (sadness, jealousy, nervousness, fear, loneliness, anger, curiosity, bravery, peace) and have a conversation about the experience.

6. How does it feel to be with someone who is experiencing these emotions?

7. How long does it take for an emotion to stay or leave? Ask them to share with examples.

```
T   M   Y   M   M   U   M   Y
A   N   L   N   E   T   A   C
R   H   E   E   M   H   V   U
T   P   X   E   O   O   Y   R
O   E   Z   N   H   U   D   I
R   P   W   E   N   G   D   O
D   C   E   E   V   H   A   U
K   E   R   A   H   T   D   S
V   P   D   V   C   S   R   A
H   B   R   A   V   E   R   Y
```

Activity : Word Search

NeeNee	Tartor	Bravery
Thoughts	Curious	Mummy
Daddy	Peace	Home

What some special big people have to say to parents and teachers

"I first met the beautiful soul that is Anisa when she was 4 months old. You know how sometimes when you look into the eyes of a baby or a young child, and you see the wisdom and mystery of the whole universe? That's what it was like. Anisa is a very special human being, with very special parents – but that same potential is in every one of us. To watch Anisa dance, play and laugh – the way she just shows up perfectly herself, is a delight I'll never tire of. As she grows up, I'm quite sure Anisa will make a huge difference in the world, just by being the perfect spark of Life that she is. I love that – at the age of 5 - she is already helping to spread the message about the inside-out nature of the human experience.

Read this book, and read it to your kids – over and over again. Keep reminding them (and yourself) that deep down we are all made of love, and we are peace, wisdom and well-being walking around in form. Thank you Anisa."

Kimberley Hare Creator of the Heart of Thriving / Author of "The He'Art of Thriving: Musings on the Human Experience"

"This beautiful book will point children to the truth that all emotions are there to be experienced. There is nothing to resist. Just life to live"

Clare Dimond Author of "Real - the inside-out guide to being yourself"

"There are so many gifts that children can give us. Things that come so naturally to them that we so often forget in adult life. If we take the time to notice, they teach us how to play freely, how to learn, how to interact socially without any regard to colour, race or gender and how to be mindful.

Anisa's young wisdom comes powerfully, yet gracefully, to us all in this wonderful story. I hope you enjoy reading it as much as I did. And I hope you take as much from it as you possibly can. What a beautiful, timely gift to the world Anisa has given us with this book. "

Mel Rose Education Consultant (U.K / U.S / Spain)

"This is a wonderful book that gently introduces and describes inner states of mind to humans of all ages. I wish I could send it back in time so that my parents would read it to me in my childhood. It would be equally appropriate if I'd had it as a college textbook. I would have learned a lot. Wisdom from a 5 year old."

Jan Elfline Coach / Facilitator / co-Author of "Actor for Life"

"This is a beautiful book with a beautiful heart - and it teaches us all a lot. It really is just as helpful for parents to read, with great tips on how to answer those 'big' questions and how to understand them ourselves. But the real beauty of the book is that all this is hidden within a very gentle story. That really is the power of stories. They teach us so much, as this book does. They help us cope with tricky times - and they're stimulating, enjoyable and irresistible. We all need stories in our lives - this one is a great place to start…"

Lottie Allen, Founder/Artistic Director, Magic Box (Interactive Storytelling)

Printed in Poland
by Amazon Fulfillment
Poland Sp. z o.o., Wrocław

My name is **Birdy**, and I'm from future Earth. 2099 to be precise. My world is at risk – a giant asteroid is on a collision course with the planet.

Kalvin Spearhead, head of **END CO** – the most powerful company on Earth – plans to build a giant vortex machine to send people back in time to escape the asteroid. He has assembled a team of human-like robots, **Tick-Tock Men**, to collect seven **Artefacts of Time**. These Artefacts will be used to power his machine.

My gran, **Professor Martin**, is the head scientist at END CO. She has shown me Spearhead's plans; she doesn't think his machine is capable of transporting vast numbers of people. Even if the machine does work, it will have a devastating effect on history: it could change everything! Gran has tried to tell Spearhead, but he won't listen. I decided I had to try to stop him. I have borrowed one of my gran's old-tech time-travel vortex machines – an **Escape Wheel** – and am trying to reach the Artefacts of Time before the Tick-Tock Men do.

Luckily, I'm not alone on my journey. I've met four new friends – **Max**, **Cat**, **Ant** and **Tiger**. They have special watches that can make them shrink to micro-size … which comes in handy when the Tick-Tock Men try to stop us!

J. A.

ILLUSTRATED BY

JONATRONIX

TIME RUNS OUT

Contents

OXFORD
UNIVERSITY PRESS

The year 2099.

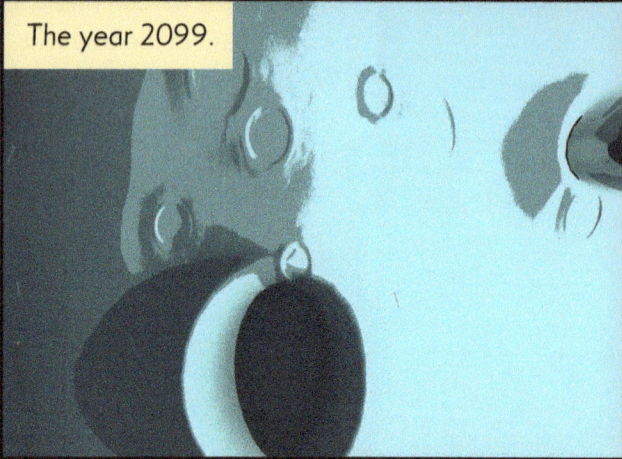

A colossal asteroid is plummeting through space …

… on a collision course for Earth.

The National Bureau of Standards (NBS), just outside Washington DC. 1949 …

… location of the world's first atomic clock.

Tick-tock,

tick-tock,

tick-tock

Meanwhile …

This is it. The NBS complex.

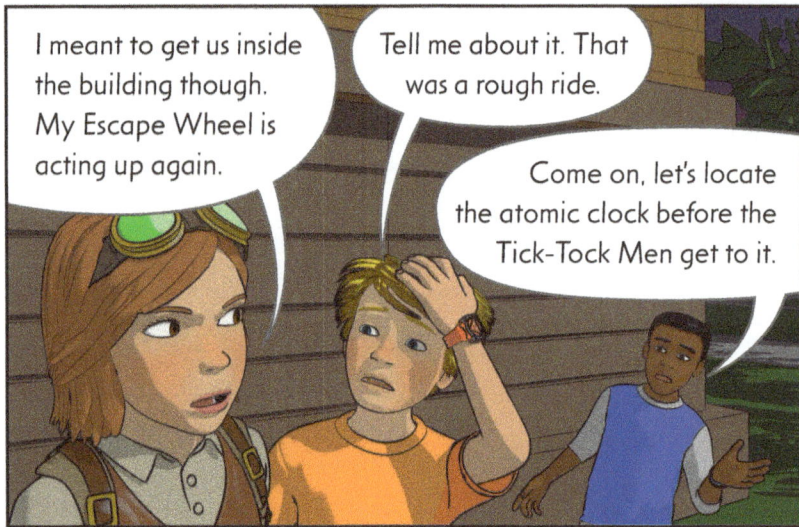

I meant to get us inside the building though. My Escape Wheel is acting up again.

Tell me about it. That was a rough ride.

Come on, let's locate the atomic clock before the Tick-Tock Men get to it.

They could already be here.

Err … I'd say that's a definite possibility.

They've already immobilized the guards.

Shhh!

Tick-tock

That's the clock? Wouldn't like to try hanging it on my wall.

Let's just try and save it shall we? It's the last artefact that Spearhead is after. We have to stop the Tick-Tock Men getting it to him.

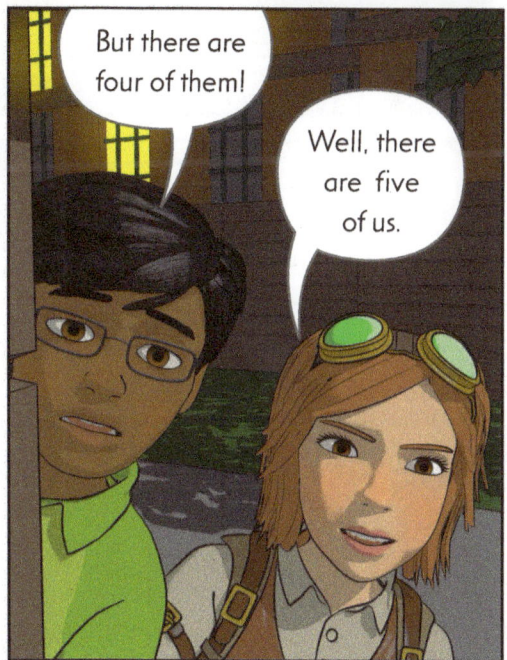

But there are four of them!

Well, there are five of us.

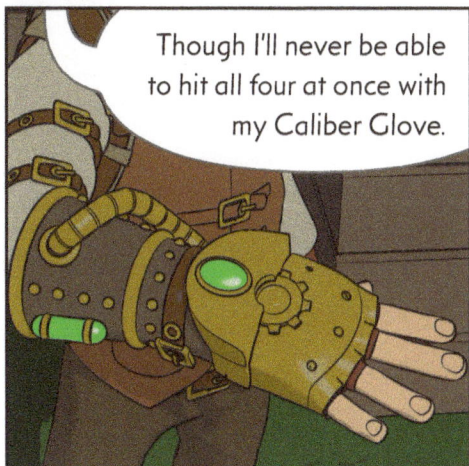

Though I'll never be able to hit all four at once with my Caliber Glove.

You won't have to. We just need to get close to the clock, then we'll go for the old small-big-small strategy.

A classic!

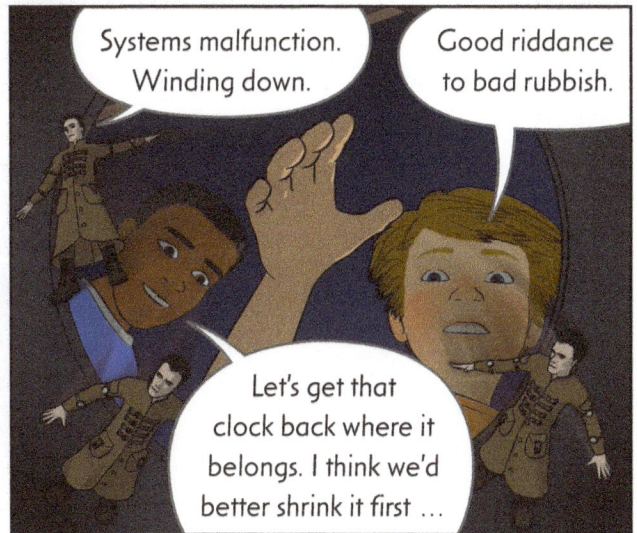

Chapter 2: Cutting it fine

Later on …

The atomic clock was the last Artefact of Time that I identified on Spearhead's plan. Now it's safe, I need to go home. I need to go back to 2099.

Hang on, you're going *back* to the *future* you mean?

No. I mean, yes. Oh … very funny.

Hold on a minute. You're saying we've completed our mission and the future is safe?

I didn't say anything about safe. We may have stopped Spearhead from getting all the Artefacts of Time, but there's still a giant asteroid poised to hit Earth.

I need to be sure that Gran has discovered a method to stop it.

Well, if this thing isn't over, then we're coming with you.

Look, Max. I really appreciate all the help you've given me so far, but you guys have all got homes to go to.

No one will have missed us. We can go back to exactly when we left, remember?

You can't risk returning alone. You've no idea what you might find.

It's true Spearhead may have his Tick-Tock army lying in wait for me.

OK, OK. You win! I know it's futile to argue with you.

Birdy took out her Escape Wheel …

Let's go. It's time we took the fight to this Kalvin Spearpoint.

It's Spearhead, Tiger. Kalvin Spearhead.

Same thing.

As the vortex began to take shape, the friends moved towards it, ready to jump. Then …

STOP!

What's wrong, Birdy?

Look!

The vortex looked wrong. The strands of energy twisted and curled as if in pain.

Fizz!

Eeeekkkk!

Ka-BOOM!

What now?

Don't panic. We can try and use the time function on our watches.

I don't think that's a good idea. You know how unpredicable they are.

Yeah, they're even worse than Birdy's Escape Wheel.

I suppose we've never tried taking anyone with us before.

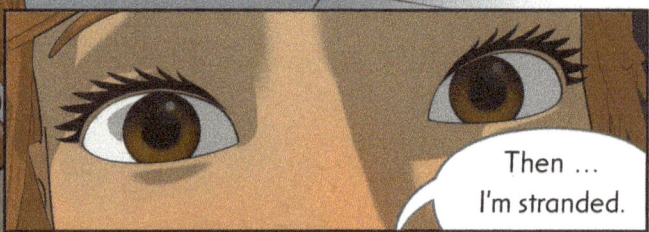

Then … I'm stranded.

Errmm … sorry to interrupt, but I think we have another problem.

Suddenly another vortex started to configure behind them.

zzzzzzz ZZZZ

Take cover!

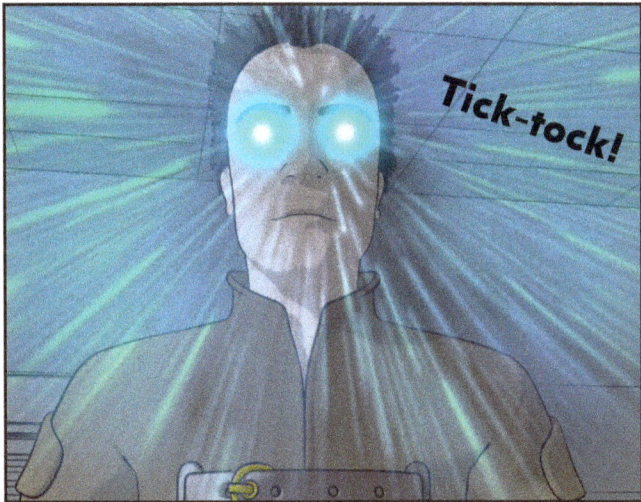

Tick-tock!

The clock!

Birdy, do something!

Come on, come on!

It must be transmitting the plans back to Spearhead.

Someone's got to stop him!

No!

VERRPP-POW!

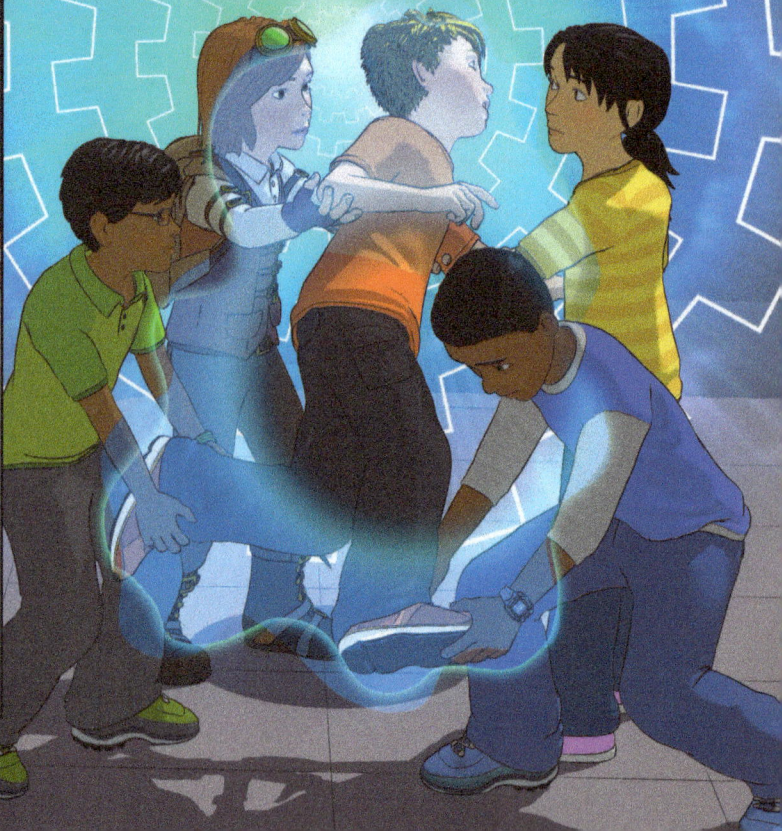

Chapter 3: Odd behaviour

The year 2099 …

There you go, Tiger. Now, try to stay out of trouble for a while!

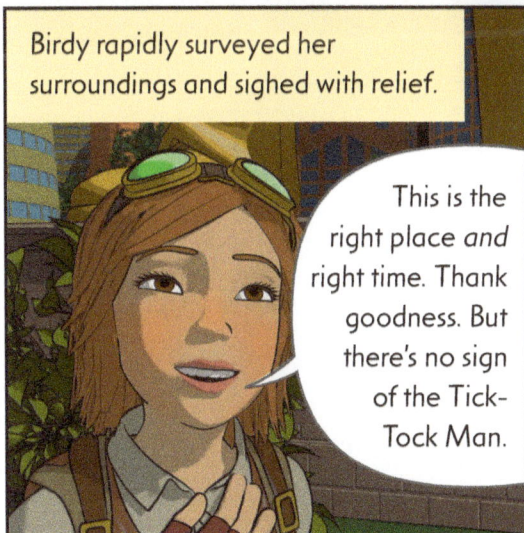

Birdy rapidly surveyed her surroundings and sighed with relief.

This is the right place *and* right time. Thank goodness. But there's no sign of the Tick-Tock Man.

Look at those scientists!

Why are they outside?

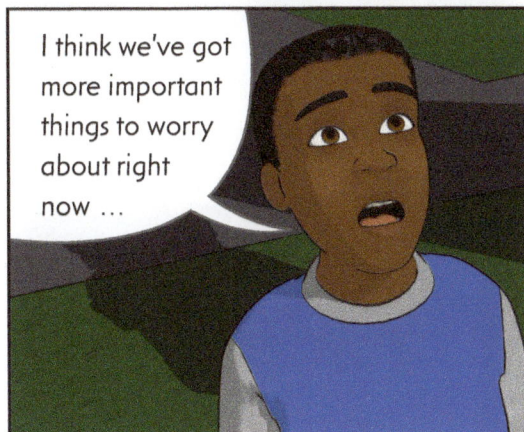

I think we've got more important things to worry about right now …

Gasp!

The asteroid!

I need to find my gran.

There was no sign of Birdy's gran among the crowd of scientists who were milling around.

What are they all waiting for?

I don't know, but I bet Spearhead's at the bottom of it.

He's such a narcissist; he's actually constructed a statue of himself! I've only been away seven days, but it seems a lot has changed.

As they watched the scientists, a man stepped out on to the balcony.

It is time!

What did I miss?

Hey, isn't that Spearmint up there?

It's *Spearhead*, Tiger! Yes, it is him.

17

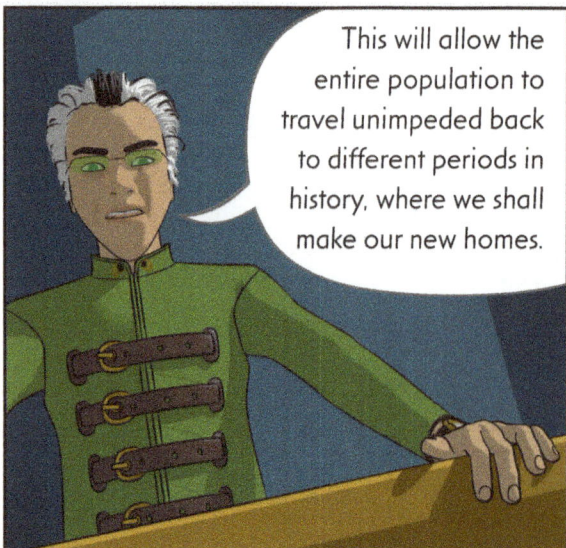

Kalvin Spearhead is in charge of END CO – a technologically-advanced communications and cybernetics business – the most powerful company on Earth. Inventing new technologies is END CO's speciality.

Kalvin was the youngest of four brothers. As a child all his clothes and toys were handed down from his siblings. It made him crave new things, and he resolved that when he was older he would only have the very best things for himself.

Kalvin worked hard at school and obtained the best results in his year. On the strength of this, he was offered a job at END CO. However, after only a few years, he was fired for alleged illegal testing of new equipment containing Hurgad 5, a dangerous chemical. Nothing was heard of him for many years after this, but he secretly bought shares in END CO and eventually had enough influence to take over the running of the company.

During his time in charge of END CO, Kalvin has overseen the development of the nanophone, the sonicplane and the Spear satellite, along with many other successful products. More recently, when news hit that an asteroid was likely to destroy the Earth, Kalvin took it upon himself to save humanity. Whether this is possible even for him, we must wait and see.

END CO HQ

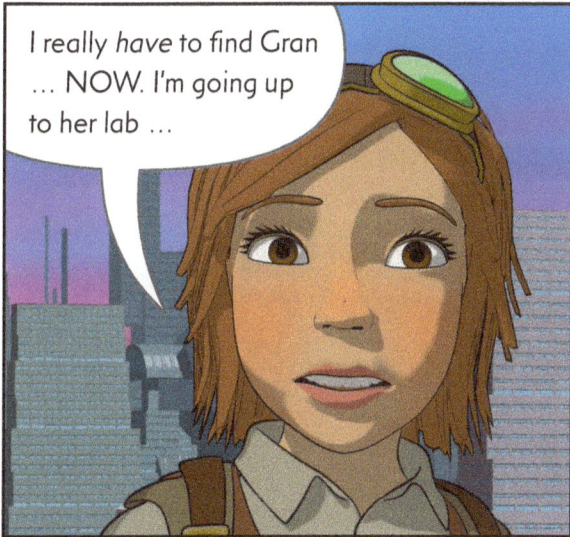

I really *have* to find Gran ... NOW. I'm going up to her lab ...

I'll come with you.

Me too.

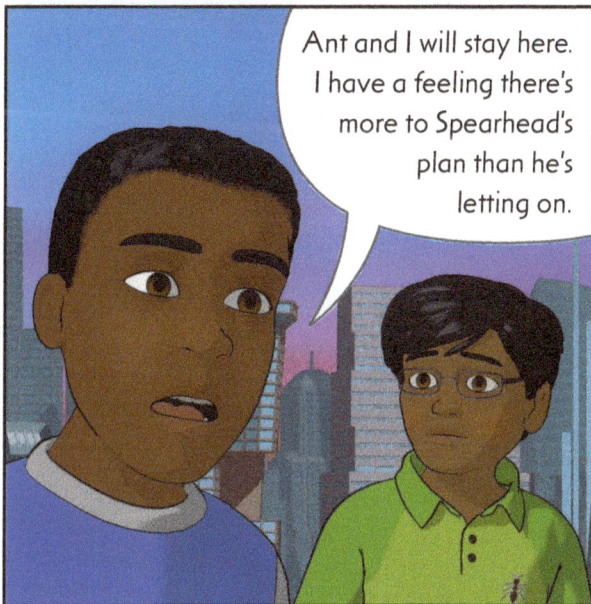

Ant and I will stay here. I have a feeling there's more to Spearhead's plan than he's letting on.

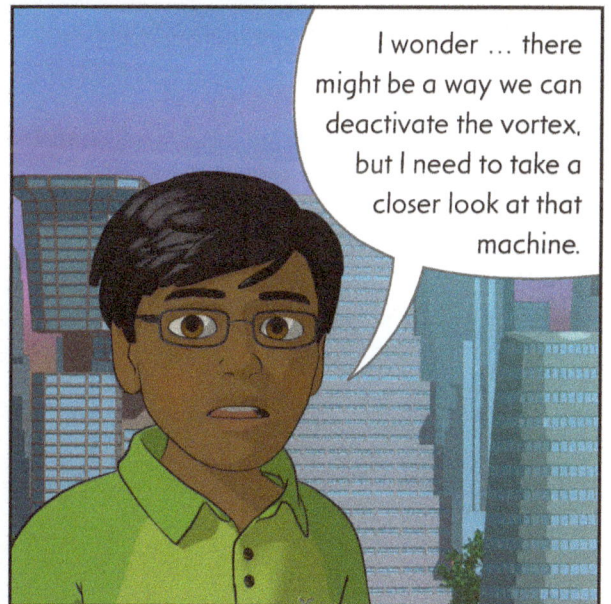

I wonder ... there might be a way we can deactivate the vortex, but I need to take a closer look at that machine.

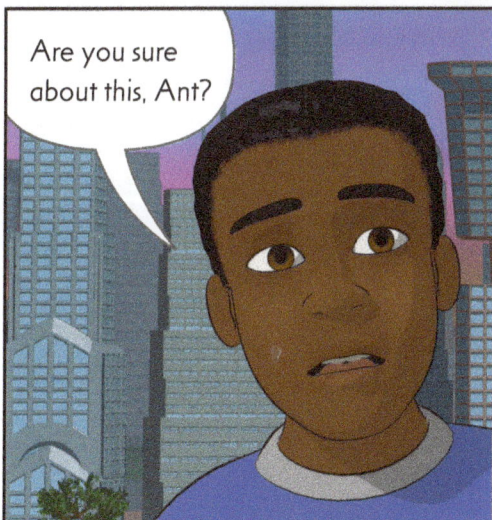

Are you sure about this, Ant?

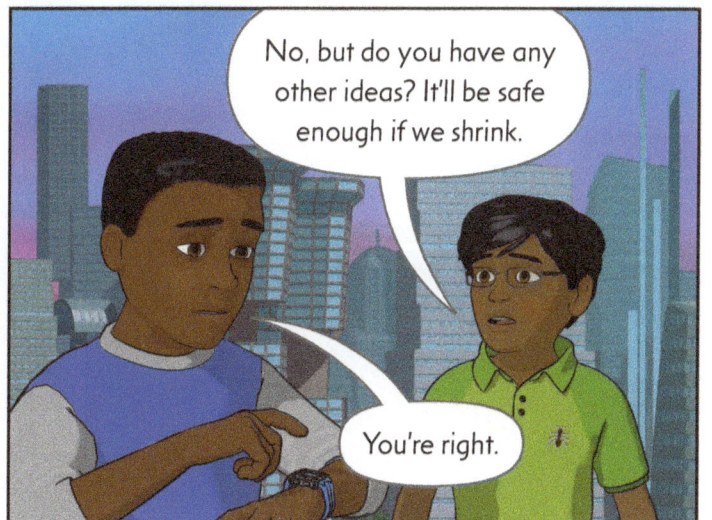

No, but do you have any other ideas? It'll be safe enough if we shrink.

You're right.

Chapter 4: Under control

In Professor Martin's lab ...

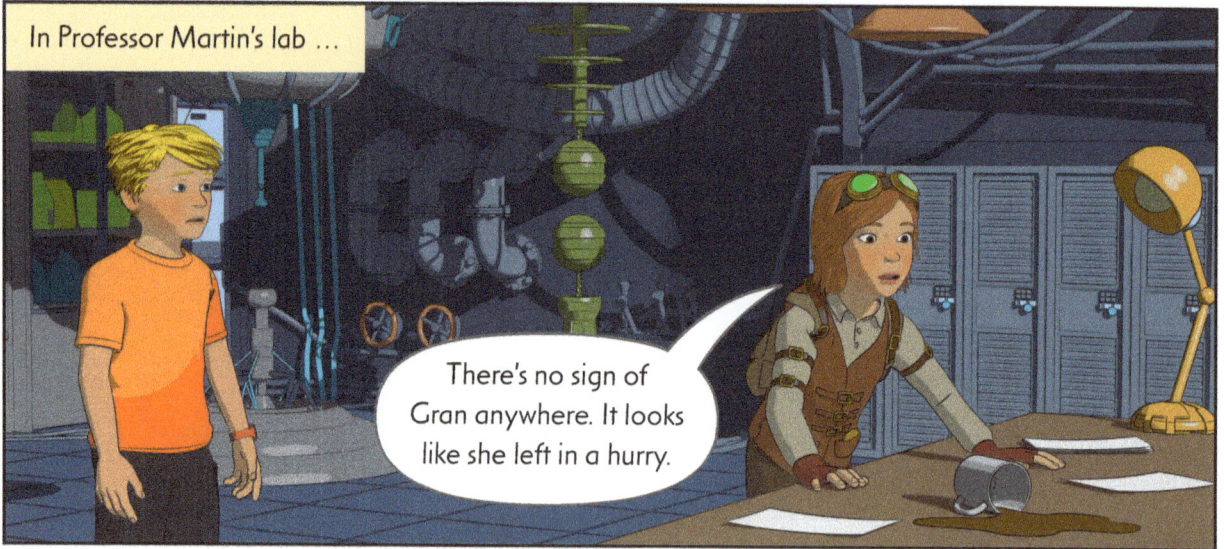

There's no sign of Gran anywhere. It looks like she left in a hurry.

There's some kind of device on Kalvin's wrist. Take a look through my magni-scope, Birdy.

It resembles a Tick-Tock controller, but it's more sophisticated. I've no idea what its purpose might be.

Spearhead addressed the crowd once more.

Bleep! Whirrr!

The time has arrived for me to activate your time trackers.

Silence descended; the crowd became motionless.

I don't like the look of this at all.

The scratch you just felt on your wrist was a micro-control device being injected into your bloodstream. Let's see if they're all working, shall we?

I wish for you all to give me a massive round of applause. NOW.

Clap, clap, clap

GRAN!!!

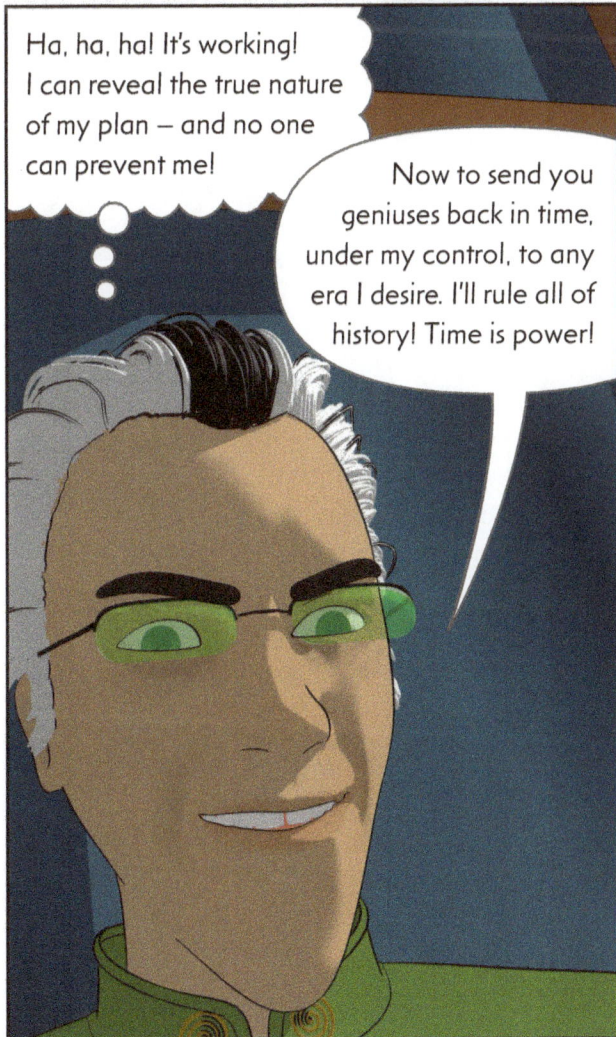

Ha, ha, ha! It's working! I can reveal the true nature of my plan — and no one can prevent me!

Now to send you geniuses back in time, under my control, to any era I desire. I'll rule all of history! Time is power!

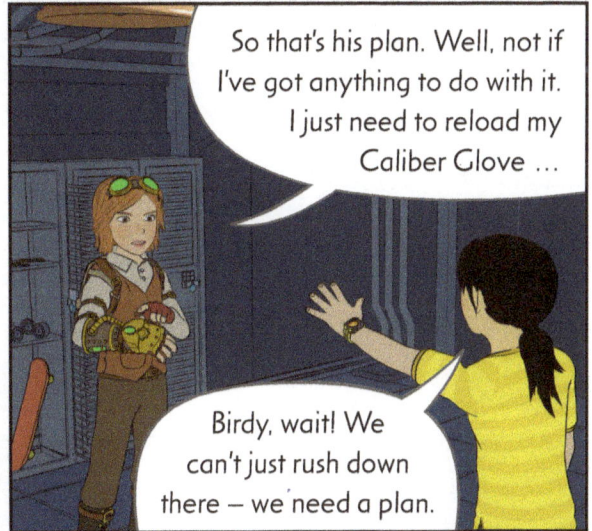

So that's his plan. Well, not if I've got anything to do with it. I just need to reload my Caliber Glove …

Birdy, wait! We can't just rush down there — we need a plan.

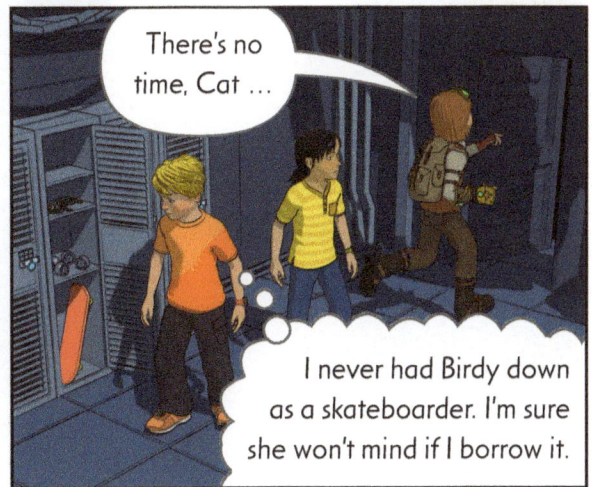

There's no time, Cat …

I never had Birdy down as a skateboarder. I'm sure she won't mind if I borrow it.

23

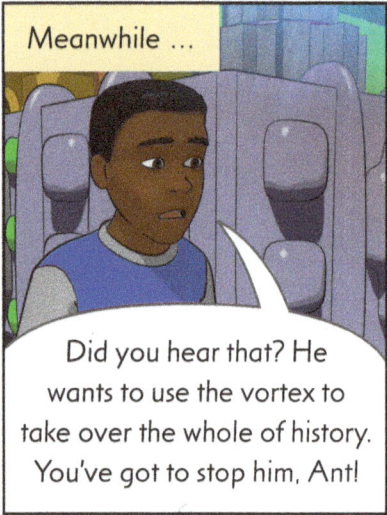

Meanwhile ...

Did you hear that? He wants to use the vortex to take over the whole of history. You've got to stop him, Ant!

It looks like the Escape Wheel has a lock on it. I'm going to have to use the power from my watch to try to reset the controls.

That's your plan?

It's the only chance we've got ... but it could attract some attention.

In which case, you'll be requiring a distraction ...

Oi! Spearhead – you won't get away with this!

I recognize you from the footage transmitted by my Tick-Tock Men.

Seize him!

28

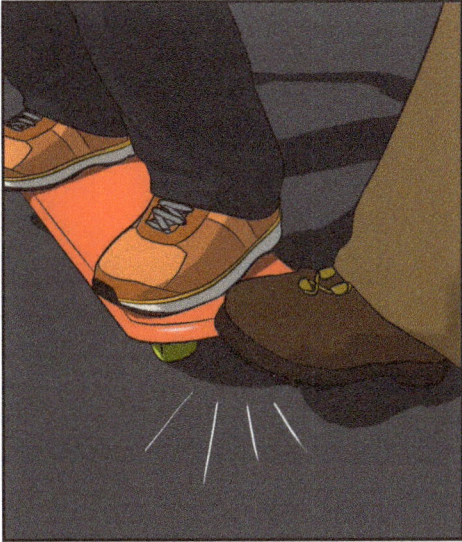

Maybe I spoke too soon!

Ooph!

Gran! It's me.

I have her, master.

And I have the other one.

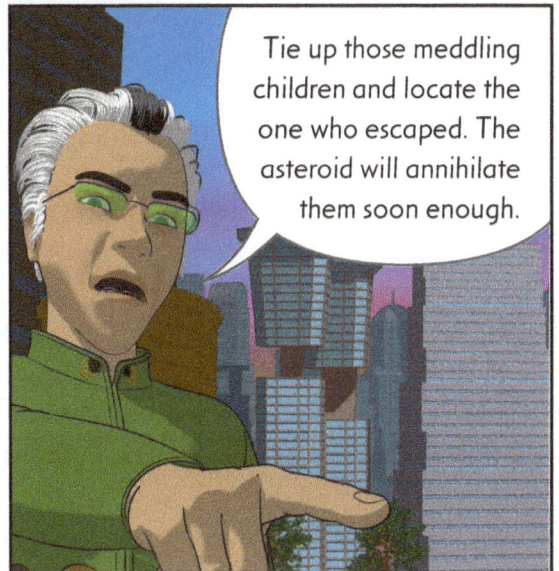

Tie up those meddling children and locate the one who escaped. The asteroid will annihilate them soon enough.

Where are Max and Ant? Time is running out!

First stop Ancient Rome. Emperor Spearhead has a nice ring to it.

Hail, Caesar!

Done it! I think …

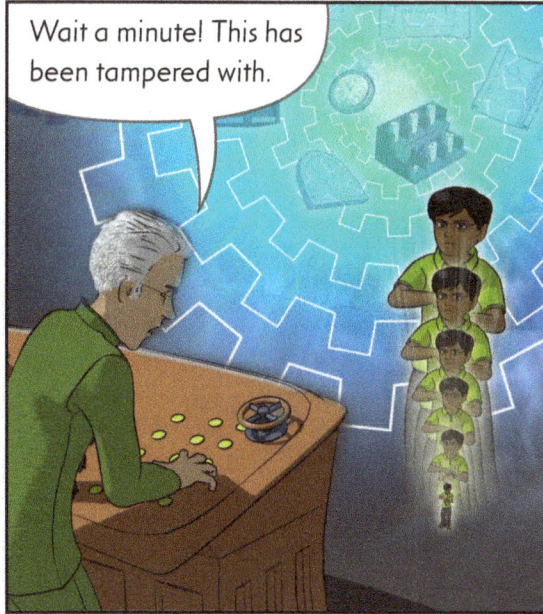

Wait a minute! This has been tampered with.

You're right there. I've reset the vortex to a time that definitely wasn't on your list of must-see destinations!

I suggest you change it back now before I make you regret it.

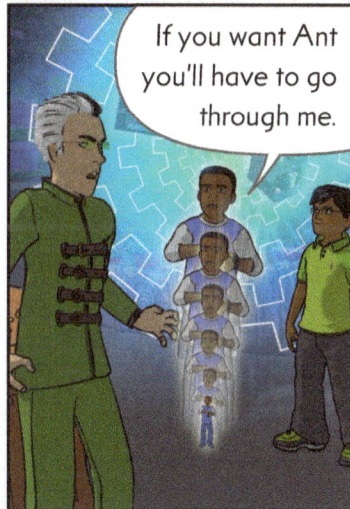

If you want Ant you'll have to go through me.

If you say so.

Whoa!

Aaarghhhh!

Max! No!

Chapter 5: Who knows when?

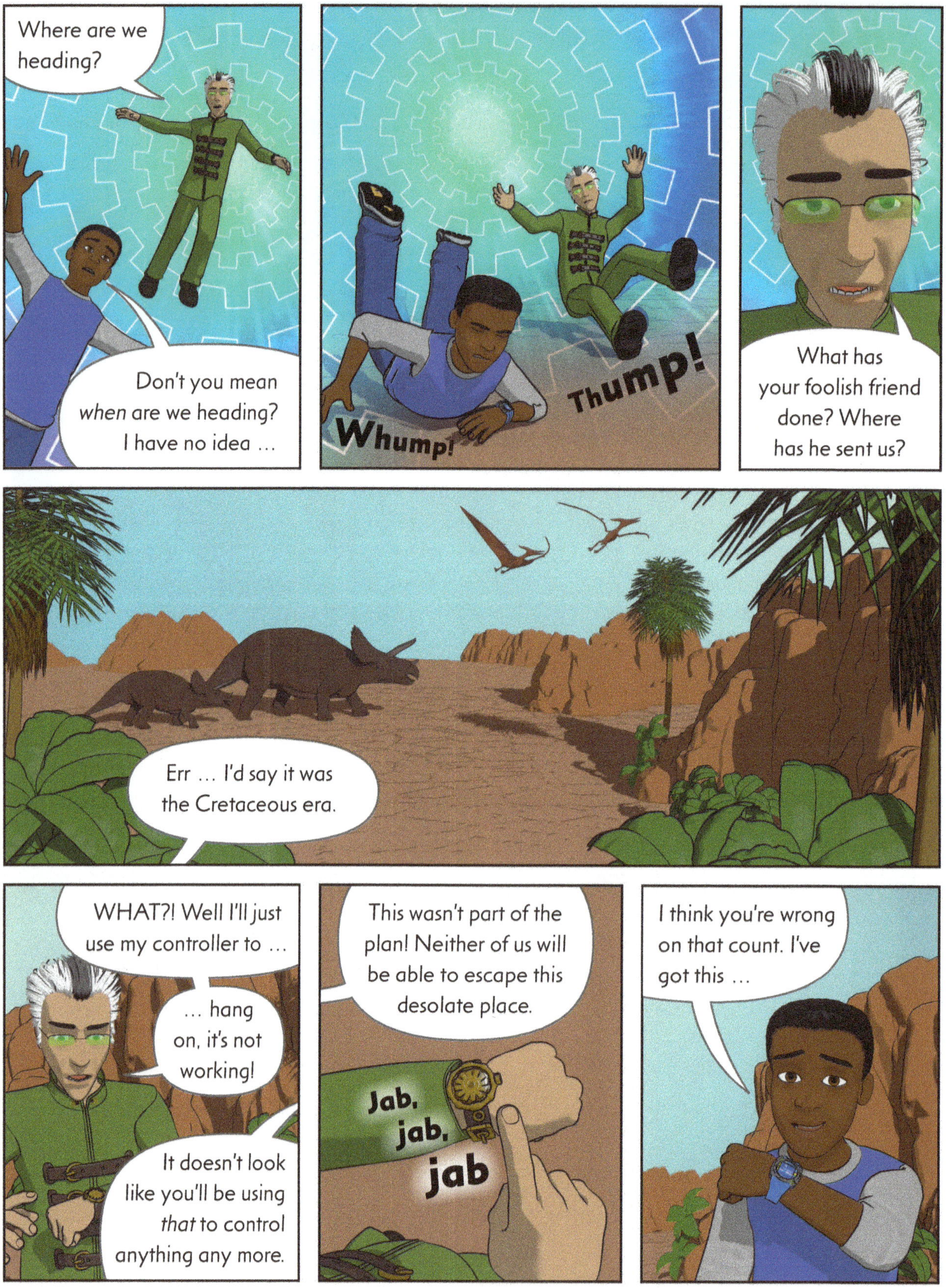

I've got it! If we synchronize the enlarge function on your watches with the time vortex, we can make Spearhead's portal big enough to swallow up the asteroid.

You can *do that?*

Of course. You're looking at the best scientists on the planet.

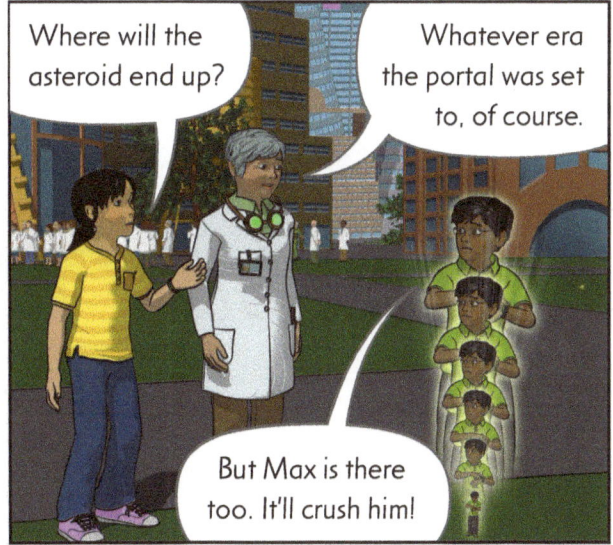

Where will the asteroid end up?

Whatever era the portal was set to, of course.

But Max is there too. It'll crush him!

Not if you shrink the vortex again, just as the asteroid enters. The rock will shrink too — and become smaller the further back in time it goes.

If we get it wrong by a split second then Max is a goner.

Better not get it wrong then.

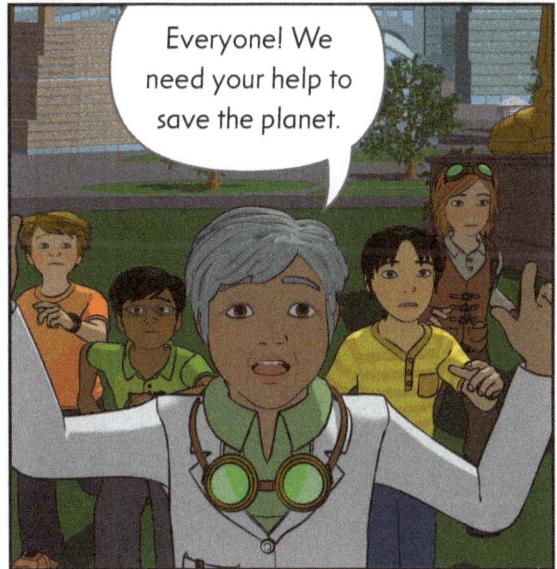

Everyone! We need your help to save the planet.

We've got one attempt at this. Let's make it count.

You think Max is all right?

Aw, you know Max. He'll have figured out a way to stay out of trouble.

37

Pat on the back for us. Well … those scientists helped a bit.

You kids saved humanity. We can't thank you enough.

I just hope Max is OK.

Chapter 6: Redemption?

Help! Kalvin, please …!

Clonk!

Well, *that* was unexpected.

It's safe to come out now, Kalvin.

You could have helped me, you know.

Now why would I do that?

Because I saved you.

Perhaps in your world everyone goes round saving each other, but not in mine. In mine it's every man for himself.

Then your world must be a very lonely place.

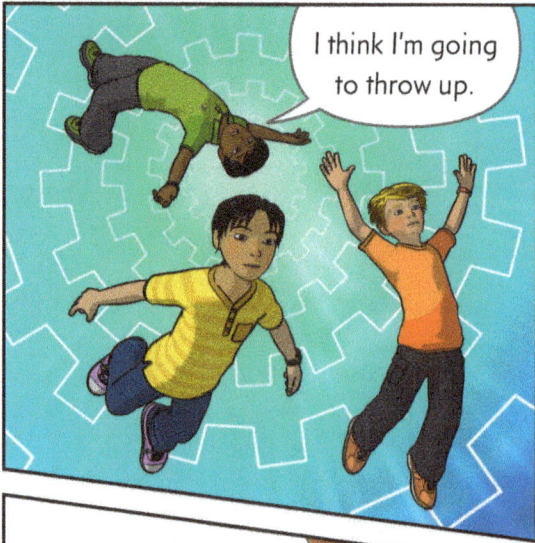

I think I'm going to throw up.

Hi guys. What took you so long?

Been busy saving the planet, while you're lazing around in the sun.

Bump

Whump

Did you know you've got an unconscious dinosaur behind you?

Yeah. I *had* noticed. Are we leaving now?

What about me?

Help is on the way. We'll be out of here soon.

Do you really think we're going to help you after what you did?

Especially after you sacrificed me to a T. rex.

But ... but ... you can't just abandon me.

Can't we? Just watch ...

RAAAAAAWR!

Please! I'm sorry for everything I've done. I truly am. I promise that if you take me back, I will resign from my position at END CO. You're my witnesses to that.

OK. We'll take you with us, but what about that …?

RAAAAAAWR!

Pffff zzzzz

Out cold again. Humans: 1 Dinosaur: 0!

Ant, where did you get that from?

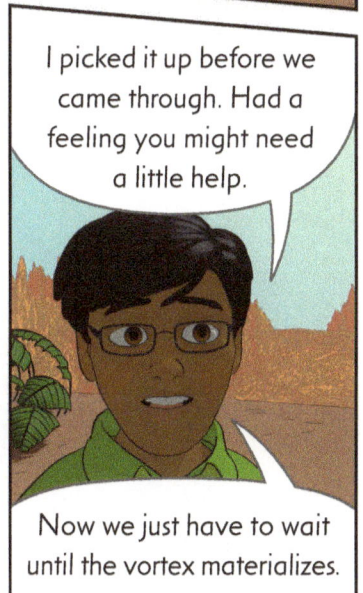

I picked it up before we came through. Had a feeling you might need a little help.

Now we just have to wait until the vortex materializes.

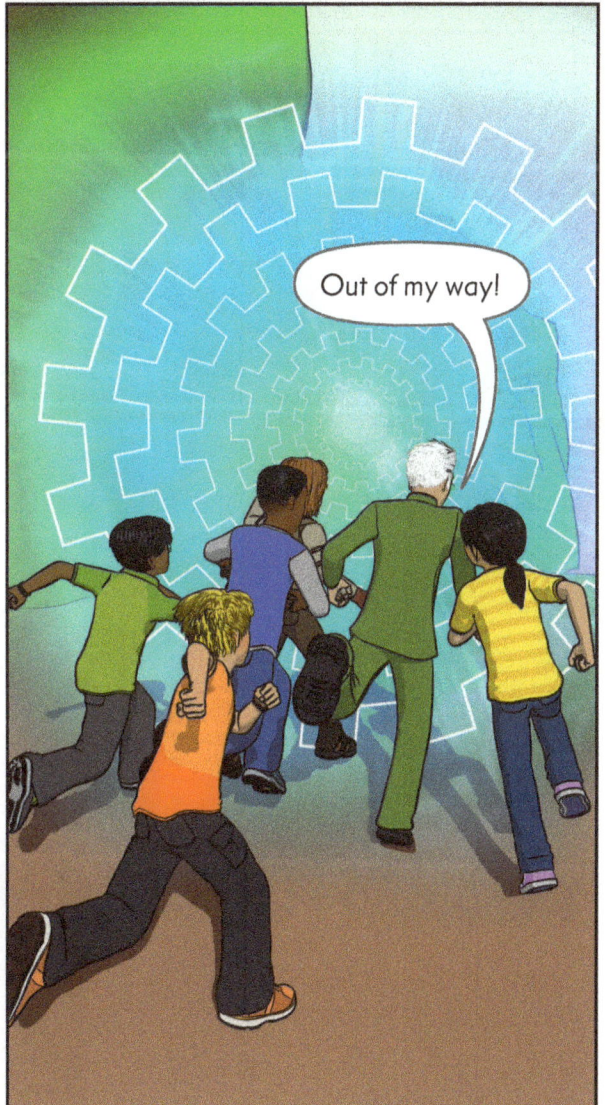

Chapter 7: It's really goodbye

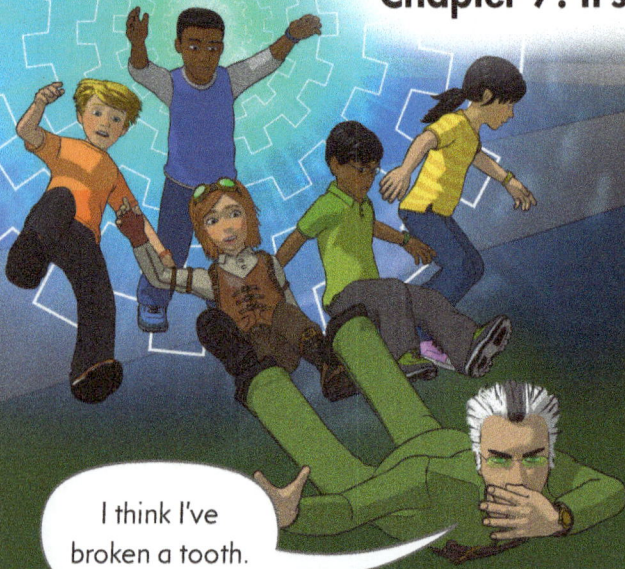

"I think I've broken a tooth."

"I've already said I'll give up the company. You don't need to take me away …"

"How can we ever thank you?"

"There's no need. Honestly."

"We, err, really ought to be getting back now though."

"So it's really goodbye this time?"

"I'm afraid so. We've got our normal lives to return to."

"I hope you know how grateful I am? I couldn't have done this without you."

"Of course you couldn't have … we're the best!"

"Seriously though Birdy, we do need to go now …"

The National Bureau of Standards (NBS) was formed in 1901, a complex of buildings built just outside Washington DC, USA. The Bureau's main function was to calculate precise weights and measurements. With all sorts of new technologies being invented, it allowed the government to set standard measurements and safety values for all sorts of products and inventions, from clothing sizes to car brakes. This may not sound important, but it was. As an example, imagine if train wheels and tracks all over the country were built in varying widths. None of them would ever be able to join up!

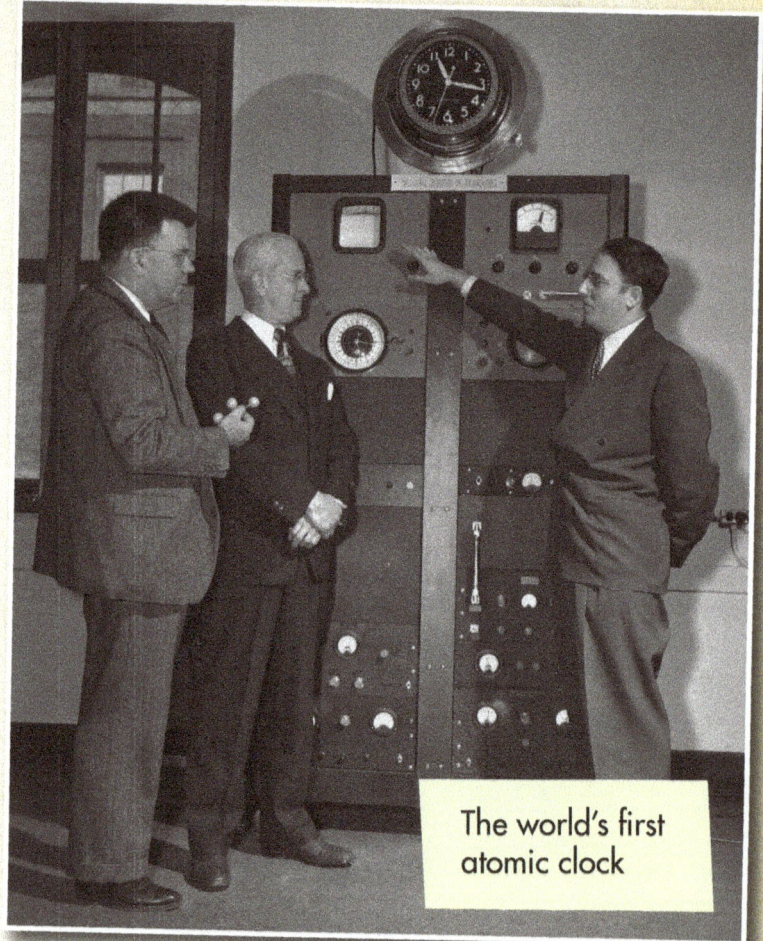

The world's first atomic clock

However, the NBS diversified into lots of other areas, such as testing planes and experimenting with radio and computer technology. In 1949 they constructed the first Atomic Clock, which used high frequency atom beams to keep time. This made it far more accurate than any previous timepiece.

The NBS eventually moved from their Washington site to Maryland and became the National Institute of Standards and Technology (NIST).

Ready for

IELTS

2nd Edition

Student's Book Pack
without Answers

Sam McCarter

macmillan
education

Contents Map

Introduction

Welcome to *Ready for IELTS*, a course which is designed to help you prepare for the IELTS Academic exam.

The book aims to help students progress from a global IELTS band score of 5 to a band score of 6.5/7. Students with a minimum score of 4/5 in any aspect of the exam can also use this book to help them achieve a global band score up to 6.5/7. For example, to achieve a global band score of 5 candidates need minimum scores of 4, 5, 5, 5, in any order, in the four modules of Listening, Academic Reading, Academic Writing and Speaking. For a global band score of 7 candidates need 6, 7, 7, 7, again in any order.

The book contains a wide range of activities aimed at improving your English and developing the language and skills you need to improve your band score. As well as providing thorough practice in reading, writing, listening and speaking, each unit of *Ready for IELTS* includes one or more *Language focus* sections, which analyse the main grammar areas that are required for the exam, together with *Vocabulary* and *Word building* sections.

Throughout the book, the following boxes help you when performing the different tasks:

- **What to expect in the exam**: these contain useful information on a particular type of task in the exam.

- **How to go about it**: these give advice and guidelines on how to deal with different types of tasks and specific questions.

- **Don't forget!**: these provide a reminder of important points to bear in mind when answering a particular type of question.

- **Useful expressions**: these contain extra words, phrases and parts of sentences to help you complete exercises.

Further information and advice is included in the four supplementary *Ready for …* units, one for each of the four parts of the exam. These are found at regular intervals in the book and can be used at appropriate moments during the course.

Each unit contains a two-page *Review* of the language covered in the unit. As you revise for the IELTS examination, you can use the *Review* pages as a quick revision guide along with the *Wordlists* and *Grammar reference* at the back of the book. Also as you progress through the course, you may want to refer back to the *Review* sections.

The *Grammar reference* contains detailed explanations of the grammar areas in the 14 units, while the extensive *Wordlist* is based on the vocabulary in each unit.

In each unit, there is practice in:

- one section of the Listening test
- a Reading Passage test using full-length passages
- either Task 1 or Task 2 of the Academic Writing test
- one or more of the parts of the Speaking test.

Each section of the Listening test is covered in turn throughout the book, so there is the equivalent of three-and-a-half full listening tests in the main units, with an additional example of each section in the *Ready for Listening* section.

Overview of the examination

The academic version of the IELTS examination consists of four tests: Listening, Academic Reading, Academic Writing and Speaking. For more information and advice on each section of the test, see the appropriate *Ready for …* unit, as well as the relevant sections in the main units.

IELTS Listening approximately 30 minutes

The Listening test has 40 questions and lasts approximately 30 minutes. You hear each section once only and you answer the questions in the question booklet as you listen. At the end of the test, you have ten minutes to transfer your answers to an answer sheet.

Section 1	A conversation between two people. The topic is usually of a social nature.
Section 2	A monologue or conversation between two people. The topic is usually of a social nature.
Section 3	A conversation involving up to four people. The situation and topic are related to education and training.
Section 4	A monologue. The context is related to education and training. Sometimes, there may be someone asking questions to a speaker.

Question types
Classification
Labelling a diagram/plan/map
Matching
Multiple-choice
Note/form/summary/table/flow-chart completion
Selecting items from a list
Sentence completion
Short-answer questions

The difficulty of the questions increases as the test progresses.

IELTS Academic Reading 1 hour

In the Academic Reading test, there are three passages, which are from various sources like books, journals, magazines and newspapers. The passages do not require specialist knowledge for you to understand them, and at least one of them contains a detailed logical argument.

Question types
Choosing suitable paragraph/section headings from a list
Classification
Completing sentences with the correct endings
Identification of information using 'True/False/Not Given' statements
Identification of the writer's claims and views using 'Yes/No/Not Given' statements
Labelling a diagram
Matching information to paragraphs/names to statements
Multiple-choice
Note/flow-chart/table completion
Selecting items from a list
Sentence completion
Short-answer questions
Summary completion – with and without wordlists

IELTS Academic Writing 1 hour

The Academic Writing test lasts one hour and there are two tasks. You are advised to spend 20 minutes on Task 1 and asked to write at least 150 words.

For Task 2, you are advised to spend 40 minutes and asked to write at least 250 words.

Task	Task type
1	Candidates are asked to describe data, presented as a graph, chart or table, or a diagram, such as a map or process, using their own words.
2	Candidates are given a question containing a point of view, argument or problem.

The rubrics in Writing Task 2 follow a range of patterns, including:

Discuss both these views and give your own opinion.

Discuss the advantages and disadvantages of …

Do you think this is a positive or negative development?

To what extent do you agree or disagree (with this opinion)?

What do you consider to be the major influence?

What do you think are the main causes of this problem/development? What effective measures can be taken to tackle (the situation/problem/issue)?

What do you think are the main causes of this problem/development? What are the effects of (the situation/problem/issue)?

IELTS Speaking 11–14 minutes

The IELTS Speaking test lasts between 11 and 14 minutes and consists of three parts. The test is recorded. Sometimes there is a video recording of the Speaking test.

The first two parts of the Speaking test are of a personal nature and the last part deals with abstract concepts/ideas.

Part	Task type
1	Candidates are asked questions about topics such as their family, job/studies or interests, and a wide range of other topics that students are familiar with. Part 1 lasts four to five minutes and includes an introduction of yourself to the examiner.
2	Candidates talk about a topic on a Task Card with prompts for one to two minutes. You are given one minute to think about the topic and make notes on a sheet of paper.
3	Candidates have a discussion with the examiner linked to the topic in Part 2. Part 3 lasts four to five minutes.

We are all friends now

Vocabulary: Describing people

1 👥 Work in pairs. Describe what is happening in each of the photographs. Then discuss the questions below.

- Do the photographs give you any clues about the personalities of the people in them?
- Which, if any, of the people would you like to be friends with? Why?

2 Match the people in each photograph with one or more of the adjectives below. Give at least one reason for each choice.

Example:

The woman in picture 3 looks very conscientious because she seems to be working late.

artistic	supportive	adventurous	talkative	reliable	patient
ambitious	sporty	creative	considerate	conscientious	helpful

3 For nouns **1–8** below, decide whether the adjective ends in: *-al, -ed, -ent, -able, -ing, -ful* or *-ous*. There may be more than one possible answer.

1 talent   **3** care   **5** confidence   **7** knowledge

2 humour   **4** generosity   **6** sociability   **8** punctuality

4 Work in pairs. Each of the items **1–8** below describe people. Match each item to an adjective from exercise 3 above.

1 My grandfather tells jokes all the time and makes us all laugh.

2 He knows a great deal about many subjects, including science, geography and history.

3 My sister plays the piano exceptionally well. I hope to be as good as her one day.

4 She's never late for any appointments, and hates it when people aren't on time.

5 Olga knows she is very good at her job and always takes the lead in business meetings.

6 She gives a lot of money away to charities and to people who need it.

7 When Mary was younger, she devoted her time to looking after seriously ill people.

8 She loves being around people all the time, meeting and making friends.

5 Think of a friend who has one or more of the qualities above. With a partner, describe the friend by explaining the qualities they have.

6 How would you describe yourself? Write down three adjectives and show the words to your partner. Ask each other about them.

Listening
Section 1

1 What numbers and letters do you find difficult to understand? Write them down and then give them to a partner. Ask him/her to dictate the letters and numbers to you in any order, for example, *f-p-t-f-g-j-l-m-f-b-d*. Write down the letters you hear.

2 Which numbers do you find difficult to understand? Write down five sets of numbers, for example, *6633, 6363, 3663, 677 331, 3553*. Give them to a partner and ask him/her to dictate the numbers to you slowly and then quickly in any order. Write down the numbers you hear.

3 You can use the questions in the test to predict the content of the conversation. Work in pairs and ask each other questions like:

Do you think the conversation is about singing classes only/adults or children?

4 For **Questions 1–10** predict which of the following is needed: a noun, name, number, adjective or adverb.

How to go about it

- Read the instructions carefully and note word limits.
- Underline the words in the questions that show you that the answer is about to be given. Try to predict the answers.
- If the answer can be (a) word(s) or a number, read the question to check which is required.

01 **SECTION 1** *Questions 1–10*

Questions 1–6

Complete the notes below.

Write **NO MORE THAN TWO WORDS AND/OR A NUMBER** *for each answer.*

Drama classes

Example
Performing arts classes with: acting, singing and dancing

Weekdays

Ages 7–11: from **1** 7.30pm to 6.30 pm Tuesday

Ages 12–15: **2** 4pm to 6 pm on Wednesday

Ages 16 and above: 6–8 pm on **3** Friday

Weekends

10 am–1 pm for those **4** 18 and over

School holidays

5 summer camps for those 16 and under in August

Performances

Each class: at least **6** 1 show per year in the summer

Questions 7–10

Complete the notes below.

Write **ONE WORD AND/OR A NUMBER** *for each answer.*

Personal details

Joining fee **7** £ 14 yearly per person

Name: Maggie Campbell

Address: 133 **8** Arbuthnot Drive

Postcode: **9** RV27 8PB

Contact number: **10** 6770435(01

What to expect in the exam

- In IELTS Listening Section 1, you listen to a conversation between two people once only. At the beginning of the recording, you are told what the conversation is about and you hear an example.
- You are given time to look at the questions before you begin and also again in the middle of the recording.
- At the end of each section, you have time to check your answers.

5 What kinds of classes have you done or do you like doing? Give reasons and examples.

Language focus 1: Likes and dislikes

1 In the conversation in the Listening, Maggie says what her children like:

They love acting, singing and dancing.

and what she'd like:

I'd like my children … to join the drama classes.

Why does she use *love + verb + -ing* in the first sentence?

G Read more about likes and dislikes in the Grammar reference on page 219.

2 🔵 Work in pairs. For **1–7** below, decide which sentences are correct.

1 Gabriella likes swimming a lot.

2 John likes to get there on time. He doesn't like lateness.

3 Would you like joining our study group?

4 Why did you hate playing football as a child?

5 Does he dislike travelling by aeroplane?

6 My grandparents loved looking after us as kids.

7 As Joseph is independent, he enjoys to do things alone.

3 For sentences **1–9** below, put the verb in brackets into the correct form. More than one answer may be correct.

1 Most of my friends dislike (play) computer games.

2 I'd like (live) near the sea as the air is fresh.

3 Certain animals hate (be) around people.

4 He likes (keep) the garden tidy, even though it takes time.

5 He enjoys (take) long walks on his own along the coast.

6 As she is so punctual, she likes other people (be) on time.

7 Sarah loves (socialise) with other people rather than (stay) at home alone.

8 He can't stand (play) sport.

9 Wouldn't you prefer (see) this film at the cinema?

4 Rewrite sentences **1–7** below using the words in brackets. Do not change the meaning.

1 The idea of living in the country appeals to me. (I'd like)

2 Nowadays people don't seem to take any pleasure in doing certain sports. (dislike)

3 I get a lot of pleasure from playing tennis. (like)

4 She gets enormous enjoyment from shopping. (enjoy)

5 He expects honesty in people he knows. (like)

6 She wants to see the film on DVD at home, not at the cinema. (would prefer)

7 He really likes to mingle with people at parties. (love)

5 🔵 Work in pairs. Ask your partner about one way of communicating with friends that they like and one way that they don't like. Use the questions below and ask for reasons and examples.

Why do you like/dislike … ?

Why don't you like … ?

6 🔵 Are the ways of communicating talked about by your partner popular in your country? Is the popularity of these means of communicating increasing or decreasing? Why?

Speaking
Part 2

1 🔵 Work in pairs. Look at the photographs below. Choose at least two adjectives to describe the adults. Use the wordlist on page 211 to help you.

2   Decide which person on page 9 appeals to you most. Look at the adjectives you chose for the person and make notes for the following:
- what kind of person they are generally
- why they appeal to you
- what they did when they were younger
- what activities are they doing now.

3   Use your notes to tell your partner about the person.

How to go about it

- Use the time given to make notes. Write them in the order of the prompts.
- Glance at the notes and develop your ideas as you speak.
- Try to use words like *for example ... , when/if ... , because ...* and *so ... .*
- If you are asked to talk about a person, name and try to think of the person and the reasons for talking about them.
- Remember the last prompt (explain why) requires more detail.

What to expect in the exam

- There are three parts in IELTS Speaking test. In Part 2, you are given a Task Card with prompts about a topic, e.g. a person, event, place, object, film, something that happened or you would like to happen, etc.
- You are given one minute to think about what to say and to make notes.
- You then have one to two minutes to talk about the topic.

4   Look at the following Part 2 Task Card. Decide which tense you are going to use for each part of the topic.

Describe a person you would like to be similar to.

You should say:

    who this person is

    what this person does

    what qualities this person has

and explain why you would like to be similar to this person.

---

5   Spend one minute making brief notes.

Example:
- *uncle*
- *teacher*
- *generosity, calmness*
- *wise, helpful, funny*

6   Work in pairs. Take turns talking about the topic, using your notes to guide you. You should speak for up to two minutes. If possible, time each other.

Reading
Questions 1–13

What to expect in the exam

- The IELTS Reading test has three Reading Passages and 40 questions: two passages with 13 questions and one with 14.
- You should spend about 20 minutes on each passage.

1   You are going to read a passage with three sets of questions. Read the title and decide what it means. Predict what methods for staying in touch you are likely to find in the passage.

2   How important is it to make friends at a new college or university? Why? Do you think students are able to keep in contact more with their family and friends nowadays compared to the past? Give reasons and examples.

3 🔊 Skim the Reading Passage and all the questions as quickly as you can. With a partner, use the questions as a guide to discuss what the passage is about. Also discuss whether your predictions in exercise 1 above were correct.

READING PASSAGE

*You should spend about 20 minutes on **Questions 1–13**, which are based on the Reading Passage.*

Questions 1–6

The Reading Passage has seven paragraphs, **A–G**.

*Choose the correct heading for paragraphs **B–G** from the list of headings below.*

List of Headings
i a comparison of male and female use of commercial venues
ii how various media affect the frequency of contact between friends
iii the ranking of the most popular communication methods
iv the reasons why teenagers like using commercial venues
v the popularity of internet friends
vi the importance of regular contact with friends met online
vii the popularity of neighbourhoods
viii the impact of mobile devices on contact between friends
ix alternative means of communication cited by teens

Example	Answer
Paragraph **A**	v

1 Paragraph B
2 Paragraph C
3 Paragraph D
4 Paragraph E
5 Paragraph F
6 Paragraph G

How teens hang out and stay in touch with their closest friends: a study of the attitudes of US teenagers aged 13 to 17

A The way young people are making friends around the world is changing. A US survey asked teens to focus on all of the ways in which they spend time and interact — both digitally and in person — with the friend who is closest to them. Many teens say they 'hang out' with their closest friend in online settings, such as social media sites or through gaming websites. More than half of teens hang out with their closest friend online on a regular basis, which is similar to the share of teens who spend time with close friends at someone's house. Teenage boys are especially likely to spend time online with close friends, as 62% do so regularly, compared with 48% of teen girls.

B Many of those who have met a friend online say they spend time with their closest friend on a regular basis online, which is somewhat higher than the 41% of teens who have not met a friend online. While this does not necessarily mean that a teen's best friend is an online friend, it does suggest a certain comfort with interacting with friends and peers in an online space for this group of teens.

C Neighborhoods also are a popular place for teens to connect with one another — 42% of teens spend time around a neighborhood with their closest friend. Boys are more likely than girls to spend time with their closest friend in a neighborhood. Nearly half of teenage boys say this is where they regularly spend time with their closest friend, compared with 36% of girls.

D About a third of teen girls spend time with their closest friend at a coffee shop or shopping centre. Roughly one-quarter of teens regularly spend time with their best friend at these places. Girls are twice as likely as boys to hang out in these locations:

30% of teen girls regularly spend time with their closest friend there, compared with only 16% of boys.

E   Frequent contact with closest friends is facilitated by mobile devices and social media. Teens today have more ways to stay in touch with friends than ever before. Beyond daily interactions at school, teens are increasingly connected by smartphones, social media, gaming, and the internet. These new avenues of communication broaden what it even means to be 'friends', changing how teens connect and how they share with one another.

F   Mobile devices help facilitate frequent connections between close friends. Teens who have mobile internet access — whether through a phone, tablet or other mobile device — are significantly more likely than those without this kind of access to be in frequent touch with their closest friend. A full 60% of these teen mobile internet users are in touch daily with their closest friend (including 42% who make contact many times a day). This compares with 47% of those without mobile internet access who communicate daily with their closest friend, including 27% who do so many times a day. Focusing in on

smartphone users, teens who have access to a smartphone also are likely to be in daily touch with their closest friend. Some 62% of teens with smartphone access are in touch with their closest friend daily, and 45% are in touch multiple times a day.

G   Phone-based methods are overall the most popular ways that teens communicate with their closest friends. Looking at the overall picture, texting comes out on top. Some 80% of teens say they use this as one of the three most common ways they get in touch. But phone calls — a technology from the analogue era — are the second most popular method overall, with 69% of teens citing it as one of their choices. This is followed closely by the 66% of teens who say social media is in their top three preferences, while just 21% of teens noted gaming in any of their choices. Other communication methods, such as video sharing, blogging and discussion sites were cited by 10% of teens or less. Some 21% of teens, however, said 'something else' to any of the three most common ways they get in touch with their closest friend. Write-in answers reveal that some teens use video chatting, such as the popular iPhone service FaceTime, to get in touch with one another, as well as email.

Questions 7–10

Complete the sentences below.

*Choose **NO MORE THAN TWO WORDS** from the passage for each answer.*

7   The majority of teenagers spend time with their closest online friend on a ....

8   The best friend of a teenager is .... someone online.

9   Almost .... of male teenagers spend time with their best friend in a neighbourhood.

10   New communication devices .... the meaning of what a friend is.

Questions 11–13

Do the following statements agree with the information in the Reading Passage?

Write:

TRUE   *if the statement agrees with the information*
FALSE   *if the statement contradicts the information*
NOT GIVEN   *if there is no information on this*

11   The use of social media and mobile devices among teenagers has little impact on their contact with their closest friend.

12   Social media are used by teenagers to exchange photographs.

13   Teenagers also use video-based communication to contact friends.

4   Do you think electronic devices, such as smartphones, and social media improve the quality of friendships? Why/Why not?

Language focus 2: Present simple, present continuous and past simple

1 Scan the Reading Passage on page 11–12 to find the following:

1 … *while just 21% of teens noted gaming in any of their choices.*

2 *The way young people are making friends around the world is changing.*

3 *Mobile devices help facilitate frequent connections between close friends.*

2 In each of the sentences above, underline the main verbs and decide whether the present simple, present continuous or past simple tense is used.

3 Match the tenses in exercise 2 with an appropriate explanation **a–d**.

a these events/actions occur routinely and repeatedly

b an action which is still going on and is not finished yet

c the event occurred in the past at a definite time

d this is always true, like a fact or a state

G Read more about the tenses in the Grammar reference on page 219.

4 Complete sentences **1–6** by putting the verb in brackets into the present simple, present continuous or past simple.

1 A mentor (help) new students integrate into university life.

2 Fewer older people (participate) in social networking compared to now.

3 The research (affect) the way the new students were helped on their arrival at the university.

4 When I was young, my parents (influence) my attitude to education enormously.

5 Researchers (recruit) students for academic research now.

6 Each time I go on the internet, I (feel) that the amount of information is overwhelming.

5 🔁 Choose three verbs you changed in exercise 4. For each verb, write a sentence about yourself. With a partner, take turns talking about your sentences.

Writing

Task 1

Verbs of movement

1 Work in pairs. Look at the graph. Match parts **1–10** with the verbs **a–j**.

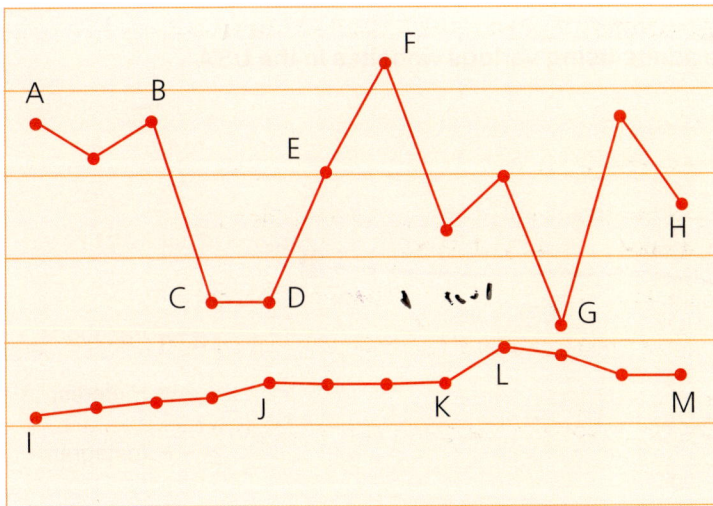

1	*A–B*	**a**	hit a low
2	B–C	**b**	fell and then levelled off
3	B–D	**c**	remained flat
4	D–F	**d**	plummeted
5	F	**e**	rose gradually
6	F–H	**f**	declined steadily
7	G	**g**	soared
8	I–J	**h**	*dipped*
9	J–K	**i**	fluctuated
10	L–M	**j**	hit a peak

2 For sentences **1–10** below, use the verbs in exercise 1 to replace the underlined text.

1 The price of laptops dropped and this was followed by a period of stability.

2 Numbers reached a high in the year 2009.

3 The amount of money spent fell slightly and then quickly recovered.

4 Visitor numbers to the website plunged in the first quarter of the year.

5 Book purchases increased steadily over the year.

6 The number of students applying to the university stabilised over the decade.

7 Attendance at the conference decreased gradually over the last five years.

8 The growth rate was erratic during the previous year.

9 Member numbers reached their lowest point in March.

10 Car sales rocketed over the period.

3   To add variety to your writing you can use nouns instead of verbs to describe movement. Choose 10 verbs from exercises 1 and 2 and decide whether they can also be nouns.

   Example:

   drop → a drop

4   Rewrite at least three of the sentences from exercise 2 using nouns instead of verbs. For three of the sentences this is not possible. Make any other necessary changes.

   Example:

   There was a (+ adjective) + noun + in …
   There was a drop in the price of laptops followed by a period of stability.

5   Compare your sentences with another pair of students.

Analysing main trends and purpose

1   Work in pairs. Read the Task 1 question below and answer questions **1–3** which follow.

WRITING TASK 1

You should spend about 20 minutes on this task.

> *The graph below shows the results of a survey among online adults on their use of various social media in the USA between 2012 and 2015.*
>
> *Summarise the information by selecting and reporting the main features, and make comparisons where relevant.*

Write at least 150 words.

The percentage of online adults using various websites in the USA

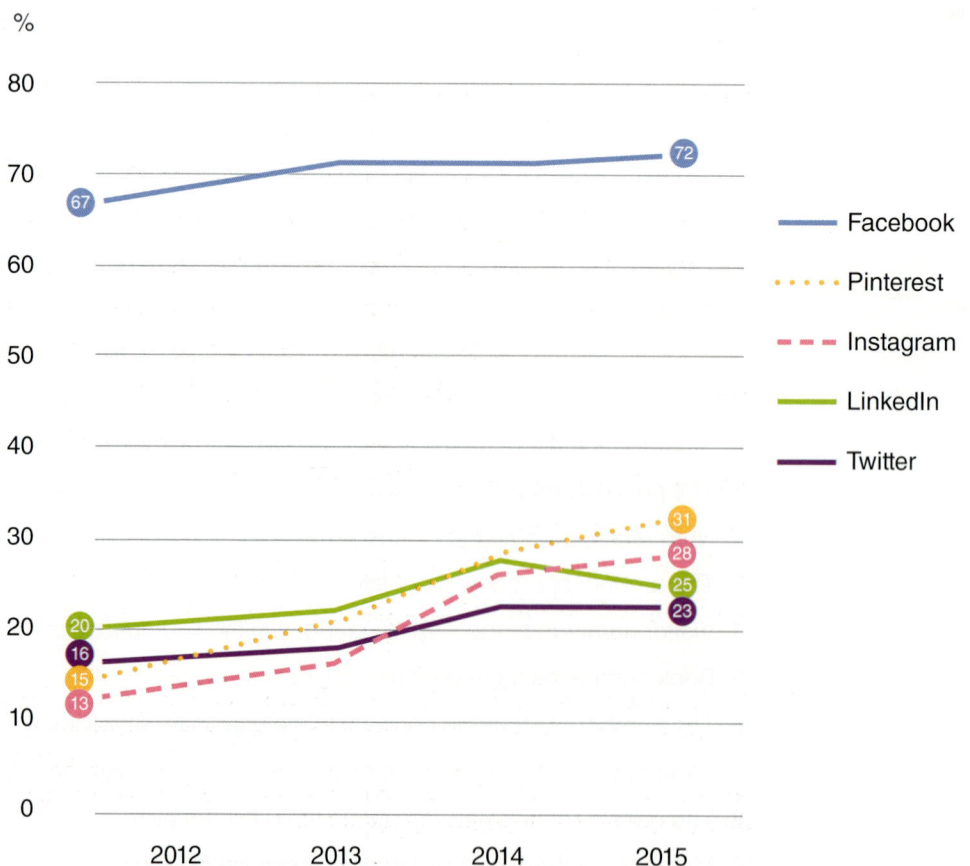

---

1 Is the trend the same for each website?

2 Are the changes in the proportions for the websites slight, dramatic, or noticeable in any way?

3 What do you think the purpose of the survey is?

    a to see if the use of social media has changed

    b to confirm that social media use is declining

2 Add the items below to the correct place in the model answer.

    a the trend in the proportion of adults using the websites is upward

    b saw a 25% increase in the proportion of online adult users

    c the proportion of the usage of Instagram jumped more than twofold

    d The graph illustrates

    e remained flat

    f A similar pattern was seen

    g there was a small rise in the proportion of

1 _____ the proportions of adults online using various social networking sites, according to a survey in the United States between 2012 and 2015.

Generally speaking, 2 _____ , with a faster increase for Instagram and Pinterest than the others, including Facebook, the most popular website overall. While 3 _____ online adults using the latter, from 67% to 72% over the period, in the last three years the trend was flat. By contrast, 4 _____ from 13% in 2012 to 28% in 2015. 5 _____ at the Pinterest site where the proportion of adult users went up more than 100% from 15% to 31%.

LinkedIn, by comparison, 6 _____ , from 20% in 2012 to 25% in 2015 with a noticeable peak of about 28% in 2014. Similarly, as regards Twitter, there was a rise from 16% to 23% in 2012 and 2014 respectively, but in 2015 usage 7 _____ .

3 Work in pairs. In the completed model answer, paraphrase the phrases **a–g** above. Use a dictionary if necessary. Compare your answers with another pair.

4 Write an answer to the Task 1 question on page 206. When you have finished, check your answer using the checklist on page 139.

1 Review

Vocabulary: Describing people

1 Use a suitable adjective to fill each blank space.

1 Do you know anyone who makes people laugh? Yes, my best friend is really _____ .

2 Is there anyone you know who talks a lot? Yes, I'm quite _____ myself.

3 Do you like people being _____? Yes, I do, because being on time is important.

4 Why do you think it's important to be _____? Well, so people can trust you and know you'll do things properly.

5 Who do you think is the most _____ person you know? My sister can sing and dance and play the piano.

6 Would you say you are _____? Yes, I work really hard at school and in my job.

7 Do you really want to succeed in life? Definitely, I'm very _____ .

8 Are you someone who plays swims and jogs lot? Yes, I think I'm fairly _____ .

2 Work in pairs and ask each other the questions and develop the answers using or paraphrasing the adjectives.

Language focus 1: Likes and dislikes

1 Match the two parts of the sentence together. Use each item once only.

1 I like	a to meet his friends rather than sit at home.
2 Anna is sociable and dislikes	b being in large crowds.
3 They don't enjoy	c playing games online with my close friends.
4 Pedro prefers	d to go to the cinema or go to the gym?
5 Would you like	e watching TV that much.
6 He's very sociable, but he can't stand	f spending time on her own.
7 This evening, would you prefer	g having to wait for buses and trains.
8 I personally prefer	h to go on holiday with a large group of people?
9 They hate	i to study with friends rather than by myself.

Language focus 2: Present simple, present continuous and past simple

1 Put the verbs in brackets into a suitable tense. If more than one tense is possible, explain the difference.

1 I (enjoy) using various online websites to buy gifts for my friends and family, but my credit cards (cause) me some difficulty at the moment.

2 What method do you and your friends (use) to contact each other? When you (first use) this method?

3 I (have) many relatives, some of whom I (contact) on a daily basis.

4 The person I (want) to describe (be) my older sister who now (live) in Australia where she (study) for a degree in engineering. She (start) the course two years ago.

5 According to the report a majority of young people (spend) a lot of time online chatting to their friends, which (be) not the case ten years ago.

6 Mobiles (have) an enormous impact on the way people of all ages (communicate) with each other.

7 People (think) Vladimir (be) very creative. He (become) a professional artist five years ago and now (run) a very successful design studio.

8 In the past, he (be) the kind of person who (like) to make people happy. He (tell) lots of jokes and (make) fun of things, but now he (be) much more serious.

9 My family (help) me a lot when I first (start) studying, but now I (support) myself.

10 Using social media does not (appeal) to everyone, which I fully (understand).

Writing Task 1

1 Rewrite the sentences below using the word in brackets.

1 There was a dramatic increase in club membership between January and March. (dramatically)

2 Visits to the museum fell steadily in 2016. (steady)

3 Online sales fluctuated noticeably. (noticeable)

4 The number of people joining the social website peaked in 2015. (reach)

5 Spectator numbers increased gradually over the football season. (gradual)

6 Overall, it is clear that the rise in numbers is erratic throughout the period. (erratically)

7 The number of visitors to the leisure centre declined slightly. (slight)

8 There was a significant rise in ticket sales to the concert. (significantly)

Accuracy in IELTS

1 Identify the type of mistake in the sentences below and then correct them. There is one mistake per sentence.

a spelling mistake	the wrong word	the wrong verb form
the wrong tense	the wrong word order	the wrong word form

1 The numbers of Friends at the museum rose drammatically after the extension opened.

2 There is a soar in the numbers of users in then morning.

3 He enjoys to be with his family at the weekend.

4 As can be seen, people prefer be time with friends rather than study.

5 The volume of users of the department rocket last weekend.

6 My best fried is very talkative and humorous.

7 Do you think pop singers are really talent?

8 I don't like large crowds of people, so I'm not going to football matches as a rule.

9 He love spending time with his family.

10 Attendances at the conference significantly during the week fluctuated.

Vocabulary: Verbs of cause and effect

1  Work in pairs. Look at the photographs and discuss the questions below.

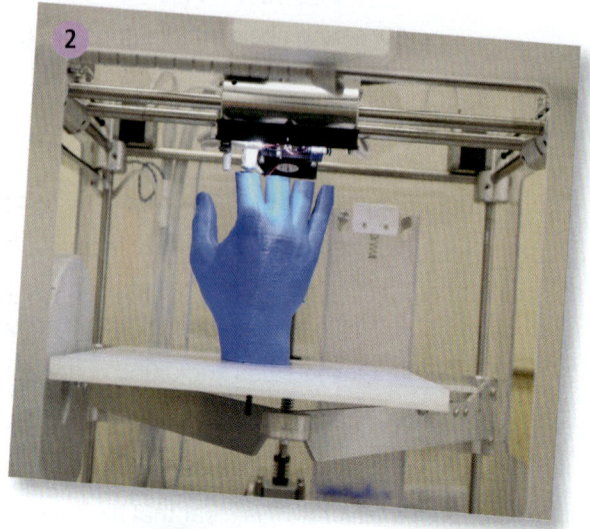

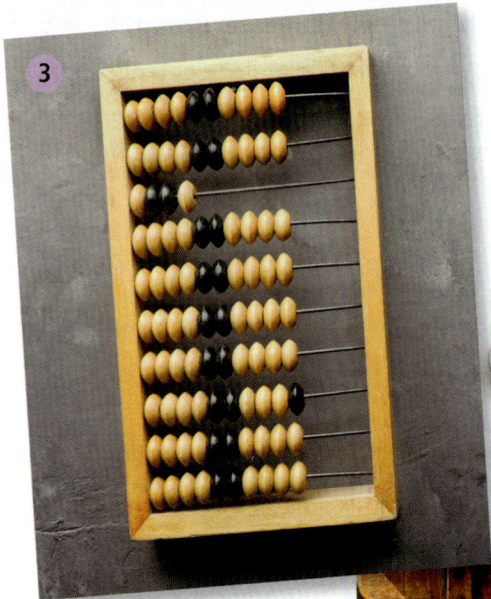

- Which two items have had the greatest influence on your life? Give reasons and examples.
- How have each of the items shaped people's lives?
- Some people think the wheel and the abacus are the most important inventions of all time. Do you agree? Why/Why not?

2 To make nouns from verbs you can add endings like *-ment* and *-ion*, e.g. *develop/development*. For some verbs the noun form is the same, e.g. *to shape/a shape*. Decide what the noun form is for each of the verbs **1–12** below. Which verb does not follow the patterns mentioned?

1 improve	_improvement_		**7** promote	_____
2 destroy	_____		**8** damage	_____
3 produce	_____		**9** ruin	_____
4 affect	_____		**10** result	_____
5 harm	_____		**11** advance	_____
6 enhance	_____		**12** deteriorate	_____

3 Work in pairs. The verbs and nouns in exercise 2 can be used to describe changes. Classify each verb and noun as a positive change, a negative change, or a neutral change.

4 For sentences **1–5** below, complete the gaps using the nouns in exercise 2.

1 Advertising companies increase sales through the _____tion of goods on TV.

2 Some pessimists argue that love of technology will eventually cause the _____tion of society.

3 _____ments in technology have gathered pace in recent years as the speed of computers has increased.

4 What recent advances have led to the _____ion of cheaper goods?

5 Some believe over-reliance on certain electronic devices can lead to the _____tion in short-term memory.

5 Rewrite sentences **1–7** below so that they contain the verb in brackets. Make any other necessary changes.

Example:

The introduction of a café and computers resulted in a significant improvement in the library's facilities. (improve)

The introduction of a café and computers significantly improved the library's facilities.

The library's facilities were significantly improved as a result of the introduction of a café.

1 People constantly debate whether television has a positive or negative influence on society. (influence)

2 The use of mobile phones is having a dramatic effect on the way we communicate. (affect)

3 Climate change has caused the destruction of many crops. (destroy)

4 Did the invention of the internet really do any harm to the way people live and work? (harm)

5 A series of new software inventions resulted in a sharp deterioration in the sales of certain mobile telephones. (deteriorate)

6 The use of technology meant that the archaeologists caused very little damage to the site. (damage)

7 Many people like Einstein and Newton have changed the shape of science. (shape)

6 Work in pairs. Discuss at least one statement or question from exercise 5. Develop your discussion using reasons and examples.

Listening
Section 2

1   Look at **Questions 11–15** and think of possible synonyms or paraphrases for the following words and phrases:

yearly   is held together   subject   during the preparation for   influence

What to expect in the exam

• In IELTS Listening Section 2 you usually listen to a monologue, but you may also hear one person answering questions.

• The topic is usually of general interest and there can be two or three sets of questions.

How to go about it

• Look at any headings in the questions.

• Use the questions to think about the answers. For example, look at the stem in Question 11. The answer is about a competition held every year. Three options are given.

• <u>Underline</u> words in the stems and options of the other multiple-choice questions which you think will help you listen for the answer. Most of the words you need to listen for are paraphrases or synonyms of these words.

• Avoid <u>underlining</u> the whole of the stem. Mark only words like nouns, names, verbs or function words like 'because', which you think will tell you the answer is about to be mentioned.

🔊 02   **SECTION 2**   *Questions 11–20*

Questions 11–15

*Choose the correct letter, **A**, **B** or **C**.*

Penwood Museum Competition

11   The yearly competition is held
    A   together with the museum's education department.
    B   as part of the museum's autumn show.
    C   along with the summer exhibition.

12   The subject of this year's competition is using technology
    A   to involve young people in the museum's activities.
    B   to form better links between local people and the museum.
    C   to improve the local community's engagement with the arts.

13   The competition was limited to those aged
    A   11–15.
    B   13–17.
    C   15–19.

14   During the preparation for the entry the competitors were
    A   able to use the museum's educational facilities.
    B   helped by the education staff at the museum.
    C   allowed to buy any of the equipment they needed.

15   According to the speaker, the prize-winning exhibits have
    A   led to traffic jams outside the museum.
    B   led to a reduction in attendances.
    C   increased interest in the museum.

Questions 16–20

The Video Commentaries

What did the older people say about each piece of equipment?

*Choose **FIVE** answers from the box and write the correct letter, **A–F**, next to Questions **16–20**.*

Equipment		Comments
16 early wooden-framed TV	....	**A** too large
17 early radios	....	**B** boring
18 microwave ovens	....	**C** more convenient
19 laptops	....	**D** exciting
20 old cameras	....	**E** well-constructed
		F still looked fashionable

2   🗣 What is the oldest piece of technology you still use?

Word building: Evaluating adjectives

1   It is important to be able to evaluate ideas and recognise when ideas are being qualified. Look at the following extract from the listening script:

We have had loads of entries from secondary schools, which is important as more local teenagers are getting involved.

Here the adjective 'important' qualifies the idea in the previous clause.

Work in pairs. Think of synonyms for the following adjectives.

unimportant   useless   valueless   harmless

2   Now think of synonyms for their opposite forms.

important   useful   valuable   harmful

3   For each adjective **1–12** below, write the opposite form in the correct column of the table.

	in-/im-	un-	-less
1 useful			
2 practical			
3 important			
4 necessary			
5 significant			
6 harmful			
7 valuable			
8 convenient			
9 effective			
10 appealing			
11 worthwhile			
12 inspiring			

4   For sentences **1–6** below, decide which adjective from exercise 3 can be used to replace the underlined words. Make any necessary changes.

Example:

Many of the early technologies we take for granted are <u>those that we cannot do without</u>.
necessary

   1 Some ideas from the 1950s were <u>not very sensible or easy to use</u>.

   2 Using hydrogen cars to combat global warming is a solution <u>that produces the desired result</u>.

   3 Satellite navigation systems have made travelling by car <u>something that requires little effort or trouble</u>.

   4 With so much business being done online, learning to build a website can be really <u>worth the time spent on it</u>.

   5 Instead of being an activity <u>which does no harm</u>, mobile phone gaming can sometimes be dangerous.

   6 The work of people like Louis Daguerre, who shaped the world of cinema, can only be considered as <u>stimulating and motivating</u>.

Speaking
Part 2

1 Work in pairs. Make notes of no more than 10 to 12 words about the topic.

┌───┐ ┌───┐
Describe an electronic device which you have bought. You should say:

> what the device is
> where you bought the device
> when you bought the device
> and explain why you bought the device.

Describe an electronic present which you have received. You should say:

> what the present was
> who bought you the present
> when you received the present
> and explain why you liked the present.

2 Compare your notes with another pair who chose the same card. Consider the following:
- the number of words in your notes
- the kinds of words you used (nouns, adjectives, etc)
- if your notes are easy to read at a glance – explain why/why not.

3 Work with a different partner who chose a different card. Take turns talking about the card using your notes to guide you. You should speak for up to two minutes. Time each other using a stopwatch. When your partner has finished speaking, give him/her feedback using the checklist on page 181.

Language focus 1: Past simple and present perfect

1 Look at the following extracts from the Listening on page 227. Then answer the questions below.

a *The first prize in this year's competition has been won by a group of seven young people who chose various exhibits from the museum's collection of equipment.*

b *They arranged them with modern versions and recorded their own reactions …*

c *… the competitors were allowed to use the educational facilities …*

1 Underline the main verbs. Which tense is used, past simple or present perfect?

2 Why do you think different tenses are used in the first two sentences?

3 In which sentences is the passive voice used? Why?

G Read more about the past simple and present perfect in the Grammar reference on page 220.

2 For sentences 1–7, underline the correct verb form in brackets.

1 Not long ago, I (began/have begun/was begun) to study another language.

2 When we (were/have been) young, we (didn't have/haven't had) many toys, but children nowadays (became/have become/have been become) used to having lots of toys and games.

3 Recently, companies (started/have started/have been started) thinking about moving into space tourism.

4 I first (went/have gone/have been gone) to South America in the early seventies, but I (never visited/have never visited/have never been visited) Asia.

5 (Did you ever see/Have you ever seen/Did you ever seen) the Northern Lights?

6 In the past five years, survival rates for people with certain illnesses (improved/have improved/have been improved).

7 Yesterday, I (did/have done/have been done) something I (did not do/have not done/have not been done) before. I (spent/have spent/have been spent) the whole day reading a novel.

3 For sentences 1–8 below, decide if the verb in brackets should be active or passive. Then put it into the past simple.

1 The invention of the plough (revolutionise) agriculture.

2 What (contribute) to the rapid pace of change in the world in the 20th century?

3 The impact of a comet (lead) to the extinction of the dinosaurs.

4 Chess first (play) in India.

5 The radio (invent) in Italy by Marconi.

6 When people (create) cities, it (shape) the way the human race (live) forever.

7 Before the advent of transport, people (travel) for days between countries.

8 The mountainous landscape in Greece (influence) the development of ancient city states.

4 Write five statements about yourself, using the structure *I have never … , but I …* and the time phrases below.

The day before yesterday …   *Last week/month/year …*
Three days/weeks ago …   *The week before last …*

5 Work in pairs. Tell your partner your sentences. Then ask each other questions to find out more details. Use the following words in your questions: *when, why, why not, what, how, who, where.*

READING PASSAGE

*You should spend about 20 minutes on **Questions 1–13**, which are based on the Reading Passage below.*

The long period of the Bronze Age in China, which began around 2000 B.C., saw the growth and maturity of a civilization that would be sustained in its essential aspects for another 2,000 years. In the early stages of this development, the process of urbanization went hand in hand with the establishment of a social order. In China, as in other societies, the mechanism that generated social cohesion, and at a later stage statecraft, was ritualization. As most of the paraphernalia for early rituals were made in bronze and as rituals carried such an important social function, it is perhaps possible to read into the forms and decorations of these objects some of the central concerns of the societies (at least the upper sectors of the societies) that produced them.

There were probably a number of early centers of bronze technology, but the area along the Yellow River in present-day Henan Province emerged as the center of the most advanced and literate cultures of the time and became the seat of the political and military power of the Shang dynasty (ca. 1600–1050 B.C.), the earliest archaeologically recorded dynasty in Chinese history. The Shang dynasty was conquered by the people of Zhou, who came from farther up the Yellow River in the area of Xi'an in Shaanxi Province. In the first years of the Zhou dynasty (ca. 1046–256 B.C.), known as the Western Zhou (ca. 1046–771 B.C.), the ruling house of Zhou exercised a certain degree of 'imperial' power over most of central China. With the move of the capital to Luoyang in 771 B.C., however, the power of the Zhou rulers declined and the country divided into a number of nearly autonomous feudal states with nominal allegiance to the emperor. The second phase of the Zhou dynasty, known as the Eastern Zhou (771–256 B.C.), is subdivided into two periods, the Spring and Autumn period (770–ca. 475 B.C.) and the Warring States period (ca. 475–221 B.C.). During the Warring States period, seven major states contended for supreme control of the country, ending with the unification of China under the Qin in 221 B.C.

Although there is uncertainty as to when metallurgy began in China, there is reason to believe that early bronze-working developed autonomously, independent of outside influences. The era of the Shang and the Zhou dynasties is generally known as the Bronze Age of China, because bronze, an alloy of copper and tin, used to fashion weapons, parts of chariots, and ritual vessels, played an important role in the material culture of the time. Iron appeared in China toward the end of the period, during the Eastern Zhou dynasty.

One of the most distinctive and characteristic images decorating Shang-dynasty bronze vessels is the so-called taotie. The primary attribute of this frontal animal-like mask is a prominent pair of eyes, often protruding in high relief. Between the eyes is a nose, often with nostrils at the base. Taotie can also include jaws and fangs, horns, ears, and eyebrows. Many versions include a split animal-like body with legs and tail, each flank shown in profile on either side of the mask. While following a general form, the appearance and specific components of taotie masks varied by period and place of production. Other common motifs for Shang ritual bronze vessels were dragons, birds, bovine creatures, and a variety of geometric patterns. Currently, the significance of the taotie, as well as the other decorative motifs, in Shang society is unknown.

Jade, along with bronze, represents the highest achievement of Bronze Age material culture. In many respects, the Shang dynasty can be regarded as the culmination of 2,000 years of the art of jade carving. Shang craftsmen had full command of the artistic and technical language developed in the diverse late Neolithic cultures that had a jade-working tradition. On the other hand, some developments in Shang and Zhou jade carving can be regarded as evidence of decline. While Bronze Age jade workers no doubt had better tools – if only the advantage of metal ones – the great patience and skill of the earlier period seem to be lacking.

If the precise function of ritual jades in the late Neolithic is indeterminate, such is not the case in the Bronze Age. Written records and archaeological evidence inform us that jades were used in sacrificial offerings to gods and ancestors, in burial rites, for recording treaties between states, and in formal ceremonies at the courts of kings.

How to go about it

For **Questions 1–6**:
- Look for words and paraphrases of words that help you scan for the answer.

For **Questions 7–12**:
- Find the words bronze, taotie and jade in the passage and (circle) them so you can see them easily.
- Read the statements and underline the information to scan for.
- Scan the passage for words and paraphrases of words in the questions.

For **Question 13**:
- Look for the title that focuses on all the information in the text, not just part of it.

Questions 1–6

Do the following statements agree with the information given in the Reading Passage?

Write:

TRUE   *if the statement agrees with the information*
FALSE   *if the statement contradicts the information*
NOT GIVEN *if there is no information on this*

1   As the migration of people to towns and cities took place, Chinese society became more unified.

2   According to evidence that has been unearthed, the Zhou people lost power to the Shang.

3   At the end of the Zhou dynasty, there were nine powers seeking to rule China.

4   Iron was introduced to China from outside.

5   There was only one type of taotie.

6   There is some proof that later jade carving was superior to earlier examples.

Questions 7–12

Classify the following descriptions as relating to

A Bronze

B Taotie

C Jade

List of Descriptions

7   Its features depended on when and where it was made.

8   Its meaning in one period of history is still a mystery.

9   Its decoration illustrates issues the elite in China dealt with.

10   It was not worked with the same degree of sophistication as in previous times.

11   It possibly sprang up spontaneously without any help from beyond China.

12   It was used for keeping a record of formal agreements between states.

Question 13

*Choose the correct letter **A, B, C** or **D**.*

Which of the following is the most suitable title for the Reading Passage?

A The importance of jade carvings

B The Chinese Bronze Age

C The decline of the Bronze Age

D How iron was introduced to China

1   *'History has nothing to teach us, so there is no point dwelling on the past.'*

Do you agree with the statement? Does ancient history have any relevance today?

Language focus 2: Habit in the past

1 *Would* and *used to* show repeated actions/activities that no longer happen. Look at the following extracts from the Listening on page 227 and answer the questions:

   a *They remembered how they would sometimes all go round to … ,*

   b *… all of whom used to have one …*

    1 Which sentence is reminiscing about the past?

    2 Which sentence is used to describe repeated actions/ activities?

    3 Which sentence is used to talk about states that no longer exist?

G Read more about *would* and *used to* in the Grammar reference on page 220.

2 For **1–8** below, decide which sentences are correct. Then decide why the incorrect sentences are wrong.

    1 I would work at the post office during holidays.

    2 Students used to play silly games, but they would enjoy them thoroughly.

    3 Pat would work as a lawyer, but he didn't do it for long.

    4 People in my hometown would always hold lots of parties.

    5 He used to fix engines and would build his own car.

    6 My brothers and sisters didn't use to go to university. They went straight into work after secondary school.

    7 As a rule, people left their doors unlocked; there never used to be any break-ins.

    8 People didn't use to throw things away as much as they do now. They mended them instead.

Adverbs of frequency

1 Look at the following sentence from the Listening on page 227 and <u>underline</u> the adverb of frequency.

They remembered how they would sometimes all go round to someone's house to watch TV as a special treat.

Decide which gap this word fits below.

1	Always	100%
2	_____	
3	Frequently	
4	_____	
5	Seldom	
6	Never	0%

2 Complete the remaining gap with a suitable adverb of frequency.

3 Decide where in the chart you can add the following words.

> occasionally   often   not often   usually   regularly
> hardly ever   rarely   commonly

G Read more about adverbs of frequency in the Grammar reference on page 220.

4 For **1–6** below, decide if the adverb of frequency in *italics* is suitable. Replace the adverbs that are not suitable.

    1 I *always* read the newspaper in the morning. I only read it in the afternoon.

    2 I would *sometimes* play games with my friends in the evenings. We used to meet up about five times a week.

    3 I *never* played computer games when I was very young, but I used to play them a lot as a teenager.

    4 The class *seldom* meet up after school. This happens only once in a while.

    5 Where I come from even strangers *usually* greet each other when they meet. It's rare for them not to.

    6 In some parts of the world people *hardly ever* leave their villages, maybe only once in a lifetime.

5 Write a sentence about your childhood and early life for each of the sentence beginnings below.

Example:

I would …

I would go to the river near my home rather than sit at home all day in front of the TV.

    1 I used to …

    2 I would sometimes …

    3 I used to always …

    4 I would hardly ever …

Writing
Task 2

1 Work in pairs. Read the Task 2 question below and answer the questions which follow.

What to expect in the exam

- In IELTS Writing Task 2, you have to write an essay on a topic of general interest.
- You are asked to write at least 250 words.
- You should spend about 40 minutes on this task.

WRITING TASK 2

You should spend about 40 minutes on this task.

Write about the following topic:

> *Some people believe that technology has led to many positive developments in their lives, while others think technology is gradually taking over control of the way people live. Discuss both these views and give your own opinion.*

Give reasons for your answer and include any relevant examples from your own knowledge or experience.

Write at least 250 words.

1 Which part of the statement contains a positive development and which part contains a negative development?

2 Which of the two views do the notes below relate to? Give reasons and examples.

  a more convenient/greater convenience

  b harmful to society

  c affecting production at work negatively

  d more practical

2 You can generate ideas by thinking of opposites. What are the opposites of the ideas in exercise 1? Can you think of examples to support them.

3 What other ways can you use to generate ideas?

4 Work in pairs. When you write an introduction it needs to reflect the structure and meaning of the writing task. Look at the following introductions for the writing task above. Decide which two are suitable and why.

  1 In some people's eyes, the influence of technology over our lives is beneficial and yet to others it is harmful.

  2 Technology is part of our daily lives. While some people see this situation has brought many improvements, others feel that technology is too controlling. Personally, I think that technology is largely beneficial.

  3 With recent scientific advances, it is argued by some that many positive changes have been brought about in people's lives by technology. Other people believe, however, that we are losing control of our lives to technology. Personally, I feel it is a mixture of both.

5 Improve the introduction which is not suitable in exercise 4 above.

How to go about it

- Two different views are expressed in this question. Make two columns A and B. Choose one of the views and write a list of ideas in column A in one to two minutes. Do not exclude any ideas. Then write a list of opposing views in column B. Select one or two ideas from each column.
- Express your own opinion either by supporting one view or balancing the two views.
- Write an introduction that paraphrases the question. Keep the introduction brief – two to three sentences is enough.
- Write two paragraphs for the views in the question and one for your own view followed by a conclusion.

6   The paragraph below develops the writer's own opinion in answer to the Task 2 question on page 26. Read the paragraph and match it to one of the two suitable introductions in exercise 4.

> To some people, technology is controlling their lives. **However**, I feel it is a mixture of positive and negative effects, **because** technology **like** smartphones has brought enormous improvements. Take, **for example**, the impact of technology on communication. Smartphones have revolutionised the way items **such as** personal and commercial messages are sent with the electronic transmission of messages. **Moreover**, very large files such as reports that were once sent by post can now be transmitted electronically **in order to** save time and money. **As a result**, people and the economy benefit.

7   Put each of the linking words in bold in exercise 6 into the correct box in the table below.

	Example	Reason	Result	Additional Information	Purpose	Contrast
Adverb						
Conjunction						
Other						

8   Decide what other words can be used to indicate examples and add them to the table.

9   Decide which words in the box below can be used to replace the words in exercises 6 and 7 and add them to the table.

> but   although   since   as   similarly   furthermore
> consequently   so   therefore   also   and so   to

10 Rewrite the paragraph in exercise 6 by doing at least two of the following:
   • changing all the examples in the paragraph
   • changing the linking words in bold in the paragraph
   • changing some of the nouns and verbs
   • changing the adjectives.

   Check that your new paragraph reads well. Compare your paragraph with a partner.

11 Write your own answer for the Task 2 question on page 209. When you have finished, check your answer using the checklist on page 139.

Vocabulary: Verbs of cause and effect

1 Identify the nouns and verbs that are related to cause and effect.

   1 In the last 10 years, considerable improvements in health care have been brought about by technology.

   2 Computer waste has seriously damaged the environment.

   3 Scientific research has led to some startling technical advances such as driverless cars.

   4 Smartphone technology has been responsible for improvements in global communication.

   5 Certain inventions such as the jet engine have had a profound effect on air travel.

   6 In future, inventions such as 3D printing will make industrial production easier.

   7 The rapid pace of advances in technology has resulted in greater stress among workers compared to the past.

   8 New techniques in design have changed the shape of the automobile world.

2 Rewrite the sentences in exercise 1 in your own words so that the effect occurs before the cause in each sentence. There may be more than one answer. Make any necessary changes.

   Example:

   Major advances in manufacturing have resulted from a sharp increase in automation.
   A sharp increase in automation has resulted in major advances in manufacturing.

3 Look at the sentences you have written and <u>underline</u> the effect in each sentence.

Word building: Evaluating adjectives

1 Remove the word 'not' from each sentence below and make the qualifying adjective positive or negative.

   1 Having advanced computer skills is not necessary for all workers.

   2 Travelling daily to an office is not convenient for modern workers.

   3 Inventions like the radio and TV are often seen as not important by some people.

   4 Using computers for long periods of time is definitely not harmless.

   5 I think having a knowledge of computer programming is not valueless.

   6 The changes in the sales figures were not significant.

   7 In my opinion, the software training was not effective.

   8 Doing the language games on the computer was certainly not a worthless exercise.

   9 It is not practical to have everyone studying the same subjects at university.

   10 The lecture on technology in the workplace was not inspiring.

Language focus 1: Past simple and present perfect

1   Use the past simple and the present perfect once each in the sentences below.

    1   Technology (transform) all professional fields, since the first commercial personal computer (come) on the market in the early 1970s.

    2   I first (visit) the science museum in my teens and (go) back many times in recent years.

    3   Last week, I (install) several maps on my phone, which (help) me enormously.

    4   The education I (receive) as a child (shape) my life.

    5   I (rarely ever use) my phone to make video calls, so this morning I (download) some new software.

    6   What (happen) education-wise at secondary school (influence) my whole life.

    7   I (need) to have a computing qualification of some kind for the job, even though I (build) up lots of experience over the years.

    8   Attendances (rise) over the whole period, even though they (dip) noticeably in 2016.

    9   The year before last (be) the most boring period in my life, yet since then everything (be) rather exciting.

    10 Communication (definitely be) less stressful since the smartphone (become) available.

Language focus 2: Habit in the past

1   In the following extract from IELTS Speaking Part 2, underline and correct the five mistakes in the verbs and verb phrases in *italics*. Decide what the candidate was asked to describe.

'The place I'd like to describe is my hometown, where I lived until I was ten years old. I **1** *hadn't visited* my hometown for the last 15 years. So recently I **2** *decided* to pay a short visit. I can't say that I **3** *would know* what to expect. Fields where I **4** *would play* with my friends **5** *were now covered* with buildings and the school I **6** *would attend* is no longer there. It **7** *has been turned* into a supermarket. A lot of famous people **8** *used to attend* the school, so I am surprised that permission **9** *was given* to knock it down.

If I remember rightly, it **10** *would rain* a lot when I was a child, but **11** *it has never seemed* to annoy us kids. We **12** *have just carried on* regardless.'

Accuracy in IELTS

1   Identify the linking words and devices below. Underline and correct those that are not used properly.

New technology has changed student life forever. Because with the internet students can access information for essays and do research from anywhere, for example, they can work at home or in cafés or on trains without going to a library. Students can now use resources such as articles, books, videos and lectures online and watch lectures that they have missed.

Furthermore, the books students need at the library can often be reserved online or they can go on the internet. In order to buy books and have them delivered next day. As a result, considerable amounts of time can be saved, though, technology may also make the studying process much more convenient, it can cut students off from each other and so it is important for them to meet face to face in seminars and lectures.

2   Decide which of these words and phrases can replace those in exercise 1 without making any changes: *moreover, like, to, consequently, since*.

3 Thrill seekers

Vocabulary: Sports

1 🗣 With a partner, describe what is happening in each of the photographs. Then discuss the questions below.

- Which of these activities would you like/not like to try?
- Which activity do you think is the most exciting/popular/risky?
- What is the attraction of extreme sports compared with activities such as playing video games or reading?

2 For **1–8** in the table below, decide what sport is connected with the place and the equipment. There may be more than one possible answer.

Sport	Place	Equipment
1	pitch	ball/goal
2	ring	gloves/shorts
3	track	shoes/spikes
4	gym	weights
5	pool	costume
6	sea	skis
7	court	racket/ball
8	course	clubs/irons

3 Work in pairs. Give at least one example of each type of sport in **1–10** below. You may use a dictionary to help you, if necessary.

1 motor	**2** water	**3** racket	**4** winter	**5** outdoor
6 table	**7** combat	**8** equestrian	**9** indoor	**10** team

4 Are extreme sports popular among your friends/in your home country? Why/Why not?

Listening
Section 3

1 Work in pairs. Look at the instructions and questions. For **21–30**, predict the part of speech for each answer (e.g. noun, verb or adjective). Then decide which words will help show you that the answer is about to be given.

What to expect in the exam

- In Section 3, there are two speakers, for example, students with or without a tutor. You need to concentrate and learn to recognise who is speaking.
- The discussion is usually about a subject of an academic nature.

How to go about it

- Skim the questions to get an idea of the topic of what you will hear.
- Mark any specific information in tables, especially headings.
- Try to decide the type of word that is required, for example, noun, adjective, noun phrase, number, verb, etc. Also try to decide whether nouns are singular or plural.
- Always check the number of words required.
- Do not write *any* words from the questions in your answers.

🎧 03 **SECTION 3** *Questions 21–30*

Questions 21–25

Complete the notes below.

Write **NO MORE THAN TWO WORDS AND/OR A NUMBER** *for each answer.*

Janson Adventure Sports Centre

Purpose of case study

- to look at why it was more **21** .... compared to other centres

Centre interviews

- at least 600 members overall
- 43 staff including **22** ....
- Interviewed around **23** ....
- Face-to-face interviews preferable to a questionnaire
- Would be able to ask for **24** .... where necessary
- Good administration/very focused managers
- Management team has **25** .... from those using the Centre

Questions 26–30

Complete the table below.

Write **NO MORE THAN TWO WORDS** *for each answer.*

Reasons for Centre's success

Reasons	Comments by researchers	Purpose
courses promoting team spirit and **26**	crucial	to maintain people's **27** .... in the Centre
quality of **28**	professional	encouraging people to reach their **29** ....
range of courses and the **30** .... available	thrilling	to become the best in their field

2 Check your answers to exercise 1 above.

3 👥 Work in pairs. Can sport help people to build confidence? How? Give reasons and examples.

Language focus 1: Adjectives with prepositions

1 Some adjectives are followed by a particular preposition. For example, in the Listening on page 228, Marco says:

'They are also very motivating leaders, who are passionate about what they do.'

For **1–10** below, underline the correct preposition in *italics*.

1 I am very keen *about/on/for* swimming, especially first thing in the morning.

2 Some people are addicted *by/with/to* watching sports. They spend all their time glued to the TV.

3 He's mad *for/to/about* parachuting. It's something I personally can't understand.

4 I'm not interested *in/by/with* going to the gym.

5 I easily get bored *in/about/with* doing nothing.

6 I can't say I'm indifferent *in/to/about* sport, but I don't like spending my time watching it.

7 I used to be very enthusiastic *on/about/with* team sports, but not anymore.

8 I'm not sure I'm capable *to/for/of* running for long distances.

9 I'm really passionate *for/about/on* travelling around the world and meeting fellow hockey enthusiasts.

10 I am fond *about/to/of* travelling, but my brother is completely fanatical *for/about/with* visiting new places.

(G) Read more about adjectives with prepositions in the Grammar reference on page 220.

2 Work in pairs. Match the sentence beginnings **1–7** with the endings **a–g**. It is possible to match some of the sentence beginnings with more than one ending.

1	I am mad	**a**	to any kind of physical activity.
2	I am not keen	**b**	about playing computer games.
3	I am bored	**c**	on team sports.
4	I am interested	**d**	in walking in the countryside.
5	I am passionate	**e**	with watching sport on TV.
6	I am fond	**f**	about doing all kinds of exercise.
7	I am indifferent	**g**	of reading sports magazines.

3 Look at questions **1–6** below. Underline the items in *italics* that are most suitable for you.

1 Which sport do you like the most?

   football   horse-riding   swimming

2 Who do you prefer doing it with?

   a colleague   a friend   nobody

3 How often do you like doing it?

   once a week   twice a week   three times a week

4 When do you normally like to do it?

   mornings   afternoons   evenings

5 How would you describe your attitude to the sport?

   interested   enthusiastic   addicted

6 Why do you enjoy doing it?

   challenging   exciting   exhilarating

4 Explain your answers to a partner using the adjectives and prepositions in exercise 1.

Speaking Part 1

What to expect in the exam

- In IELTS Speaking Part 1 you are asked about familiar topics, for example, common pastimes in your country now compared with the past.
- In Part 1, the discussion is more personal (for example about yourself, your home and the country where you live).

1 Make examiner's questions from the following lists of words.

1 what kinds/sports/popular/your country?

2 do you/the same sports now/past?

3 are/same games/popular/as in past/where you live?

4 do young people/more physical activities/extreme sports/now/past?

5 what makes these games/interesting/people?

6 sports/challenging/now than they/in the past

7 young people/challenged more/nowadays/in the past?

2 Work in pairs. Take turns playing the role of the examiner and the candidate. Ask and answer the questions.

Word building: Adjectives ending in *-ing/-ed*

1 Look at the extracts from answers to questions **1** and **2** of the speaking practice opposite.
I feel sports are more challenging than they used to be.
Younger people can feel challenged by some sports at school.

- What is the difference between the two types of adjective made from the word *challenge*?
- Now complete the gaps by adding *challenging* (x 2) and *challenged* (x 2) to the following:

Verb + *-ing*: *challenging* Something is _____ if it makes me feel _____.

Verb + *-ed*: *challenged*   I feel _____ because something is _____.

Adjectives ending in *-ing/-ed* like *challenging* and *challenged* are used to evaluate or express an opinion about something. You can use adjectives like this in your speaking and writing to express your judgement about an idea, event, experience, etc.

2 For **1–8** below, underline the correct adjective in *italics*.

1 Do you find sports like parkour *thrilling/thrilled* to watch?

2 Do you think people become *irritating/irritated* by the constant encouragement to do something physical?

3 Why do you think people are *interesting/interested* in extreme sports?

4 Do you think sports stars are as *inspiring/inspired* for young people now as in the past?

5 What makes funfair rides like roller coasters *exciting/excited*?

6 Are you the sort of person who considers sports programmes on TV *annoying/annoyed*, or do you get *annoying/annoyed* by other types of programmes?

7 Do you think extreme sports are more *challenging/challenged* than other sports?

8 Do you feel *invigorated/invigorating* when you do any type of energetic activity?

3 Work in pairs. Choose three questions from exercise 1 to ask your partner. Take turns asking and answering the questions. Give reasons and examples in your answers.

4 Work in pairs. For **1–8** below, use a form of the word in brackets (noun, verb or adjective) to complete the sentences.

1 It is rare to see a whole stadium (excite) by a player's performance.

2 These days I don't think people feel (challenge) enough physically at school or work.

3 Where I come from people find football more (interest) than other sports.

4 Some extreme sports like snowboarding seem to be (fascinate) for young people.

5 Being (motivate) helps with improving and achieving your potential at a particular sport.

6 For some people computer games are as (excite) as real sports.

7 People often feel (refresh) after doing activities like yoga.

8 Other people may find as much (excite) in reading a book as in climbing a mountain.

5 Work in pairs and make two questions about sport with an adjective ending in *-ing/-ed*. Ask your questions to students in another pair.

Speaking
Part 3

What to expect in the exam

- In Part 3 you have a discussion with the examiner which is linked to the topic of Part 2. However, the questions are more abstract and you need to talk about general ideas, not about yourself and your own experiences.

How to go about it

- Develop your ideas by using simple linking devices to express purposes, results and contrasts.
- Give reasons and examples.
- Make sure you speak fluently, but not rapidly.
- As the discussion is about turn-taking, be aware of the examiner's desire to ask you questions as you speak.

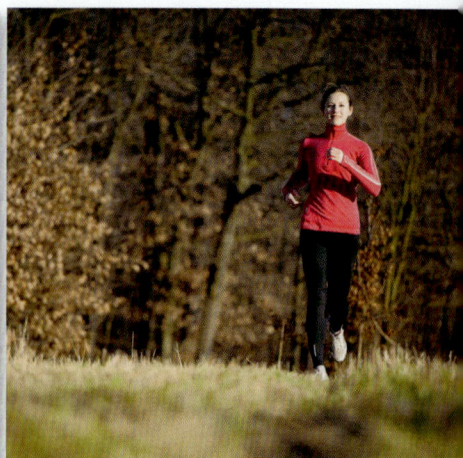

1 Decide which three of the following phrases describe the main reasons for people doing sport. Then discuss your answers with a partner, giving reasons and examples.

   1 to keep fit

   2 so they can lose weight

   3 so that they can make friends

   4 in order to help them relax

   5 so as to get an adrenaline rush

   6 in order to improve their performance

2 Underline the words in **1–6** above that indicate purpose. Then use these phrases to write your own sentences explaining why you do sporting activities.

3 It is important to give variety to what you say. Rephrase items **1–6** using the following structure: *because they + want/would like/would rather/would rather not/like to … .* Make any necessary changes.

4 Work in pairs. Look at the Part 3 questions below and choose one or two questions from each set. Briefly discuss them using the expressions of purpose in exercise 1. Then take turns asking each other the questions. When your partner has finished speaking, give him/her feedback using the checklist on page 181.

Physical activity

Do you think that doing physical activity is important nowadays? Why/Why not?

What are the advantages and disadvantages of doing any kind of physical activity?

In what ways can people be encouraged to adopt a less sedentary and more physically active lifestyle?

Benefits of sport

What are some of the social benefits of doing sporting activities? Which is the most important?

Are we more risk averse than we were in the past, that is, do we seek to avoid risks nowadays? Why is this?

Some people think that there are benefits to the individual and society of people being involved in sports. To what extent do you agree or disagree?

---

1 Work in pairs. Look at the photograph. Describe what kinds of rides you would expect to find in an amusement park or fairground.

READING PASSAGE

You should spend about 20 minutes on **Questions 1–13**, *which are based on the Reading Passage below.*

Readers can join a unique experiment to discover what goes on in our brains and bodies at the fairground

Roger Highfield reports.

A For decades, thrill-seekers have happily queued to experience a few seconds of the adrenaline-spiking, intestine-twisting thrills of roller coaster and other funfair joy rides. Nowadays, people also spend hours living out the virtual excitement of computer games.

B An experiment will soon lay bare the science of thrills and help to build the foundation of the next generation of funfair rides and sensational computer games. Brendan Walker, a self-proclaimed 'thrill engineer', is curating this extraordinary venture where people can become a guinea pig. Fairground: Thrill Laboratory, at the Science Museum's Dana Centre, will include three different rides over three weeks — the Booster, to measure the physiology of excitement and thrill; a ghost train, to measure fear and the tingle of anticipation; and Miami Trip, a gentler ride designed to explore pleasure.

C One of the collaborators in the thrill lab is Prof Tom Rodden. Its impetus is the blurring of the boundary between the real and the digital worlds, he explained: 'Today, trainers count footsteps, wrist watches can measure heart rate, satellites can detect where we are and, all the while, computer games are being played in the streets not just the living room, and computer accessories such as joysticks are being replaced with real-world objects such as tennis racquets.'

D Doctors already understand the broad effects of joy rides. As a roller coaster puts the body through weightlessness, high gravitational forces and acceleration, the brain struggles to make sense of conflicting and changing signals from the senses. There are effects on the vestibular system, located in the inner ear, that detects position and motion, and on the somatic nervous system, which controls voluntary systems in the body, such as heartbeat.

E Added to the confusion of these signals are the messages from the eye, which may be different from those of the other systems. This can lead to peculiar effects such as the vection illusion (think of when you are stopped at a traffic light and the car next to you edges forward — you feel as though you are moving).

F Overall the brain responds to an exhilarating ride by triggering the release of a potent cocktail of biochemicals to deal with the body's stress, including more adrenaline (epinephrine) and norepinephrine which can suppress pain and boost the glow of euphoria that follows. The result can be pleasure but can also be nausea. Military and Nasa researchers have studied the problem for half a century, calling it 'simulator sickness'.

G But engineers and scientists have not figured out how to fool the senses at the same rate at the same time. They still don't know for sure who might get sick. Meanwhile, the latest rides are pushing the boundaries of endurance. The human body cannot take much more of a G-force than the latest rollercoasters, so we need to understand more about what distinguishes a spine-tingling thrill from a gut-emptying fright to ensure the experience is memorable for the right reasons.

H   At the thrill lab, volunteers will be asked to try the fairground rides while hooked up to special equipment. This includes an accelerometer that measures the G-force their body is subjected to; a measure of blood oxygen levels; measures of skin conductance (sweating) and an ECG monitor that keeps track of their heart rate. In addition, a helmet-mounted video camera will film their expressions, from the first gasp to the last scream. As with astronauts and test pilots, information will be beamed in real time to a computer. And measurements will be displayed publicly. Aside from providing amusement for onlookers, participants can relive their terrifying experiences.

I   This study will help designers of amusement parks to squeeze more shrieks out of people by creating the illusion of imminent death, said Prof Rodden. Equally, the next generation of rides will sense when too many people feel nauseous and wind down accordingly. In short, they will be able to distinguish terror from titillation. This work will also help computer games to escape the boundaries of the Xbox and PlayStation. Steve Benford, of the mixed-reality lab at the University of Nottingham, believes that the thrill lab will help to design more immersive rides and games, 'real-time adaptive spaces'.

How to go about it

For **Questions 1–6**:
- Read the instructions carefully and check if you can use any letter once only or more than once. In this instance, you can use any letter more than once.
- Check if any of the information in the phrases looks as if it might fit together in the same paragraph.
- Check if any pieces of information will follow other information in the list.

Questions 1–6

The Reading Passage has nine paragraphs, **A–I**.
Which paragraph contains the following information?
NB You may use any letter more than once.

1   the types of rides involved in the experiment
2   what happens chemically in the brain as a result of thrill rides
3   the fact that the volunteers will be filmed during the rides
4   the way the experiment will help computer game designers
5   the impact on the human auditory system
6   what the lab experiments will show members of the public

Questions 7–12

Do the following statements agree with the information given in the Reading Passage?
Write:
    TRUE   *if the statement agrees with the information*
    FALSE   *if the statement contradicts the information*
    NOT GIVEN *if there is no information on this*

7   The excitement from computer games is different from that of thrill rides.
8   The brain has little difficulty processing information it receives during thrill rides.
9   Thrill rides have a greater impact on the heart than the eye.
10   The most recent thrill rides take the body close to its G-force limits.
11   The lab volunteers will consist of equal numbers of men and women.
12   Future rides will be able to adapt to people's reactions.

Question 13

Choose the correct letter *A, B, C,* or *D*.

Which of the following is the most suitable title for the Reading Passage?

A   Roller coasters and their effects on the brain
B   What makes fairground rides so thrilling?
C   The equipment used to test the efficacy of thrill rides
D   How the brain copes with fear in response to thrill rides

2 Do you find funfair rides 'thrilling'? Why do you think people enjoy extreme rides?

Language focus 2: Comparison

1 Look at the following extracts from the Reading Passage on page 35.

    a … *Miami Trip, a gentler ride designed to explore pleasure.*

    b … *the thrill lab will help to design more immersive rides and games …*

Underline the comparative adjectives in the two sentences then answer the questions below.

  1 What is added to the adjective to make a comparison in **a**? Can *more* be used instead? Why/Why not?

  2 How is the comparative formed in **b**? Can it be formed by adding an ending to the adjective instead? Why/Why not?

G Read more about comparison in the Grammar reference on page 221.

2 Complete the table below.

Adjective	Comparative	Superlative
		the worst
	better	
noisy		
wet		
tasty		
cheap		
lively		
appetising		

3 For **1–8** below, put the word in brackets into the correct comparative or superlative form.

  1 People who do some physical activity are supposed to be (happy) than less active people.

  2 It's much (easy) to find places to do specialist sports outside cities and towns.

  3 With more people taking it up, professional bowling is far (popular) than it used to be.

  4 Which sport do you think is (energetic) of all?

  5 It is becoming (difficult) for people to organise their lives around work nowadays.

  6 Is work the (stressful) aspect of modern life?

  7 Is mental activity (important) than physical activity?

  8 People don't realise that racing drivers are (fit) individuals in sport.

4 Work in pairs. Look at sentences **1–8** in exercise 3. Decide what the noun form of each adjective is. Then decide which nouns can be used with these verbs.

have	need/require	enjoy	experience

5 Rewrite sentences **1–8** in exercise 3 using a noun instead of an adjective. You may need to use the verbs above and make any necessary changes.

Example:

People who do some physical activity are supposed to enjoy/have greater happiness than less active people.

6 The questionnaire below contains some mistakes. Rewrite the questions that are incorrect.

Do you agree that …

  1 football is exciting than swimming?

  2 athletics is the most boring activity to watch on TV?

  3 sports like sky-diving are dangerouser than hiking?

  4 you need to be fiter to go cycling than walking?

  5 table tennis is not most exciting sport in the world?

  6 people are lazier now than they were in the past?

  7 rowing is a sport only for fittest people?

  8 tennis is more exhilarating than skiing?

  9 watching sport on TV or the internet is less exciting than seeing it live?

 10 racket sports like squash and tennis are tiring than many other sports?

---

7 Use the questionnaire to interview other students in your class. Ask for reasons and examples. If someone agrees with a statement, put a tick (✔) next to the question.

Writing
Task 1

How to go about it

- Make sure your introduction does not just copy the information in the rubric.
- Write a clear overview.
- Select and compare specific data, but make sure you do not just write a list.

1   Work in pairs. Study the table below and prepare questions about the data using comparative adjectives where possible.

Example:

What is the proportion of men walking for exercise?

Is the proportion of men walking for exercise greater/smaller than women?

WRITING TASK 1

You should spend about 20 minutes on this task.

> The table below shows the participation of people over 15 in selected sports and physical recreation activities by gender in Australia during the period 2011–12.
>
> Summarise the information by selecting and reporting the main features, and make comparisons where relevant.

Write at least 150 words.

Participation in selected sports and physical recreation activities

	Males (%)	Females (%)
Walking for exercise	16.5	30.4
Fitness/Gym	15.1	19.1
Cycling/BMXing	9.8	5.4
Jogging/Running	8.7	6.4
Golf	8.2	0
Swimming/Diving	7.5	8.0
Tennis	4.9	3.4
Netball	0	4.5
Football (outdoor)	4.1	0
Basketball	2.8	0
Yoga	0	3.3
Total	**77.6**	**79.4**

2   Work in pairs. Look at sentences **1–8** below. Find a sentence which does not give true or false information about the data (not given). Then decide whether the other sentences are true or false.

   1 A smaller percentage of men than women went swimming or diving.

   2 There was a far greater proportion of men than women involved in walking.

   3 Proportionately, males were less likely than females to take part in sporting activities.

   4 Nearly twice as many men as women went cycling/BMXing.

   5 The table compares data about male and female involvement in a selection of activities in Australia in 2011/12.

   6 A small percentage of men (2.8 per cent) played football, while no women played.

   7 Jogging/running was the least popular activity overall.

   8 Overall, there are some noticeable differences in the proportions of male and female involvement in the selected activities.

3   Rewrite the sentences in exercise 2 which give false and not given information to make them true.

4   Work in pairs. Match each of the sentences in exercise 2 to a section **a**, **b** or **c** below.

   a the introduction   **b** the overview   **c** specific data

5   Work in pairs. Look at the overview in question **8** of exercise 2. Paraphrase the sentence using the following:

   It is clear that the participation of _____ .

6   Explain how you paraphrased the sentence and suggest other ways of paraphrasing.

7   <u>Underline</u> the words and phrases used to make comparisons in questions **1–8** in exercise 2.

8   Rewrite sentences **1–6** below using the words and phrases in the box. Make any necessary changes.

a smaller proportion of	a third of the number of	40% of	three-quarters
half five times the number of	over 50%		

Example:

Twice as many cars were sold in June compared to March.

Half as many cars were sold in March compared to June.

   1 The football match was attended by three times as many spectators as the rugby match.

   2 The sports department was visited by only 20 per cent of the shoppers in February 2009 when compared to February 2008.

   3 More than four out of every ten competitors were from the main city.

   4 The bulk of players were from overseas rather than home-grown.

   5 A quarter of the members of the sports club paid by cash rather than credit card.

   6 The team lost just under half of the games they played last season.

9   Write your own answer for the Task 1 question on page 206. When you have finished, check your answer using the checklist on page 139.

Vocabulary: Sports

1 Add these words to the correct space below.

water	outdoor	table tennis	track-and-field
racket	boxing	winter	baseball	car-racing

1 He enjoys doing _____ sports such as skiing and ice-skating.

2 Team sports, for instance football and _____ , are good for developing social not just physical skills.

3 To practise for _____ sports like athletics, good running shoes are essential.

4 Participation in motor sports like _____ can be expensive.

5 Practising _____ sports is problematic if you don't have access to a lake or the sea.

6 _____ sports like rugby still attract many fans even in bad weather.

7 People can participate in indoor sports like badminton and _____ all year.

8 Tennis is a _____ sport that can be played both indoors and outdoors.

9 Combat sports include ju-jitsu and _____ .

Word building: Adjectives ending in -ing/-ed

1 Make an adjective ending in -ing or -ed using the word in brackets below.

1 I was (thrill) by the football match, even though I rarely find sport on TV (thrill).

2 After a day's work, people are often not (motivate) enough to do exercise.

3 The extreme sport I think is the most (excite) to watch is snowboarding, but I do get (excite) by other sports.

4 Some extreme sports are (fascinate) to watch; I am always (fascinate) by people's reasons for getting involved in something so dangerous.

5 I know a work out at the gym is (invigorate), but I sometimes find gyms really (irritate).

6 Sports commentators on TV can be (annoy), but no doubt speaking live is (challenge).

7 Whether you are (interest) in one type of team sport or another depends on what type of interaction you find (interest).

Language focus 1: Adjectives with prepositions

1 Make seven sentences using the items below. Two items cannot be used.

I'm addicted	As a keen motorist, I'm not interested	with life.	for travelling
She's very fit and capable	to all kinds of video games.	about is gymnastics.	on fitness.
of playing tennis for a long time.	in walking holidays.	I'm a cyclist and keen	As my grandfather's very active, he's the sort of person who rarely gets bored
The sport that I am most enthusiastic	It's my sister that's mad	by singing.	about football, not me.

Language focus 2: Comparison

1 Put the adjective in brackets into the correct comparative or superlative form.

1 Is your neighbourhood usually (lively) than this?

No, it's (dull) area in town.

2 The park is (quiet) for running in the morning compared to the afternoon.

I agree. It's much (noise) after the schools finish.

3 She's (energetic) student on the sports field.

Yet she used to be (lazy) than everyone else.

4 Cycling is (difficult) sport of all.

No. I think it's much (easy) than long-distance running.

2 Choose an appropriate ending to complete sentences **1–6**.

fitter	expensive	popularer	better
sadder	important	more happy	popular

1 As people seek more adventure, extreme sports are now definitely more …

2 Of all the benefits from participating in any kind of sport, fitness is the most …

3 Walking is as good as any sporting activity if people want to be …

4 If we compare indoor and outdoor sports, I think the latter is much …

5 Even with the stresses of modern life, do you think people are happier or …

6 Do you think out of all sports motor racing is perhaps the most …

Accuracy in IELTS

1 Correct the mistake in each sentence below.

1 Nearly twice as many spectators watched the football match live on the internet compare to the last time.

2 There were far fewer men than women involving in walking.

3 Generaly speaking, similar proportions of males and females participated in each sport.

4 Males were less likly than females to take part in running.

5 A greater proportion of women than man participated in badminton.

6 The table compare data about male and female involvement in a range of sports in New Zealand last year.

7 Compared to last year, more than twice as many male took up keep-fit classes.

8 In 2016, a much large proportion of girls (15.89%) played football in sharp contrast to 2015.

9 Kayaking was the less popular extreme sport.

Introduction

The IELTS Listening test has 40 questions and lasts approximately 30 minutes. There are four sections each with ten questions.

The first two sections are of a social nature. Section 1 is a conversation between two people and Section 2 is usually a monologue. However, Section 2 can also be a conversation between two people. Sections 3 and 4 are connected with education and training. Section 3 is a conversation involving up to four people and Section 4 is usually a monologue.

You hear each section once only and answer the questions in the question booklet as you listen. A brief description is given at the beginning of each section. At the beginning of Section 1 an example is always given. You are given time to check your answers at the end of each section. At the end of the test you have *ten minutes* to transfer your answers to the answer sheet. The question types used are:

- classification
- labelling a diagram/plan/map
- matching
- multiple-choice
- note/form/summary/table/flow-chart completion
- selecting items from a list
- sentence completion
- short-answer questions.

Section 1

Section 1 is a conversation between two speakers in a social setting (for example, enrolling in a club or buying something), which involves the exchange of information like personal details.

The section has two parts. You will be given time to look at the questions before each part. Note a range of question types is used in Section 1, not just form completion.

1 🎧 04 Listen and follow the instructions.

SECTION 1 *Questions 1–10*

Questions 1–6

Complete the form below.

Write **NO MORE THAN TWO WORDS** *for each answer.*

Health Centre Registration

Example	
Reason for visit:	Registration and appointment

Registration for the entire	1 ....
Name:	Clara 2 ....
Date of birth:	3 1990
Old address:	72 Crocket Street
Current address:	4 ....
Post code:	5 ....
Acceptable documents:	Tenancy 6...

Questions 7 and 8

Complete the sentences below.

Write **NO MORE THAN TWO WORDS** *for each answer.*

7 Clara has to .... her daughter from school.

8 Clara's appointment is at 4 pm on ....

Questions 9 and 10

Label the map below.

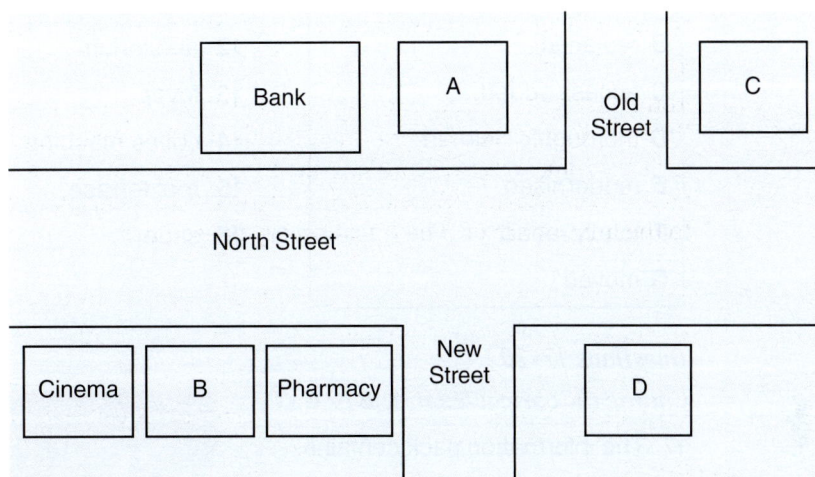

9 Health centre ....

10 Small park ....

2 Work in pairs. Look at the listening script on page 228 and check your answers. Underline the words in the questions which show the answer is about to be given. Match these words with the underlined answers in the script.

3 With your partner, discuss the type of questions you have problems with, for example, writing down numbers, words with plural endings, or answers which are close together or far apart, or completing diagrams. Compare them with another pair of students. Keep a record of the problem areas and think about them while you are studying by yourself and before you do a test.

Section 2

In Section 2 you will *usually* hear a monologue of a social nature like a radio broadcast or a talk about a place, but be aware than you may also hear a conversation between two people.

There may be two or three types of question. The recording is divided into two parts, but you will be given time to look at the questions before each part.

1 In Questions **11–16** on page 44, decide which you think you should listen for first: items **A–G** or the parts of the theatre **11–16**.

2 Work in pairs. Decide what synonyms you might hear for the words in **A–G**.

3 For Questions **17–20**, underline the word or words which show the answer is about to be given.

4 🎧 05 Listen and follow the instructions.

SECTION 2   *Questions 11–20*

Questions 11–16

Which change has been made to each part of the theatre?
*Choose **SIX** answers from the box and write the correct letter, **A–G**, next to Questions 11–16.*

Theatre changes	Part of the theatre	
A enlarged	11 façade	....
B replaced	12 auditorium	....
C access added	13 foyer	....
D thoroughly cleaned	14 coffee machine	....
E modernised	15 roof terrace	....
F totally rebuilt	16 shop	....
G moved		

Questions 17–20

*Choose the correct letter **A**, **B** or **C**.*

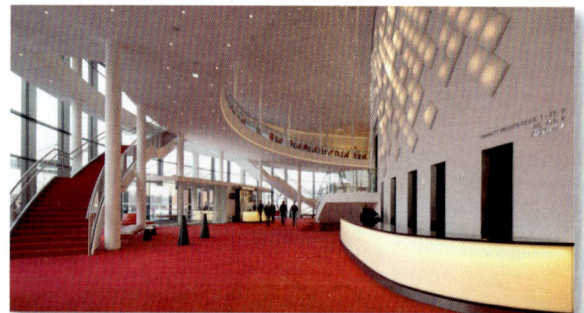

17 The information pack contains,

    A a programme for the evening.

    B details about events over the summer.

    C a list of the event organisers.

18 How many free tickets will those below 16 years of age be allocated for the matinee performance?

    A 100.

    B 200.

    C 300.

19 On Wednesdays, the reduction on ticket prices for theatre members will be

    A 25%.

    B 50%.

    C 33%.

20 A new development at the theatre is the

    A regular lectures and cinematography classes.

    B weekly workshops and master classes.

    C regular lectures and master classes.

Section 3

In Section 3 you will hear a conversation between two to four people on a topic connected with education or training, such as preparing for a tutorial or receiving feedback on an assignment.

There may be only one type of question or up to three. The recording is divided into two parts, but you will be given time to look at the questions before each part.

1 Work in pairs. For Question **21**, decide which word(s) in the stem help prepare you for the answer. Decide what synonym(s) you might hear for each.

2 For Questions **22–24**, decide which aspects of research you think are most likely to be still undecided at the beginning of a research project. Then think of paraphrases for the words in **A–G**.

3 For Questions **25–30**, decide which answers are numbers and which could be plural.

4 🔊 **06** Listen and follow the instructions.

SECTION 3 *Questions 21–30*

Question 21
*Choose the correct letter **A**, **B** or **C**.*

21 Zahra's talk is about how

    A smartphone technology makes young people's lives easier.

    B certain new discoveries led to smartphone technology.

    C the technology of smartphones affects people's lives.

Questions 22–24
*Choose **THREE** letters, **A–G**.*

Which **THREE** of the following elements of conducting Zahra's research are mentioned as not yet decided?

A length of the questionnaire

B images to use

C volume of statistics

D duration of interviews

E period of research

F age of interviewees

G exact aims

Questions 25–30

Complete the table below.

Write **ONE WORD AND/OR A NUMBER** for each answer.

Questionnaire on gadgets

Thomas's smartphone	Use	Score
Communication	Excluding phoning • for almost **25** .... • less for texts	8
Studying	Preparing assignments and recording **26**	**27** ....
Entertainment	For listening to music, etc and for TV **28**	7
Other	Eventually for organising his whole domestic **29**	**30** ....

5   Work in pairs. Look at the listening script on page 229 to check if any of the words or phrases you chose for exercise 2 were used.

Section 4

In Section 4 you will hear a talk or lecture of an educational/academic nature. You do not need any specialist knowledge to understand the talk.

There may be only one type of question or up to three. There is no break in the middle as in Sections 1 to 3, but there is a pause of a few seconds. You will be given time to look at all of the questions before you begin.

1   Work in pairs. For Questions **31–35**, decide which words in the stem indicate the answer is about to be given. Then think of paraphrases for the alternatives **A–C**.

2   For Questions **36–40**, study the diagram carefully and make sure you know the sequence the information is given in.

3   🎧 07   Listen and follow the instructions.

SECTION 4   *Questions 31–40*

Questions 31–35

*Choose the correct letter **A**, **B** or **C**.*

Cloud-seeding to provide rain

31   Boreholes provide water for

     A   industrial use.

     B   agricultural purposes.

     C   domestic consumption.

32   According to the speaker, in the past people have tried to induce rain by

     A   supernatural means.

     B   using fires.

     C   special dances.

33 There is some proof that seeding clouds increases rainfall by

    A 15%.

    B 55%.

    C 25%.

34 According to the speaker, why do some people not support cloud seeding?

    A The benefits of the practice are limited.

    B The costs of the equipment are too great.

    C The effects of playing with nature are unknown.

35 With the amounts of money involved in agriculture, weather control

    A deserves more investment.

    B is worthy of attention.

    C is a surprising success story.

Questions 36–40

Label the diagram below.

Write **NO MORE THAN TWO WORDS** *for each answer.*

How cloud seeding works

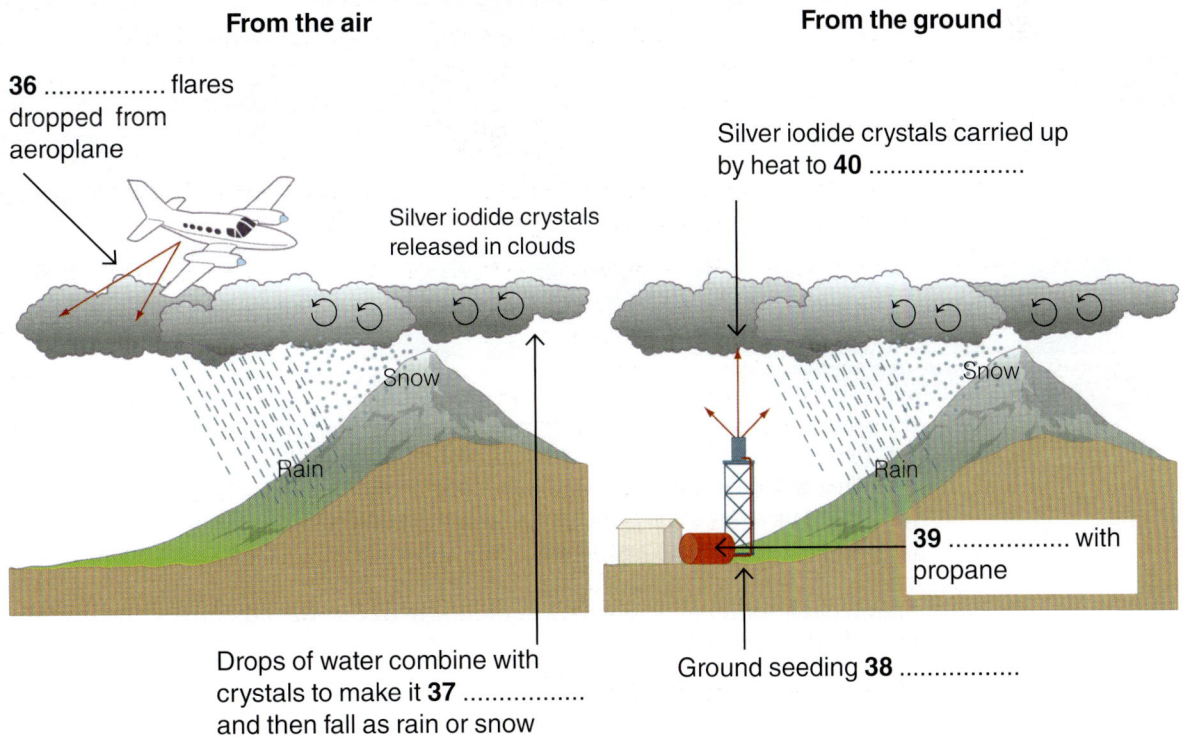

From the air   **From the ground**

36 .... flares dropped from aeroplane

Silver iodide crystals released in clouds

Silver iodide crystals carried up by heat to **40** ....

Snow

Rain

39 .... with propane

Drops of water combine with crystals to make it **37** .... and then fall as rain or snow

Ground seeding **38** ....

4   Check your answers in the listening script on page 230.

4 Global issues and opportunities

Vocabulary 1: General nouns

1 👥 With a partner, describe each of the photographs. Then discuss the questions below.

- Describe your reaction to each photograph.
- What global issues are presented in the photographs?
- Do you think any of the photographs present opportunities? Give reasons and examples.
- Do you think problems and difficult situations can present us with opportunities? Why/ Why not?

2 Match each sentence **1–8** with a sentence **a–h**. Use the adjectives and nouns to help you identify the connection.

1 I lost my wallet last week.

2 My parents and my brother came to my graduation.

3 After leaving college, I found myself with lots of free time and money.

4 Both sides refuse to talk to each other.

5 Access to too much information can overwhelm as well as help people.

6 I was offered a scholarship to go to university.

7 The number of cars sold fell.

8 All participants at the meeting agreed on the necessary action.

a It was too good an opportunity to miss.

b It is a rather awkward situation.

c Some think it is a growing problem, while for others it opens up many possibilities.

d It caused a company crisis.

e It was a very special occasion.

f It was an annoying incident, which I reported to the police.

g These were the perfect circumstances to write my first novel.

h It was a good outcome.

3 Look again at the sentences in exercise 2. Which nouns are general?

Example: opportunity

4 Which noun in exercise 2 completes both the gaps below?

*Computer waste is a serious world _____ . It is now accumulating everywhere.
The _____ , however, can be solved by …*

In pairs, discuss the reasons for your answer.

5 Match each group of adjectives **1–10** with a noun **a–j** that collocates with all of the adjectives in the group.

1	growing/serious/insurmountable	**a**	cause
2	golden/excellent/perfect	**b**	problem
3	main/likely/probable	**c**	opportunity
4	ideal/dangerous/difficult	**d**	event
5	imaginative/effective/perfect	**e**	issue
6	memorable/festive/state	**f**	occasion
7	significant/political/current	**g**	situation
8	adverse/unfavourable/trying	**h**	solution
9	burning/controversial/major	**i**	impression
10	favourable/false/good	**j**	circumstances

6 Complete sentences **1–8** with a word from the box below. Make any necessary changes.

> issue   incident   outcome   problem
> possibility   impression   cause   event

1 I would like to describe an amusing _____ that happened at work.

2 There is a faint _____ that the plan will succeed.

3 The most likely _____ of overcrowding in cities is a rise in birth rates.

4 A series of significant _____ occurred in the early part of the 19th century, which changed the face of transport forever.

5 Instead of being seen as a serious _____ , the situation should be thought of as a golden opportunity.

6 Energy costs have been a burning _____ over the last few decades.

7 The natural forest made a profound _____ on me.

8 The _____ of the talks was not totally unexpected.

7 👥 Work in pairs. Choose one or more of the following situations and describe what happened to your partner:

- an event that made a profound impression on you
- a serious problem that you solved
- a golden opportunity you seized

Useful expressions

*I'm going to talk about …
I'd like to describe …
What I'd like to describe is …
It was … , because …
Another reason is …*

49

What to expect in the exam

- In IELTS Listening Section 4, you usually listen to a monologue once only. The topic is of an academic nature but does not require specialist knowledge.
- You are told at the beginning of the recording what the topic is about. Sometimes there is a heading.
- There is a short pause in the middle of this section.

How to go about it

- Skim questions **31–37** quickly to get an idea of the content.
- Circle words, dates, etc. that help you anticipate the answer.
- Sometimes, the answers come close together and sometimes there is a big gap between them. Make sure you do not lose concentration.
- Check the number of words or numbers that you need to write. Decide what type of words are required: nouns verbs, adjectives or adverbs.

1 👥 Work in pairs. Discuss the following questions:
- What forms of public transport are used in your country?
- How do you prefer to travel? Give reasons and examples?

👤 08   **SECTION 4**   *Questions 31–40*

Questions 31–37

Complete the notes below.

*Write **ONE WORD ONLY** for each answer.*

Notes on social and economic opportunities of railways

Historical background

- Timeline of important **31** .... in 19th-century railways in the UK
- Opening of Liverpool to Manchester line (1831)
- First modern railway with goods and passengers carried on scheduled **32** ....
- Progress resulting from earlier **33** ....
- In 1825, success of Stevenson's engine *Locomotion*
- **34** .... poured into north-west of England due to pace of **35** ....

Social and economic impact

- Between both Liverpool and Manchester by 1834 almost half a million passengers a year
- Merchandise such as coal and **36** .... transported
- Increased railway passenger travel and transport of goods led to a reduction in other **37** ....

Questions 38–40

*Choose **THREE** letters, A–F.*

Which **THREE** of the following improvements from modern railways are mentioned?

A Increased passenger satisfaction   **D** Greater competition

B A rise in living standards   **E** Better transport facilities

C The creation of jobs   **F** New trade links

2 👥 Do you think trains could replace aeroplanes in the future? Why/Why not?

Language focus: Countable and uncountable nouns

1 In the Listening on page 230 you heard the phrases below. <u>Underline</u> the nouns and decide which are countable and which are uncountable.

… high-speed links around the world … more merchandise, including coal …

2 Match each uncountable noun **1–10** with a countable noun **a–j** that is associated with it. What other countable nouns can you add in each category?

1	furniture	**a**	shirts
2	clothing	**b**	chairs
3	luggage	**c**	oranges
4	cash	**d**	flats
5	fruit	**e**	goods
6	accommodation	**f**	coins
7	media	**g**	burglaries
8	merchandise	**h**	magazines
9	crime	**i**	bottles
10	rubbish	**j**	suitcases

G Read more about countable and uncountable nouns in the Grammar reference on page 221.

3 For sentences **1–8** below, <u>underline</u> the correct word in *italics*.

1 There is now no need for people to throw away *equipment/equipments* like *computer/computers*.

2 The *weather/weathers* deteriorated rapidly with severe *storm/storms* forecast.

3 *Information/Informations* like bank *detail/details* should not be revealed for security reasons.

4 *Business/Businesses* done on the internet can save *business/businesses* large amounts of money.

5 *Accommodation/Accommodations* such as small *flat/flats* could help reduce homelessness.

6 *Furniture/Furnitures* is made by skilled craftsmen working in *wood/woods* from different *tree/trees*.

7 *Rubbish/Rubbishes* such as bottles and food tins ought to be recycled.

8 People sometimes need to do other *job/jobs* besides their permanent *work/works* to earn more *money/moneys*.

4 Look at the countable and uncountable nouns in the box below. Replace the words in *italics* in sentences **1–8** with one of these nouns. Make any necessary changes to the verb.

suggestions	machines	information	behaviour
opportunities	robberies	language	litter

1 Some *machinery* is expensive to maintain.

2 Some individuals and businesses have changed their *actions* as a result of environmental pollution.

3 *Details* about the damage appeared in the newspaper.

4 *Crime* is surprisingly on the decrease.

5 Modern railways offered countries the *chance* to increase trade links.

6 *Advice* from the right person about which career path to follow is useful.

7 The *words and phrases* all children pick up follow fairly similar patterns.

8 Removing *cans and bottles* from streets improves the appearance of towns and cities.

5 Expand **1–7** below into sentences. Put the nouns into the singular or plural and use the correct form of the verb.

Examples:

vocational and technical skill/help/people/find/work

Vocational and technical skills help people find work.

modern business/technology company/provide/many employment opportunity

Modern businesses such as technology companies provide many employment opportunities.

1 useful information/be/available/nowadays/the internet

2 social media/help/people/make/new friends

3 transport/bus and train/lead/development/communities

4 accommodation/become/very expensive/in many major cities

5 technological waste/computer and phone/be/now/a growing problem

6 leisure activity/help/people/relax

7 electronic good/refrigerator/cause/considerable harm/the planet

6 👥 Work in pairs. Ask each other questions about the sentences in exercise 5.

Examples:

What kind of information?

Can you give examples of social media?

Can you give any reasons and other examples?

1 In IELTS Speaking Part 1 you may be asked to talk about food products and manufactured goods, such as cars and refrigerators. Look at the Part 1 questions below. Underline the countable nouns and circle the uncountable nouns.

Food

1 Tell me about the most common types of food in your country.

2 What food products do you buy weekly?

3 Do people prefer home-grown food to imported food? Why/Why not?

4 Do you think people eat a wider range of food nowadays than in the past? Why/Why not?

Manufactured goods

1 What types of electronic equipment are common in your country?

2 What handmade goods are produced in your country?

3 Do you think it is important for your country to produce manufactured goods? Why?

4 Is the merchandise sold in the shops in your country the same as in other countries you have visited? How?

5 Do you prefer clothes and furniture that are handmade or machine-made? Why/Why not?

2 Work in pairs. Choose three or four of the questions in exercise 1. Take turns asking and answering the questions. Pay particular attention to the nouns and verbs.

1 Work in pairs. Do you think skills are more important than knowledge in the modern world? What do you think are the three most important skills that young people need to have a good job? Give reasons and examples.

READING PASSAGE

You should spend about 20 minutes on **Questions 1–14**, *which are based on the Reading Passage below.*

Is there REALLY a skills shortage in the engineering industry, or are employers just not paying up?

It is common knowledge in the engineering industry that there's a skills shortage. Apparently, 50% of the entire workforce is due to retire within the next five years. How are we going to fill the positions if nobody has the skills? So more needs to be done to encourage young people to take up engineering and technology jobs if the sector is going to be able to fulfil its need. But actually, is there more to it than meets the eye?

Marcus Body, a consultant in the Brand and Insight team at employer marketing company ThirtyThree (and engineering graduate), believes that employers need to stop shifting the blame onto jobseekers' skills, or apparent lack of. Let's start with degrees. Does a degree have any value anymore? Marcus says: "There's an enormous elephant in the room in graduate recruitment, which is that some universities are better than others."

This implies that you could be studying engineering right now at university and already be at a disadvantage if your institution isn't prestigious enough. He goes on to say that: "The reality is that first stages of screening are done by people – either in-house or at third party suppliers – who know nothing about engineering, so they will use crazy criteria, from degree grade through to spelling." If this is the case, then it's no surprise when companies have problems with recruiting a new generation of engineers and technicians. Could it be that companies are simply being far too fussy with their criteria? They cannot expect a graduate to be able to replace someone who's about to retire – and has probably been in the job for over thirty years – like-for-like.

According to The Institute of Engineering and Technology (IET) Annual Skills Survey for 2014, approximately 40% of its

respondents indicated that they have trouble recruiting engineering graduates. When asked why they don't expect to be able to recruit suitable candidates over the next 4 to 5 years, over 70% of respondents said it was due to lack of suitably qualified candidates, and half of the respondents said shortages or difficulties with specific skills. The worrying term used here is the word 'specific'. How specific are companies willing to get with jobseekers' requirements?

On the other hand, apprenticeships seem to be increasingly popular among companies looking for fresh talent, which is reassuring. The IET's Annual Skills Survey says that over the next five years, over half answered that they believe they will employ more apprentices in technical roles than they have in the past. Marcus Body isn't surprised by this statistic. He says: "Apprenticeships are really taking off – loads of good ones in engineering, and employers are keen. The difficulty is in getting the infrastructure together to manage those apprentices – trainers, supervisors etc." Over a third of respondents in the 2014 Skills Survey said that they would focus more on apprentices and graduates when recruiting the people they need in the next four to five years – so the demand could be there very soon, which is good news for graduates.

Eventually, these things come down to money. Marcus Body reckons that if the UK industry offered a higher salary, there wouldn't be any shortages at all: "Sectors steal the best graduates with more money. Before we can declare a skills shortage, we should double the salary offered and see if they're still unfillable." However, companies

are reluctant to use this as a tactic to lure in graduates. Less than 20% of the IET's survey respondents said they would create more attractive salaries when asked how they would recruit the people they need over the next 4 to 5 years.

There's also one more area where any shortages in the engineering industry can be rooted: education. There are plenty of news stories out there saying that schools need to work harder to attract students towards STEM subjects (science, technology, engineering and maths). However, does the 'STEM' discussion need to really come to an end? Marcus states that the whole discussion of 'STEM' as one thing entirely unhelpful. "There is no such thing as a 'STEM' employee. There are areas that are harder to recruit (like very specific disciplines of engineering), and areas where we have a surplus – e.g. the 20,000 per year psychology graduates we produce and don't have psychology jobs for."

It seems the consensus is quite uncertain. It can be debated that companies are using the skills shortage argument when in reality they should spend more time and effort recruiting or luring graduates with better salaries. Some companies are ahead of the game by offering more apprenticeships to get staff up to a suitable standard before the predicted retirement influx in the near future. There is no shortage of actual people. Applications to study engineering at UK universities having increased by seven per cent on the previous year. On the other hand if businesses want to replace staff due to retire; they're going to need to give a little slack on the application process.

How to go about it

For **Questions 1–9**:

- Look at the title and decide whether the summary relates to one part or the whole of the passage. A title can help you decide where to look in the passage.

- Skim the summary. Decide what type of word is needed for each space and think of your own word. The answers can be nouns, verbs, adjectives and adverbs.

- Skim the wordlist and predict the answer where you can, using your knowledge of grammar and collocation. Then skim the passage and check your predictions. Note, some answers in the summary can be in a different order from the passage.

For **Questions 10–14**:

- *Yes/No/Not Given* questions check the views or claims of the writer. Underline the words in the questions that will help you scan for the information in the passage.

Questions 1–9

*Complete the summary using the list of words, **A–Q**, below.*

Reasons for a lack of engineers

It is well-known in the engineering industry that a **1** .... exists. Moreover, as half of the workforce is expected to enter **2** .... in the near future young people need to be **3** .... to enter the engineering and technology **4** .... Marcus Body suggests that the **5** .... is not to do with the skills of **6** .... , but is connected with such people being at a **7** .... because of the **8** .... of their university training in engineering and the **9** .... at the interview stage.

A disadvantage	**B** quality	**C** retirement
D encouraged	**E** adult skills	**F** employment
G excess	**H** skills shortage	**I** jobseekers
J educational experience	**K** time	**L** employers
M dilemma	**N** advantage	**O** screening process
P issue	**Q** profession	

Questions 10–14

Do the following statements agree with the claims of the writer in the Reading Passage?

Write:

YES	*if the statement agrees with the claims of the writer*
NO	*if the statement contradicts the claims of the writer*
NOT GIVEN	*if it is impossible to say what the writer thinks about this*

10 The IET's annual survey was more extensive in 2014 than in previous years.

11 A small proportion of respondents said their graduate recruitment problem was to do with the suitability of candidates' qualifications.

12 It is possible employers will recruit more apprentices in the future.

13 A greater focus on higher salaries is essential for increasing the recruitment of engineers.

14 According to Marcus Body, thinking of all STEM subjects as one idea has a negative effect on shortages in the engineering industry.

2 🗣 Do you think anything can be done to deal with the situation of skills shortages in all areas? Give reasons and examples for your answer.

Vocabulary 2: Developing ideas

1 In IELTS, you can use words that are similar in meaning to explain and develop your ideas. <u>Underline</u> the correct verb in *italics*.

    1 Positive health education on TV can be motivating. It can *encourage/frighten* people to improve their lifestyle.

    2 The scale of crime in some cities has been shocking. It has even *stunned/tempted* the police.

    3 Some people find buying consumer goods very satisfying. Sometimes it is just the act of buying that *pleases/coaxes* them.

    4 I found the festive occasion really interesting. It *bothered/fascinated* me so much I had to read more about it.

    5 Cities are becoming more appealing to young people. The vibrancy *attracts/disturbs* them enormously.

2 Look at **1–5** again. <u>Underline</u> the words in the second sentences that replace nouns in the first sentences. What type of words did you <u>underline</u>?

3 For **1–4** below, write a second sentence of your own to develop the idea.

    1 Pollution is a growing problem around the world.

    2 The news on TV is sometimes very worrying.

    3 The education results were alarming.

    4 Disaster movies are very appealing to many people.

Speaking
Part 3

1 Work in pairs. Look at each Part 3 question below and answer the following:

- Which nouns, verbs and adjectives help you to work out the purpose of each question?

- Which other nouns, verbs and adjectives could you replace these with to develop your ideas?

How to go about it

- Develop your answers with reasons and examples.

- Use synonyms of words in the questions where you can.

- Use words like *but* and *although* to show, contrast and concession.

- Use adjectives to evaluate ideas. Then explain and develop the evaluation.

> **World problems**
>
> Do you think that individuals should do more to solve global issues such as rising unemployment?
>
> What do you think are the main problems facing the world today?
>
> Some people think that change brings more opportunities than problems. To what extent do you agree?

2 With your partner, match the response below to one of the questions in exercise 1. Explain your choice.

I think such problems are difficult for people to tackle alone. They need the help of governments and large companies. They are challenging issues, which …

3 Take turns asking and answering the questions in exercise 1, asking additional questions where necessary. Choose two or more of the bullet points in the 'How to go about it' box to check as you listen to your partner. Give each other feedback.

Writing
Task 2

How to go about it

- Decide what type of writing task it is. In this case a problem is presented and you are asked to write about the causes and solutions.
- Organise the answer by writing:

either

- an introduction with a paragraph stating two or more causes followed by two paragraphs with solutions and then a conclusion.

or:

- an introduction, followed by three paragraphs each with a cause and a solution and then a conclusion.

1 👥 Work in pairs. Read the Task 2 question below and answer questions **1–3** which follow.

WRITING TASK 2

You should spend about 40 minutes on this task.

Write about the following topic:

> *Homelessness is increasing in many major cities around the world. What do you think are the main causes of this problem and what measures could be taken to solve it?*

Give reasons for your answer and include any relevant examples from your own knowledge or experience.

Write at least 250 words.

---

1 Look at the first statement of the task. Is it a positive or negative development?

2 What things do the questions that follow ask you to write about?

3 What else does the task ask you to do? Why?

2 Work in pairs. Look at the two outlines, A and B, for the body paragraphs for the Task above. Circle all the causes, and then tick each solution.

Outline A

The main cause of homelessness is the cost of accommodation. One solution is to subsidise accommodation for people.
Another reason is the shortage of land to build cheap homes. Cities should build more tower blocks with flats.
The migration of people to cities is another factor that contributes to the problem of homelessness. The economies in rural areas could be improved/revitalised.

Outline B

The main cause is the cost of accommodation. Another cause is the shortage of land to build cheap homes.
The best strategy is for governments to provide cheaper accommodation.
Revitalising the economies in rural areas is another possible measure that can be taken.

3 Look at the two outlines again. What are the similarities and differences between them? Which outline do you prefer and why?

Suggesting causes and solutions

1 👥 Work in pairs. Look at the four statements. Discuss what you think might be the causes of the problems. What are the possible solutions?

1 Rising temperatures are causing problems in some parts of the world.

2 Many species of animals are becoming extinct.

3 Many cities are becoming overcrowded.

4 Water is becoming scarce in various regions.

2 Rewrite sentences **a–d** below using the modal verbs in brackets.

Example:

The most important step is to prevent the situation from becoming worse. (should)
The situation should be prevented from becoming worse.

a The best solution is for governments to encourage people to return to the countryside. (ought to)

b One possibility is to put protection orders on all wild animals. (can)

c There is a slim chance that water desalination plants will work in some regions. (might)

d I think that planting more trees is a good option. (should)

3 Match each problem in exercise 1 to a suggestion in exercise 2.

(G) Read more about making suggestions in the Grammar reference on page 222.

Developing a topic sentence

1 You need to develop ideas in a topic sentence with reasons and examples and then to link them. In the paragraphs below on homelessness, decide if the linking device needed for each gap introduces: *an example, result, contrast, reason, purpose* or *concession*.

One factor contributing to homelessness is the lack of cheap accommodation. Many major cities like New York face homelessness problems, mainly **1** _____ there is a shortage of family houses along with high property rents. **2** _____ there are many empty properties in these cities, which could be used to alleviate the situation.

Governments should **3** _____ encourage property owners to rent out the properties to those without homes. **4** _____ , incentives could be offered to owners by giving tax relief or subsidies **5** _____ help make empty properties available. Such measures would **6** _____ help to alleviate the situation. **7** _____ this is not a complete answer, it ought to be considered.

2 Complete the gaps in exercise 1 with the following linking words: *for example, therefore, yet, in order to, because, although, then.*

3 Are the linking words and phrases below adverbs, conjunctions or both?

| however | nevertheless | though | nonetheless | although |
| still | but | yet | even so | while | even if | much as |

4 For sentences **1–5** below, <u>underline</u> the correct word in *italics*. There may be more than one possible answer.

1 People tend to be pessimistic about their present circumstances. *But/However,/Although* I think the human race is eternally optimistic; otherwise, how would we survive?

2 Man-made problems such as the plastic soup in the Pacific Ocean are a disaster, *but/ however,/although* steps like recycling could reduce their impact.

3 *While/Although/However*, green technology is certainly beneficial, there are issues that we need to be careful about.

4 *Even so,/Even if/Though* urban dwellers face problems such as overcrowding and traffic congestion, there are many effective solutions to tackle such issues.

5 Many people believe that the changes we see in the world are a result of natural causes. *Even so,/Nonetheless,/Whereas* there is compelling evidence to the contrary.

5 Work in pairs. Answer the Task 2 question on page 209.

Vocabulary 1: General nouns

1 Circle the four adjectives below which are in the wrong place and write the correct noun.

1 a burning issue	**7** a difficult situation
2 a serious problem	**8** a major cause
3 a profound opportunity	**9** a trying possibility
4 a state occasion	**10** a golden impression
5 faint circumstances	**11** an unexpected outcome
6 an imaginative solution	

2 Add an adjective or a noun from exercise 1 to complete each blank space. You may have to use a singular or plural noun.

1 The gathering of representatives from various countries lasted through the night, but the _____ of their discussion was not totally _____ .

2 There is a _____ _____ that there will be perfect weather for the occasion.

3 Some people think that overcrowding in cities is to blame for a rise in crime, but this is a less likely _____ than many others.

4 Advances in technology are changing the world for many people. While this is a _____ which is welcome in many cases, it is at times _____ for governments and people to deal with.

5 What would you say is the most insurmountable _____ facing people in their daily lives today?

6 I'd like to talk about a news item on the TV which made an _____ on me that was so _____ it made me want to change my career.

7 Deforestation is a major issue in the world today. Do you think there are any _____ to this problem that can be _____ ?

Vocabulary 2: Developing ideas

1 Underline the adjective in each sentence below.
   1 The volume of electronic waste in the world is now dangerous.
   2 People sometimes feel motivated enough by health adverts to change their lifestyle.
   3 Certain situations such as flooding can be very alarming.
   4 Action video games are appealing to people of all ages.

2 Match the sentences below to those in exercise 1.
   1 They encourage people to exercise.
   2 They are very frightening for people.
   3 Throwing away your old computer endangers the environment.
   4 The characters, story and graphics are attractive to many people.

Language focus: Countable and uncountable nouns

1   Choose an uncountable noun that relates to each group of words.

Example:

suitcase, bag, rucksack   *luggage*

   1 apple, orange, banana, pineapple
   2 flat, house, apartment, tent, caravan
   3 bottles, paper, plastic bags
   4 trousers, shoes, shirts, blouse
   5 newspapers, magazines, radio, TV
   6 news, facts, details, data
   7 tables, chairs, sofa
   8 words, phrases, sentences

2   Use the countable nouns from exercise 1 to answer the questions below.

Example:

What type of fruit do you like?

I like fruit such as/like apples and oranges.

   1 What type of fruit do you like?
   2 What kind of accommodation have you lived in over the years?
   3 What kinds of rubbish do people throw away?
   4 What clothes do you like to buy?
   5 Which media do you access daily?
   6 What kind of information can be found on the internet?
   7 What kind of furniture do you have in your house?
   8 What do you do to study a language effectively?

Accuracy in IELTS

1   Find the nine words or phrases that are used in the wrong way. They include nouns, adjectives and linking devices. Replace them with suitable alternatives. More than one answer may be possible.

> Many people think that all media such as TV and newspapers nowadays focus too much on bad news. They think that this is a trying issue for society to consider, because it can lead to many other serious problems such as bad behaviour, vandalism and burglaries. By watching graphic images of such details on TV people become hardened and then find it difficult to distinguish between right and wrong. However, I agree that this is a major issue, I think that instant access is a more important contributing measure to a rise in crime and violence. As example, we now live in a 24-hour world where news from a wide range of media such as the internet, mobile phones and TV is at our fingertips. Although I acknowledge the benefits of such instant access, I also think it definitely makes the event worse. As regards actions, I think the best measure is to encourage the media to have more positive stories for balance the negative and positive occasions.

Language focus: Ways of looking at the future

1 👥 Work in groups. Look at the photographs below. Which represents your view of what the future will look like? Why?

2 Work in pairs. Ask and answer the questions below. Discuss your predictions by giving examples and reasons.

- Do you think machines will have a positive impact on your life in the future? In what ways?
- In what ways will accommodation be different in the future?
- Do you think people will live on other planets like Mars in the future? Why/Why not?

3 Read statements **1–6** below and decide whether each is a prediction, plan or fixed schedule.

1 We're going to visit an exhibition about future air transport this afternoon.

2 I'm leaving in 50 minutes.

3 I think people will be living on Mars in 20 years.

4 By 2050, machines like robots will have changed the way people work and live.

5 Civilisation as we know it will no longer exist. It will be very advanced technologically.

6 According to the programme, the NASA presentation begins at 10 am.

4 Complete the descriptions **a–f** with the correct future form. Then match the descriptions to sentences **1–6** in exercise 3.

| simple future |
| going to |
| present continuous |
| future perfect |
| future continuous |

a _____ is used for fixed arrangements.

b _____ is used for intentions or plans.

c _____ is used for predictions or instant decisions.

d _____ is used for a situation which will be happening at a particular time in the future.

e _____ is used for a completed action at or before a point of time in the future.

f _____ is used for events that relate to a schedule/timetable.

G Read more about different ways to talk about the future in the Grammar reference on page 222.

5 For **1–5** below, complete the sentences by putting the verbs in brackets into the correct form.

1 As we're flying tomorrow morning at 8 am, I _____ (arrange) an alarm call for 5 am.

2 Why's the government _____ (spend) less money on research into urban life in the future?

3 By tomorrow, we _____ (complete) the planning project, and it _____ (work) perfectly.

4 Some people believe virtual reality _____ (be) the next big techno craze, but is it _____ (last) long?

5 When she _____ (arrive) tomorrow, she _____ (carry) a red bag.

6 Replace the verb that is in the wrong future form.

1 People will be living in space in the year 2050, but will they really have enjoyed it?

2 According to the timetable, the train arrives at noon. I'll sit at the front if you are looking for me.

3 I'm staying at the Braganza Hotel for four days next week, so I'll have met you on Tuesday.

4 The government are going to change the law next month. At least that's their intention, but I bet something is happening to make them change their minds.

5 The public will have become better informed about healthy eating by then, and are thus going to improve their general well-being.

7 Work in pairs. For sentences **1–6** below, decide whether you can rewrite each one using the tense in brackets. Decide what the difference is.

1 I'll be seeing the doctor next Wednesday at 2 pm. (present simple)

2 Society is not going to change dramatically by 2030. (future perfect)

3 Ageing populations are going to be a global issue in the future. (present continuous)

4 The world will certainly have changed for the better by then. (*going to*)

5 The human race will be living in more closely-knit communities in the future. (*will*)

6 My diary is full, but perhaps I'll be able to meet you on Saturday. (*going to*)

8 👥 Work in pairs. Make predictions about what your life will be like next year, five years from now and ten years from now, in terms of education and employment. Give reasons and examples.

Speaking
Part 3

1 Work in pairs. Use the picture below to help you talk about the world in the future. Describe the following:

- what will be happening
- what will happen
- what will have happened.

Don't forget!

- Remember to talk in more abstract terms rather than personally, e.g. in Russia, in the UK, the people in China, etc.

Useful expressions

In 10/20/50/100 years' time …

Over the next century …

Before the end of the century …

By the time we reach the end of the century …

In the coming decades …

2 Work in pairs. Look at the Part 3 questions below. Then take turns asking and answering the questions. Make sure you give reasons and examples in your answers. You can use the notes to help you. When you have finished, give each other feedback using the checklist on page 181.

City life in the future

In what ways do you think city life will have changed by 2030? Why?

Do you think life in urban areas will be more or less stressful than today's world? How? Give reasons.

Do you think city life will be more popular than rural life in the future?

Future developments

How do you think modern civilisation will develop over the next half century?

What do you think will be the most important developments in the future? Give reasons and examples.

Why do you think people make predictions about the future?

- More sophisticated entertainment
- More sophisticated hospitals
- More crowded
- Better facilities
- Richer culturally
- More jobs

Vocabulary: Adjective/Noun collocations

1   Work in pairs. For **1–8** below, use an adjective from the box to replace the words in *italics* to make a common adjective/noun collocation.

general	governing	agricultural	indigenous
modern	dominant	thriving	urban

1   a civilisation *that is current and contemporary*

2   societies *that live off the land*

3   a culture *that is stronger than other cultures*

4   communities *that are doing well and are successful*

5   the public *that is made up of ordinary people*

6   populations *that live in towns and cities*

7   the elite *that controls and runs a country*

8   a people *that live in a particular region*

2   Complete each gap in the following paragraph with a collocation from exercise 1.

The **1** _____ has widely different views about what life will be like in years to come. Some pessimists predict that **2** _____ as we know it will collapse in the near future, and that people will end up living in **3** _____ just as their ancestors did before the Industrial Revolution. Others think that **4** _____ will increase in size so much that there will be no agricultural land left, or that there will be one **5** _____ rather than the multicultural world of today with a **6** _____ made up of robots controlling everything and everyone.

3   Work in groups. What is your reaction to the predictions in exercise 2? Do you think life will be very different in the near future? Why/Why not?

Listening
Section 1

1   Work in pairs. You will hear someone enquiring about and booking an exhibition. Work with a partner. Before you listen to the conversation, check the meaning of the following words and phrases and give examples of each.

Example:

booking office: *collection of ticket*

1   preview

2   the week after next

3   restrictions

4   sign up for

5   come up

6   register

7   range

09 **SECTION 1** *Questions 1–10*

Questions 1–4

Complete the notes below.

Write **NO MORE THAN TWO WORDS AND/OR A NUMBER** *for each answer.*

Notes on Exhibition

Example	Answer
Title of Exhibition:	<u>Futuristic</u> Home Design

Preview on: **1** ....

Two free: **2** ....
No entry on certain days

Days chosen by caller: **3** .... and ....

Reference number: **4** ....

Questions 5 and 6

Choose **TWO** *letters, A–E.*

Which **TWO** of the following eating facilities are available for the public at the exhibition?

A stalls
B local restaurants
C a canteen
D cafés
E sandwich bars

Questions 7–10

Complete the table below.

Write **ONE WORD OR A NUMBER** *for each answer.*

	Number and destination	Frequency	Stop/Location	Cost
Bus	**7** .... to Brookfields	every 12 minutes	Stop W near the station	£3.20 or weekly pass for £15
River bus	Route A to the **8**	every 20 minutes	**9** .... minutes' walk from station	**10** £ .... No weekly pass

2 👥 Work in pairs. Do you like going to exhibitions? Give reasons and examples.

Do you like to book in advance or do you prefer to turn up on the spur of the moment? Why/Why not?

Word building: Forming adjectives from nouns

1 Work in pairs. Make adjectives from the nouns in the box below using one of these three suffixes: *-al, -(i)ous* and *-ful*. Make any necessary changes.

use	luxury	technology	success	population	space
beauty	agriculture	tradition	nation	danger	industry

2 For **1–8** below, complete the gaps with a suitable adjective from exercise 1.

1 At the moment some houses in my community are very _____ , but in the future they will not be so big.

2 I cannot say it is a _____ society at the moment, but as the internet and computers spread that will change.

3 The area where I was brought up is very _____ with lots of trees and stunning gardens, but I think all this beauty will be destroyed by future developments.

4 My home town still survives on the production of _____ crafts, but I think that modern industry is beginning to creep in.

5 We have many _____ monuments, but people forget their significance.

6 _____ office blocks with all the latest modern facilities and expensive furniture will replace old factories and buildings.

7 I come from one of the most _____ regions of the world, and I think it will become even more crowded in the future.

8 My home town is _____ in attracting tourists, with many visiting in the summer.

3 Talk about one or more statements from exercise 2 giving reasons and examples.

Reading
Questions 1–13

1 Work in pairs. Look at the title of the Reading Passage and decide what predictions could be made about ideas A–D. Then skim the passage and check your answers.

A developments in personal transport   **B** adapting people's perceptions

C the design of buildings   **D** the interaction between people and machines

READING PASSAGE

You should spend about 20 minutes on **Questions 1–13**, *which are based on the Reading Passage below.*

Life in 2045

The film, *Back to the Future II*, released in 1989, made a series of outlandish predictions about 2015, the year its key characters travel to from 1985. Although several of the film's predictions, like video calls and wearable technology, came true, *Back to the Future II* showed the pitfalls of making long-term forecasts. The world of 2015 was one of hoverboards, flying cars and power clothing, and instead we got Snapchat and selfies. Several experts have made their predictions about what the world of 2045 will look like. Alex Ayad, head of Imperial College London's Tech Foresight Practice forecasts that people will be able to purchase high-quality emotions online. Emotion-sharing experiences are the latest fad in 2045. Imagine your friend at a music festival can post a photo on Instagram and with it comes bundled a faint twinkling of what she was feeling right there in that moment, so you too can share emotionally in her social experience. Recently, techniques for direct brain stimulation, like optogenetics, have made it possible to not only read but also write information into single neurons. At the moment data transfer rates are still very slow, the best we can do is a few bits per second, but this could well increase to kilobits or maybe reach broadband speeds by 2045. This means the range of human perception could expand beyond its current design limitations.

Our cities will be made from living, dynamic materials that respond to the environment. In 30 years, tall buildings made of glass and twisted steel will be seen as relics from a bygone era, in the same way we think now of 1970s concrete tower blocks: ugly, out-dated and unfit for contemporary purpose. The urban environment of 2045 blends architecture with living materials that are mouldable, adaptable, responsive and disposable.

Entirely new synthetic life forms, or biological machines, made of engineered living cells from bacteria, fungi and algae will grow and evolve with the changing needs of a building's inhabitants. They breathe in pollutants, clean wastewater, and use sunlight to make useful chemicals, energy, heat and vibrant vertical gardens. We will start to see a convergence between biology and technology, to the point where there is no longer a perceptible difference between the two.

Invisibility cloaks, according to Alex Ayad, will be used to 'disappear' ugly objects. Invisibility has forever been a tantalising prospect. The key to cloaking lies in the way the electromagnetic spectrum (including visible light) interacts with objects. The human eye picks up electromagnetic radiation that falls and scatters from objects and we perceive this as light. In recent decades, scientists figured out using mathematics that it might just be possible to imagine a new class of artificial materials made of intricate tiny features with light- (and sound-) bending properties. They named them metamaterials.

And Tamar Kasriel, founder and MD of Futureal, a future-focused strategy consultancy, has forecast that we won't be able to tell the difference between VR hoverboards and real hoverboards. By 2045 quite a few of us might have a hoverboard, but it will be struggling to compete with the thrill of the virtual reality version. What we are likely to see is the breakdown of much of the current distinction between the real and the digital, and the artificial and the human.

Driverless cars will just be ... cars. And for many driving will have become only a leisure pursuit, a kind of sport, and buildings will power themselves. Being optimistic, Marty and Doc won't find themselves in a smoggy apocalypse in 2045. Rather, a powerful mix of sense and/or fear will have continued the momentum behind increasing the efficiency and reducing the cost of alternative power sources. Solar panels will be built into lots of different building materials, so whole neighbourhoods can quietly and cleanly power themselves.

Richard Watson, futurist, writer and founder of online magazine *What's Next*, predicts phones, cars or homes will be able to read people's feelings and adapt accordingly. Machines will be able to sense and then adapt themselves to the emotional state of an individual user. At the moment machines can work out where someone is, who someone is and perhaps what they are doing or 'like' but that's about it. The next stage will be for machines to intuit human feelings. This can be done by 'harvesting' facial expressions, body language, heart rate, voice and so on. If you are typing text into a computer the computer might consider the speed you are typing, decide you are stressed and conclude that this isn't the best time to allow you to read negative emails.

If you are driving a car, the car might consider how you are driving and infer certain conclusions. If the car decides you are angry and in danger of driving unsafely, it might adapt itself to make things safer. On the other hand a shop might use this technology to work out when customers are more likely to buy things, including things they probably don't really want.

Maybe the predictions above will be realised fully in the year 2045 or maybe life will turn out to be even more fantastical than we can now imagine.

How to go about it

For **Questions 1–7**:
- Skim the summary to decide whether it relates to the whole passage or part of it.
- Look at the names to work out what is summarised.
- Check the word limit.
- Think about the types of words needed.
- Don't use any words from the summary in your answers.

Questions 1–7

Complete the summary below.

*Choose **NO MORE THAN TWO WORDS** from the passage for each answer.*

Alex Ayad predicts that by 2045 **1** .... will be available for sale online. He also thinks that construction materials in cities will be 'alive' and react to their surroundings and that invisibility cloaks will be employed to hide **2** ....

Tamar Kasriel forecasts that by 2045 it is probable people will not easily make a **3** .... between the real, human world and what is **4** .... or .... He also thinks there will be driverless cars and buildings that **5** .... Among Richard Watson's forecasts are that people's belongings will have the ability to read their **6** .... and then adapt to an individual's **7** ....

How to go about it

For **Questions 8–11**:
- Read the stem and underline any words that you think will be paraphrased.
- Read each option as a complete sentence by combining it with the stem.
- Find the information in the text.

For **Questions 12–13**:
- Think about whether the answers might overlap with the questions.
- Think about the dates in the questions and look for words in the text that paraphrase words in the questions.

Questions 8–11

*Choose the correct letter **A**, **B**, **C** or **D**.*

8 The film *Back to the Future II* forecasts for 2015

    A were not completely wrong.

    B were not all related to technology.

    C did not turn out to be true.

    D led to several important inventions.

9 By 2045, certain brain stimulation techniques

    A are unlikely to affect human perception.

    B will have no impact on the way humans perceive.

    C could alter human perception.

    D will reach the limits of the human perception.

10 According to Alex Ayad, in 2045 cities will have

    A tower blocks with a special type of steel and glass.

    B structures that are built with reusable materials.

    C more attractive buildings than in the past.

    D buildings that are partially alive.

11 New man-made life forms will

    A help architects create stunning buildings.

    B respond to the requirements of the people living in them.

    C help buildings to remove all pollutants from the environment.

    D allow buildings to monitor people.

Questions 12 and 13

Answer the questions below.

*Choose **NO MORE THAN THREE WORDS** from the passage for each answer.*

12 What will have become less expensive by 2045?

13 What might computers of the future prevent people from seeing?

Vocabulary 2: Verbs of prediction

1 Underline the four verbs in the box below that cannot be used to indicate prediction in an IELTS Writing Task 1 answer.

predict	prophesy	forecast	assume	foretell
project	estimate	anticipate	expect	foresee

2 Decide what the noun and adjective forms are for the correct verbs in exercise 1.

3   Rewrite sentences **1–7** below using the words which follow each sentence.

Example:

Computer sales will increase by 20 per cent.

… are predicted …

Computer sales are predicted to increase by 20 per cent.

Passenger numbers will be rising dramatically towards the end of the year.
It is forecast …

It is forecast that passenger numbers will be rising dramatically towards the end of the year.

1   By the year 2030 the population will have increased to nearly 70 million.
… it is estimated …

2   Spectator numbers will be rising dramatically towards the end of the year.
… are forecast …

3   The projected sales next month will be lower than this month.
It is projected …

4   Sales will climb at the rate of 20 per cent a year.
… are predicted …

5   Attendances will decline gradually in the next two years.
… are anticipated …

6   Advances in technology are not expected to slow down in the coming years.
It is expected …

7   The estimated recovery in ticket purchases will happen in the third quarter.
… are estimated …

Writing
Task 1

1   Look at the Task 1 question below. Then put the verbs in brackets into the correct tense in the model answer.

WRITING TASK 1

You should spend about 20 minutes on this task.

> *The pie charts below compare the proportion of energy capacity in gigawatts (GW) in 2012 with the predictions for 2030.*
>
> *Summarise the information by selecting and reporting the main features, and make comparisons where relevant.*

Write at least 150 words.

Energy capacity in 2012 and 2030

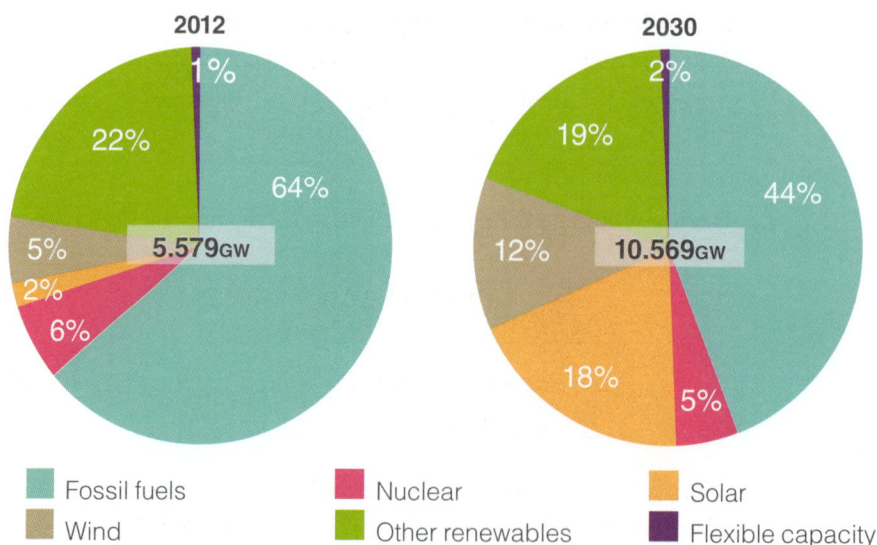

2012

22% • 1% • 64% • 5% • 2% • 6% • **5.579**GW

2030

19% • 2% • 44% • 12% • 18% • 5% • **10.569**GW

- Fossil fuels
- Nuclear
- Solar
- Wind
- Other renewables
- Flexible capacity

The charts **1** _____ (show) the expected changes in energy capacity in 2030 compared to 2012.

The most noticeable feature **2** _____ (be) the drop in the proportion of the annual gross capacity of fossil fuels, with the projected capacity almost doubling from 5.579 to 10.569 gigawatts. It **3** _____ (expect) to experience a significant decline, falling from 64% in 2012 to 44% in 2030. By contrast, it **4** _____ (predict) that there **5** _____ (be) a dramatic rise in the proportion of energy capacity from solar energy with a jump from 2% to 18% in 2030. While the proportion of the capacity for wind **6** _____ (anticipate) to increase more than twofold from 5% in 2012 to 12% in 2030, it **7** _____ (estimate) that other renewables **8** _____ (account for) a smaller proportion with a decrease from 22% to 19%.

The projected proportion for nuclear energy **9** _____ (be) 5% in 2030, a slight decline from 6% to 1% with flexible capacity expected to double from 1% to 2%.

It is clear that despite the decline in the proportion of energy capacity from fossil fuels and the rise in solar and wind sources, the former **10** _____ (remain) a major energy source in 2030.

2 For **1–5**, <u>underline</u> two suitable words or phrases in *italics* to link the information.

1 By 2030, it is predicted a greater proportion of energy capacity will be accounted for by solar sources than in 2012 (18% as against 2%). *In contrast/While/By comparison* the capacity from wind sources is anticipated to comprise 22% and 19% respectively.

2 In the year 2030 it is projected the proportion of capacity from nuclear energy will constitute 5%. *By contrast/Whereas/Meanwhile*, flexible capacity is expected to increase to 2%.

3 In 2012 the proportion of energy capacity for other renewables comprised 22%, *but/whereas/in contrast* the proportion for wind totalled only 5%.

4 The majority of the energy capacity was made up of fossil fuels in 2012 at 64%. *Meanwhile/But/In contrast*, the proportion from other renewables accounted for 22%, followed by nuclear and wind with 6% and 5% respectively.

5 The proportion of energy capacity accounted for by fossils fuels is expected to decrease to 44% by 2030, *whereas/whilst/meanwhile* it is forecast that the proportion for energy capacity from solar energy will rise from 2% to 18%.

3 Complete the sentences below. Add the relevant data from the charts.

1 Fossil fuels in 2012 accounted for _____ of the total energy capacity, while in 2030 they are forecast to constitute _____ .

2 It is estimated that the proportion of capacity from wind in 2030 will be _____ in contrast to _____ in 2012.

3 In 2012, fossil fuels made up the bulk of energy capacity with _____ of the total but in 2030 this is forecast to drop to _____ .

4 in 2012 flexible capacity and nuclear energy accounted for _____ and _____ respectively.

5 The proportion of capacity from solar energy is predicted to rise dramatically climbing from _____ to _____ in 2030.

6 Fossil fuels are expected to experience a significant drop, with a fall from _____ in 2012 to _____ in 2030.

Don't forget!

- Write an overview.
- Summarise and compare the data. Don't just write a list.

4 Write your own answer for the Task 1 question on page 207. When you have finished, check your answer using the checklist on page 139.

Vocabulary: Adjective/Noun collocations

1 For **1–6** below, use an adjective/noun collocation to replace the words in *italics*. Make any other necessary changes.

    1 Do you think that developments in science will change *the civilisation of today*?

    2 As urbanisation advances around the world, don't we have a duty to try to protect the remaining *societies that live off the land*?

    3 How do you think *populations that live in towns and cities* will deal with expansion in future?

    4 Do *cultures that are stronger than other cultures* such as that of Rome generally last for a long time?

    5 Why do you think there are lots of small *communities that are doing very well* employing thousands of creative people?

    6 In what way do the *public at large* benefit from the modernisation of facilities and amenities?

Word building: Forming adjectives from nouns

1 Add the adjectives made from the words in brackets to the correct blank space.

    1 I think people's living conditions in major cities today will seem _____ to people in the future as accommodation then will be less _____ . (luxury/space)

    2 It is _____ for any country not to invest in _____ skills. (danger/tradition)

    3 The place that I would like to describe is a _____ park, which is considered by many people as the most _____ in the country. (nation/beauty)

    4 Do you think the _____ evolution we're now going through will replace _____ skills? (technology/tradition)

    5 To be _____ in the future, the _____ world will need to adapt to rapid changes in the workplace. (success/industry)

    6 Do you think it's _____ to have _____ skills in the modern world? (use/tradition)

    7 As countries become more _____ , the amount of land available for _____ purposes will decline. (population/agriculture)

    8 At a _____ level, it is _____ to develop strategies combining local skills and _____ advances. (nation/use/technology)

Language focus: Ways of looking at the future

1 Put the verbs in brackets below into the correct tenses. In some cases, there is more than one answer.

    1 I'm not sure but I think that there is a possibility that people _____ (land) on Mars in the next 20 years. I also think that by 2050 or even earlier people _____ (live) on the moon.

2 Life _____ (change) dramatically in both urban and rural areas by the end of the next decade. Life _____ (be) less stressful and people _____ (access) to a wide range of leisure facilities and amenities.

3 I'd say I'm fairly optimistic about the future. Although I think we _____ (face) more challenges regarding developments in fields like education, medicine and industry, they _____ (increase) life expectancy.

4 We _____ (meet) this Friday morning at the café at the airport where we _____ (be) able to chat more about what we _____ (do) on the holiday.

5 The museum _____ (close) as usual at 6 pm this evening, but the new extension to the museum _____ (open) to the public for the first time from 6.30–10 pm for a preview.

2 Match the questions to **1–5** in exercise 1.

a Where are you meeting before you fly off?

b What time does the building close this evening?

c Will the way we live have changed by 2030?

d Are you optimistic about the future?

e Do you think the human race will live on other planets in the near future?

Accuracy in IELTS

1 In each sentence below there are two mistakes: a word is missing and a letter is missing. Correct the mistakes.

1 By the year 2025, the proportion of graduate in the workforce will risen significantly.

2 It estimated that shopper number in the department store will increase next month.

3 Next year, there will a noticeable ris in smart TV sales to 5,000 units a month.

4 The trend in energy consumption is predicted to dramaticaly increase during next decade.

5 The projected sale figures for next year show that will be a slight decline.

6 The use of industrial robots anticipated to continue increasing wordwide.

7 In the last quater of the year, it is expected that registrations at the gym will rising again gradually.

8 Overall, it expected that a clear upward tend will be seen in the funding for space research.

2 Transform the first four sentences using the following words:

1 there

2 are estimated

3 noticeably

4 it is predicted

6 The fruits of nature

Vocabulary 1: Lifecycles and processes

1 Work in pairs. Describe what is happening in each of the photographs below.

2 Skim each of the short texts **a–d** and match them to the four photographs.

a When it has flowered, fruit is produced which in turn becomes seeds. These either fall to the ground or are carried by birds or animals to other places, or they are carried along by the wind. When they drop to the ground they wait until the spring of the next year. Then they germinate and grow, and the process repeats itself.

b Once it blooms, the crop is picked by hand or machine. Next it is collected and taken to a factory where the crop is crushed and the oil is extracted from the plant. It is then made into an essence, which is used in perfumes and toiletries.

c It lays its eggs on the leaves of plants. When the eggs hatch, the caterpillars eat the leaves. They then weave or form a cocoon, from which a new insect emerges.

d The plants produce flowers. When the flowers open, they attract insects, which pollinate the plant.

3 Look at each text again. <u>Underline</u> the words that helped you answer exercise 2.

4 Work in pairs. Choose a process in exercise 2 and describe it in your own words.

72

Reading
Questions 1–14

1   Look at the picture and the title 'The fruit of the olive tree'. What kind of information do you think the passage will contain? Decide if the passage is descriptive/factual or argumentative.

2   Scan the Reading Passage. Which paragraphs contain the following information:

How to go about it

- Look at the title. What kind of information will the passage contain?
- Will the passage be descriptive/factual or argumentative?

1   a description of the olive tree and fruit

2   a reference to the time of harvesting

3   a history of olive cultivation

READING PASSAGE

You should spend about 20 minutes on **Questions 1–14**, *which are based on the Reading Passage below.*

The fruit of the olive tree

A   Olive trees (*Olea europaea*), which are widely distributed across the Mediterranean region, Africa and Asia, have long represented wealth, abundance, power and peace. The olive has been a symbol of the Mediterranean since time immemorial and has a reputation for long life, nourishment and its ability to thrive in tough conditions. There are claims of 1600-year-old trees still producing fruit.

B   The tree's primary product, olive oil, is revered throughout the world for its distinctive flavour. Homer called it 'liquid gold'. In Ancient Greece athletes rubbed olive oil over their bodies and winning competitors received no trophies or medals – instead the symbol of supreme honour was the olive wreath placed on their heads.

C   *Olea europaea* is an evergreen shrub or tree, which grows up to 15m tall. It is slow to mature but can live for hundreds of years. The leaves are borne in opposite pairs. The leaves are evergreen, 3 to 9cm long, elliptic, and silvery in appearance. The flowers are borne in axillary clusters, with a four-lobed calyx, and a four-lobed corolla. The two stamens (male parts) project beyond the mouth of the flower. The fruit has a hard endocarp (the olive stone), which is surrounded by a fleshy, edible mesocarp.

D Grown in the Mediterranean for over 5000 years, the olive has shaped the landscape and culture of the region: 90% of all olives are produced in the Mediterranean. It is the region's most versatile and valuable crop with the fruit, oil and leaves having been used for food, fuel, medicine and embalming.

E The birth of olive-farming is shrouded in the mists of time. Discoveries of olive stones at archaeological sites in the Middle East show at least 20 000 years of use and by 5000 years ago olives had been taken into cultivation and spread throughout the Levant. Domestication may have taken place in the eastern Mediterranean region, or in the region of the Nile Delta where the climate of the time would have been more suitable for cultivation. Today, there are thought to be around 1000 million olive trees in the world.

F The harvesting of the olives occurs in autumn. If they are to become table olives, they are soaked in water for five days to extract the bitter phenolic compounds such as oleuropein. The fruit is then cured in brine for around four weeks. Green olives are unripe, whereas black olives are ripe and less bitter. Olives are eaten as snacks or appetisers with a variety of accompaniments, and are a key ingredient of Mediterranean cooking.

G The oil is obtained from the fruit shortly after harvesting. The fruit is cleaned and processed into a paste from which the oil is extracted. Olive oil is classified according to the production method and the oleic acid content. A refined olive oil is obtained with the use of heat or solvent extraction and requires further processing to yield edible oil (it contains up to 3.3% oleic acid). The leftover cake is used as a source of inedible industrial-grade oil (containing more than 3.3% oleic acid), and is also used in livestock feed and compost.

H The oil is used for food, cooking and for a multitude of therapeutic purposes. The safe dosage for adults is two tablespoons (28g) of olive oil per day. Evidence suggests that people whose diets include olive oil have a reduced risk of developing certain cancers. Likewise, a diet rich in olive oil (and low in saturated fats) is associated with reduced risk of cardiovascular disease, high cholesterol levels and high blood pressure.

I The beneficial qualities of olive oil have been attributed to the fatty-acid composition and the presence of phenolic compounds, which seem to have antioxidant, vasodilating, antiplatelet and anti-inflammatory effects. At the Botanical Gardens in Kew in London, investigations are being carried out on how the waste products of olive oil production could be used as sources of compounds for medicines to treat cardiovascular disease.

J In the Arboretum Nursery at Kew young olive plants are grown from seed. It has been noted that germination is spasmodic, taking from a few weeks to a few months. The compost used as a growing medium is an open, gritty, free-draining mix. The seedlings are pricked out into 'air pots'. Air pots prevent the plants from becoming pot-bound by encouraging the roots to grow outwards rather than spiralling. Planting out into the required position in the garden can be carried out straight from the air pot. The glasshouse zone in which the seedlings are grown is kept at a minimum temperature of 5°C. Only natural light is provided. The young plants are well watered and not allowed to dry out.

Questions 1–5

The Reading Passage has ten paragraphs **A–J**.

Which paragraph contains the following information?

1 the places where olive trees were supposedly grown first for domestic purposes

2 research into the health benefits of the leftovers from producing olive oil

3 the process involved in making olives suitable for eating

4 a method that benefits plant growth

5 the link between olive oil consumption and improvements in health

Questions 6–9

Do the following statements agree with the information given in the Reading Passage?

Write:

TRUE   *if the statement agrees with the information*
FALSE   *if the statement contradicts the information*
NOT GIVEN *if there is no information on this*

6 Olive trees are found in only one continent of the world.

7 For the winners in Ancient Greek athletic competition games, an olive crown represented victory.

8 There are few fruit trees that have a longer life span than olive trees.

9 Olive tree cultivation has had little impact on the Mediterranean countryside.

Questions 10–14

Complete the flow-chart below.

Choose **NO MORE THAN TWO WORDS** *from the passage for each answer.*

Stages in the extraction of olive oil

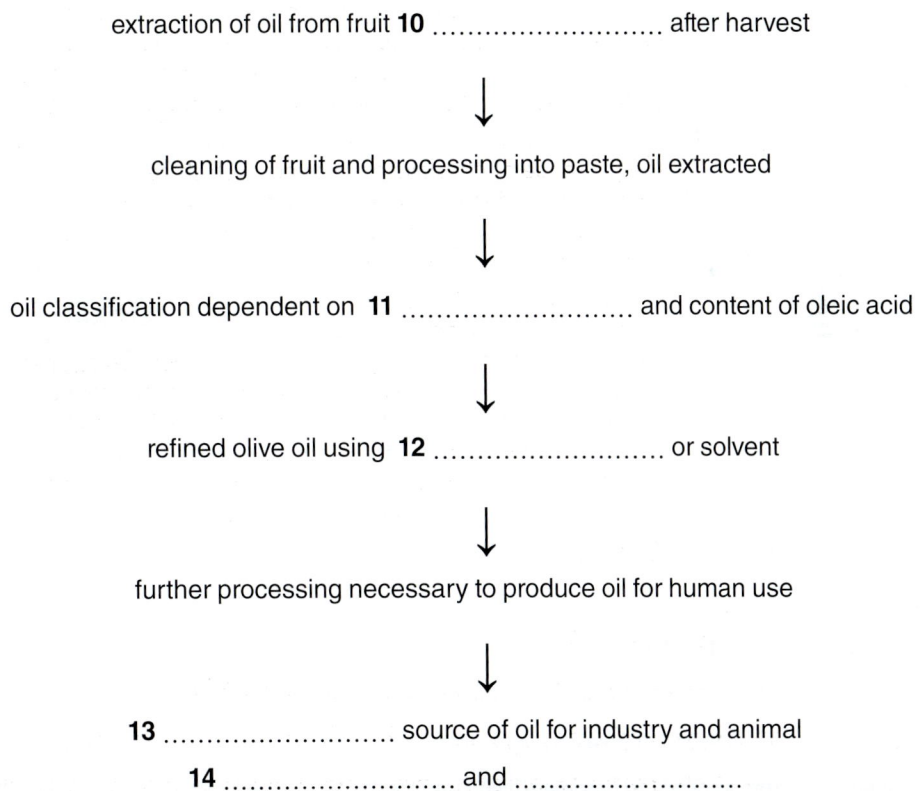

extraction of oil from fruit **10** .... after harvest

↓

cleaning of fruit and processing into paste, oil extracted

↓

oil classification dependent on **11** .... and content of oleic acid

↓

refined olive oil using **12** .... or solvent

↓

further processing necessary to produce oil for human use

↓

13 .... source of oil for industry and animal
14 .... and ....

How to go about it

For **Questions 10–14**:
• Flow-charts usually have a heading so use this to locate the relevant part of the text.
• Treat the flow-chart like a summary. The text may be in note form, so pay particular attention to the grammar.
• Sometimes, the information in the flow-chart may be in a different order from the Reading Passage.

Don't forget!
• For questions that require you to complete information, check the number of words required for each blank space.

3 Is it important for us to know how things such as trees, plants, insects and animals grow? Why/Why not?

How common is it for people in your country to grow their own produce? Is it less common now than in the past? Give reasons and examples.

Language focus: Transitive and intransitive verbs

1 Look at the following sentences from the Reading Passage on page 73. Underline the verbs.

1 *The harvesting of the olives occurs in autumn.*

2 *The fruit is cleaned and processed into a paste from which the oil is extracted.*

3 *In the Arboretum Nursery at Kew young olive plants are grown from seed.*

2 Read the explanations. Match the explanations to the verbs in exercise 1.

a the verb takes an object and can be used in the passive. (transitive)

b the verb cannot take an object and cannot be used in the passive. (intransitive)

c Which of the verbs can be used both transitively and intransitively.

G Read more about transitive and intransitive verbs in the Grammar reference on page 223.

3 The verbs in the box below can all be used to describe processes and lifecycles. Decide whether the verbs in the box are transitive, intransitive or both and write them under the correct heading in the table.

make	look	produce	decrease	weave
happen	collect	rise	sow	become	flow
process	pick	emerge	occur	crush

Transitive	Intransitive	Both
make	look	decrease

4 Work in pairs. Use your own knowledge to answer questions 1–6 below using suitable singular or plural nouns.

1 What sets every day in the evening?

2 What is harvested to make bread?

3 What leaves are picked to make a hot drink from China?

4 What is white and is used to make a very light cloth?

5 What emerges from a cocoon to become a flying insect?

6 What are colourful, grown in gardens and look and smell very nice?

5 Write an answer for each question 1–6 in exercise 4. Where possible, replace the verbs in the question with one of the verbs in the box below or a verb of your own.

| gather | harvest | come out of | bloom | go down |
| produce | plant | cultivate | weave | utilise |

6 Work in pairs. Underline the intransitive verbs in the box below.

plant	pollinate	grow (tall)	disperse
become (bigger)	prune	sprout
transplant	harvest	ripen	appear
open up	cultivate	bear

7 Decide which verbs in exercise 6 can be used with each of these nouns.

| seeds | saplings | branches | tree |
| buds | flowers | fruit |

8 Work in pairs. Look at the diagram of the lifecycle of an apple tree and describe it in your own words.

9 Complete the gaps in the text below using suitable verbs in the present simple.

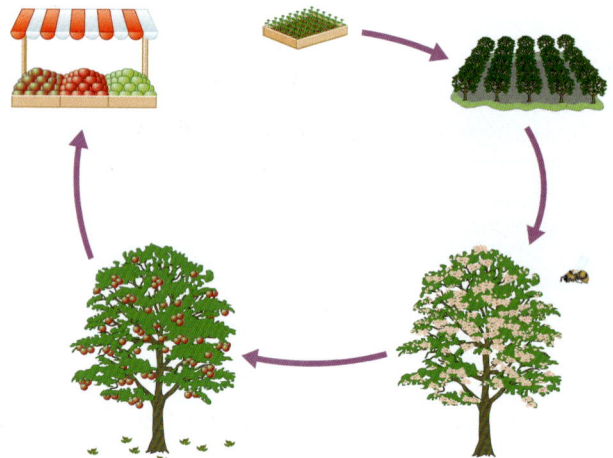

The life of an apple tree

The seeds of the apple tree 1 _____ in trays where they grow until they reach a certain size. After that they 2 _____ into the fields. When they reach a certain height, the saplings are 3 _____ to increase the production of apples. As the trees 4 _____ taller, the branches become bigger and they 5 _____ leaves. The tree blossoms attract bees that, in turn, 6 _____ the flowers. In the autumn, the fruit begins to 7 _____ and the leaves fall. The fruit is then 8 _____ and the apples are graded, sorted and taken in special refrigerator lorries for storage or distribution to the market.

Speaking
Part 2

1 ⬥ Work in pairs. Choose a photograph and describe it to your partner. What kind of impression does the photograph make on you? Why?

Don't forget!

- Write your notes, briefly, clearly and in order.
- Write the notes vertically so you can read them easily as you speak.
- Glance at your notes as you speak and expand your ideas.

2 ⬥ 10 Look at the Part 2 Task Card below. Then listen to a student giving a possible response to the Task. Which stages in the Task Card does the student mention?

Describe a place of outstanding natural beauty that you like.

You should say:

  where the place is

  when you first went to the place

  who you first went to the place with

and explain why you like the place.

---

3 ⬥ Listen to the extract again and complete the notes below using one word or a number.

- a place that is very beautiful
- a picnic area on a **1** _____ top on the north coast of **2** _____
- I went there for the first time when I was about **3** _____ years old with my **4** _____
- the surrounding **5** _____ is breathtaking.
- the **6** _____ of the countryside below the mountain are really spectacular
- the area is very **7** _____
- it is usually **8** _____ as few people go there.
- it is very **9** _____ and somewhere to **10** _____ from the world
- it is a place to **11** _____

4 Work in pairs and check your answers. Then match items **1–11** to the stages (where, when, who and why) on the Task Card.

5 ⬥ Make short notes for the Part 2 Task Card in exercise 2. Work with a new partner. Take turns talking about the topic, using your notes to guide you. When you have finished, discuss with your partner whether you followed the notes.

Vocabulary 2: Conservation

1 Work in pairs. Choose a word, **a–d**, to complete each of the gaps. Think of the type of word you need and whether it might be singular or plural.

1 Tree _____ is crucial, because trees are the _____ of the planet; we chop them down at our peril.

   a extinction   **b** heart   **c** lungs   **d** conservation

2 Where I come from the countryside needs _____ , because it is being _____ by more and more buildings.

   a spoilt   **b** broken   **c** protection   **d** defence

3 In the _____ season, the countryside is not at all _____ as it is buzzing with activity.

   a plant   **b** tranquil   **c** tranquillity   **d** planting

4 A huge factory, which is now derelict, _____ the landscape, but the scenery is still _____ with wooded hills and streams.

   a rules   **b** dominates   **c** extravagant   **d** spectacular

5 From the mountain top you have a _____ view of the coastline, with beaches _____ into the distance.

   a stretching   **b** panoramic   **c** panorama   **d** stretch

6 People go to New York to shop and to take in the _____ like the Statue of Liberty, but they also like to visit open _____ like Central Park.

   a sightings   **b** spaces   **c** sights   **d** spacing

7 I think it is necessary to _____ the environment, because wildlife will _____ .
   a disappear   **b** depart   **c** safeguard   **d** uphold

8 People come from miles to admire the _____ across the valley, because the area has a breathtaking _____ .

   a scenery   **b** scenic   **c** outlook   **d** view

2 For sentences **1–6** below, complete the gaps with a word from the **a–d** choices in exercise 1. Make any necessary changes.

1 The coastline has some breathtaking _____ , which attract people from all over.

2 As trees produce oxygen they keep us alive, which is why they are often called the _____ of the planet.

3 The beach _____ for miles with lots of wildlife, but it is in danger of being _____ if we don't conserve it for future generations.

4 Tourists spend a lot of money when travelling around and take in as many _____ as possible in a city.

5 Wildlife like lions and tigers should not be kept in zoos, but how can they be _____ from extinction?

6 Forest _____ schemes protect areas of national importance like the Amazon rainforest.

3 Work in groups. Discuss the questions below using the words from exercises 1 and 2.

1 How important do you think it is to have conservation schemes to protect the environment?

2 In what ways can people safeguard the countryside?

3 Do you think natural environments around the world will be destroyed or conserved in the future? Give reasons and examples.

Listening
Section 2

🎧 11 **SECTION 2   Questions 11–20**

Questions 11–13

Choose the correct letter, A, B or C.

11 The woodland and countryside programme began

    A 5 years ago.

    B 10 years ago.

    C 15 years ago.

12 Not all young people like the programme initially, because

    A smartphone use is allowed only in the evenings.

    B the use of all electronic gadgets is discouraged.

    C watching TV is discouraged at all times.

13 The programme receives most of its income from

    A donations.

    B the nursery.

    C courses.

How to go about it

For **Questions 14–17**:

- Study the map carefully. Do not assume that 'A' will be the first thing you hear, the description is more likely to start at 'the Entrance'.

- Think of words that are related to sequence, for example, *then*, *next*, etc., as these will indicate steps in the sequence.

- North is marked on the map, so think about the four points of the compass.

Questions 14–17

Label the map opposite.

Write the correct letter, A–J, next to Questions 14–17.

14 Beech Lodge   ....

15 Chestnut Lodge   ....

16 Family Area   ....

17 Plant Nursery   ....

Moorland Countryside and Woodland Centre

Woodland

A J I B C D H E F G

Entrance

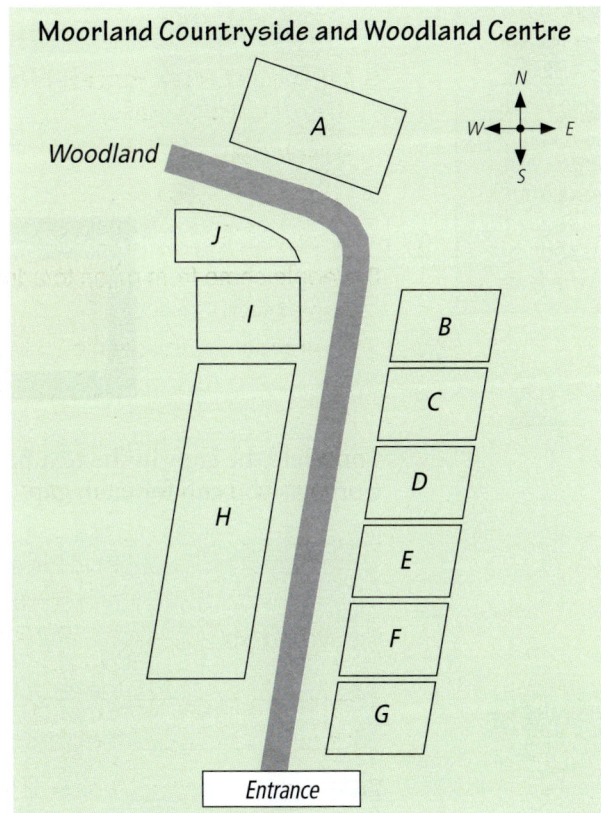

Questions 18–20

Complete the sentences below.

*Write **NO MORE THAN TWO WORDS** for each answer.*

18 As the centre is high up, there are spectacular …….........................…… of the surrounding area.

19 As no trees have been cut down, the …….........................…… has not altered for centuries.

20 During woodland walks, people are requested not to remove …….........................……
    or …….........................….. .

Writing
Task 1

How to go about it

- Write an overview using words to describe sequences such as *stage*, *step* and *phase*.

- Use the correct tense to describe the sequence. As this is a cycle that is repeated, use the present simple.

- Make sure that you use transitive and intransitive verbs correctly.

- Make sure that you use the active and passive correctly.

- Use linking words related to sequence, for example, *first, then, next, after that, subsequently, once, as soon as, when, where,* etc.

1   Work in groups. Describe the steps in the process below. Try to use as many of the words in the box as possible.

throw away	recycle	crush	buy	rubbish tip	landfill	collect
transport	separated	colour	crush	recycled	new bottles	

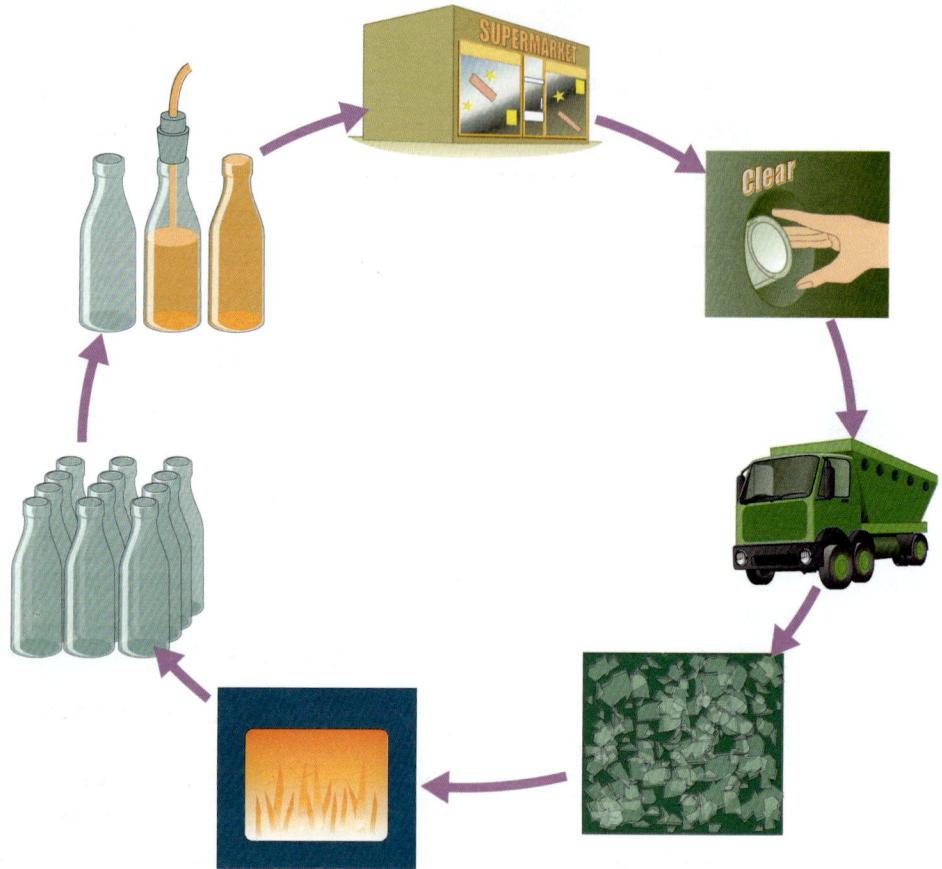

2   Complete the gaps in the text below with suitable linking words. Think of as many linking words as you can for each gap.

The fizzy drink is bought in the shop. **1** _____ it is drunk, the bottle is either thrown away, in which case it is thrown into a rubbish tip, or it is put into a recycling bin.

2 _____ the recycled bottles are collected and taken to a special centre,

3 _____ the glass is sorted. After this step, the glass is crushed and

4 _____ it is used for making new glass. This glass is

5 _____ made into new bottles which are delivered to various bottling

plants, **6** _____ the various drinks are added.

Don't forget!

- Make sure you write an introduction which paraphrases the rubric. Do not just copy the rubric.

- Write a minimum of 150 words.

3   Find the word *step* in the text in exercise 2. Which other words can you use instead of *step*?

4   Write an introduction and an overview for the text in exercise 2.

Describing sequences

1   Decide which one of the following linking words or phrases in the box below cannot be used to describe sequences.

initially	first	at first	next	as soon as	after
before	following that	finally		when	where

2   Work in pairs. <u>Underline</u> the linking words in **1–7** below and find the first step in the sequence. Then decide what is being described and put the sentences in order.

   1   If it is the latter, the broken components are mended.

   2   and the phone is then sent for sale.

   3   Once a device is broken, it is either thrown away or sent for recycling.

   4   These are then shipped to a different factory for assembly.

   5   First, the various internal components like the chip are manufactured in one place.

   6   After that they are dispatched to a central warehouse for distribution.

   7   At the same time, the case and the SIM card are produced.

3   Compare this manufacturing process with the natural lifecycle described in the life of an apple tree on page 76. Decide which contains the most transitive verbs.

4   Match **1–6** below with a sentence or part of a sentence **a–f** to complete the sequence.

   1   As soon as the wheat is fully grown,

   2   Before it is wrapped,

   3   Once the mangoes are ripe, they are picked,

   4   The components are imported and then put together.

   5   When the tea bush reaches a certain height, the leaves are picked.

   6   Milk production goes through various stages. When the cows are milked, the milk is taken to a dairy where various products are made.

   a   the chocolate is put into moulds and left to cool.

   b   It is heated to kill bacteria to make it suitable for drinking, or churned to produce butter.

   c   and sent to the market for sale, or kept in a cold refrigerator for export.

   d   it is reaped.

   e   They are then dried, sorted, blended and wrapped in packets for sale.

   f   After that the machines are put into boxes and transported to warehouses or to shops.

5   Match each of the words below to a sequence in exercise 4.

packaging	storage	delivery	pasteurisation	harvesting	assembly

6   Decide what the verb form is for each noun in exercise 5.

7   Write your own answer to the Task 1 question on page 207. When you have finished, check your answer using the checklist on page 139.

6 Review

Vocabulary 1: Lifecycles and processes

1   Match an item in column A with an item in Column B. You may use each item only once.

	A	B
1	blossoms	produce
2	trees	fruit
3	butterflies	thread
4	harvest	appear
5	plant	trees
6	weave	emerge
7	prune	sprout
8	leaves	branches

2   Write a short sentence using each noun phrase from exercise 1 above.

Example: blossoms appear   *Blossoms appear on plants and trees in spring.*

Vocabulary 2: Conservation

1   Complete the sentences below with a suitable word beginning with the letter given.

1   From the top of the building, you have a p_____ view of the city, with buildings s_____ into the distance.

2   The scenery in this part of the countryside is s_____ with streams and wooded hills and an old brick mill that that dominates the l_____ .

3   People go to London to shop and to take in the s_____ like Tower Bridge, but they also like to visit open s_____ such as Hyde Park.

4   As there are some breathtaking v_____ along the coast, people travel miles to admire the s_____ .

5   The conservation of the natural e_____ is vital to help prevent the e_____ of wildlife.

6   It is necessary to s_____ the natural world, so wildlife will not d_____ .

7   The woodland around my hometown is being s_____ by the construction of factories and houses nearby and is in urgent need of p_____ .

Following directions

1   The following sentences take you on a tour through the map below. Follow the line and decide whether the sentences are correct or not. Correct the sentences that are wrong.

1   We start off here at the bottom of Theed Street.

2   The tour takes us past Wren House on the right.

3   We then turn left into Chatham Street.

4   We go past Brompton Palace which is on the north side of the street on our left.

5   Just after the palace we immediately turn right into Manor Way, where we stop and look at the building of the College of Music, which is on our left.

6   We then turn left into Weston Avenue to look at the Old City Hall, which is on the north side of the street.

7 We continue to the end of Weston Avenue where we go south.

8 We then turn left and finish our tour on the north side of the Old City Hall.

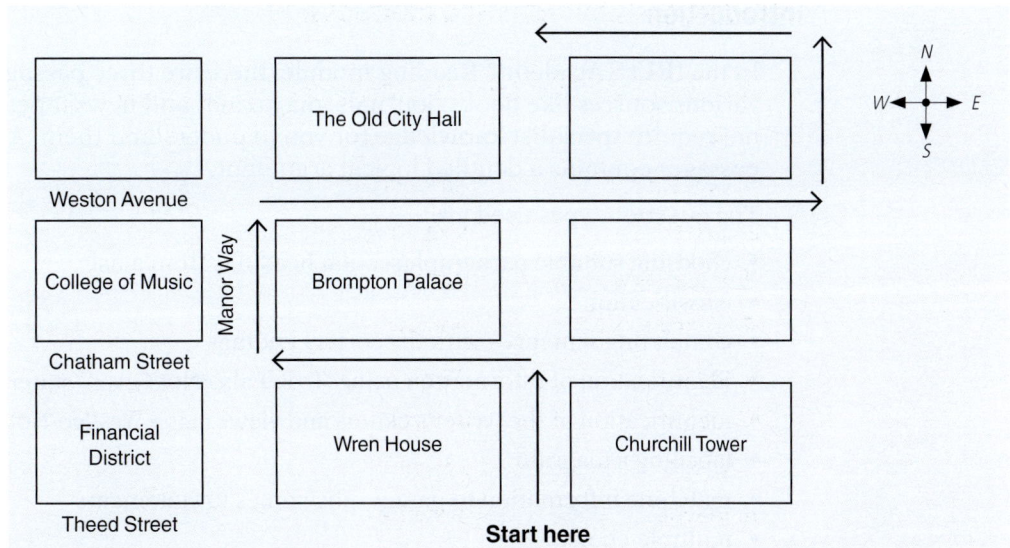

Language focus: Transitive and intransitive verbs

1 Match the words from column A with corresponding words in columns B and C. You should use each word only once.

	A	B	C
1	sun	produce/utilise	bread
2	wheat	emerge	garden/spring
3	cotton	goes down/sets	cocoon
4	flowers	cultivate/harvest	evening
5	butterflies	bloom	cloth

2 Write a short sentence using each word group from exercise 1 above.

Example:

Sun/goes down/evening

I enjoy watching the sun go down in the evening.

Accuracy in IELTS

1 In sentences **1–9** below, there is either a letter *s* missing or there is one too many. Find the mistakes and correct them. Try to complete the exercise in less than two minutes.

1 When the seed germinate, the plant begins to grow.

2 As soon as the wood is burnt, carbon dioxide is released into the atmospheres, which can then cause serious problems.

3 The diagram show how the water is purified.

4 Trees are the lung of the planet as they purify the air we breathe.

5 If the plant produces fruit, it releases the seed which are either carried away by the wind or birds.

6 More conservation projects need to be organised if we are to save the countrysides.

7 Pomegranate are now found in many countries in the world.

8 What are the most common fruits in your parts of the country?

9 It is clear that there are seven step in the process.

Introduction

In the IELTS Academic Reading module, there are three passages which are from various sources like books, journals, magazines and newspapers. The passages do not require specialist knowledge for you to understand them. At least one of the three passages contains a detailed logical argument.

The question types used are:

- choosing suitable paragraph/section headings from a list
- classification
- completing sentences with the correct endings
- identification of information using 'True/False/Not Given' statements
- identification of the writer's claims and views using 'Yes/No/Not Given' statements
- labelling a diagram
- matching information to paragraphs/names to statements
- multiple-choice
- note/flow-chart/table completion
- sentence completion

You will have one hour to answer 40 questions, which is about 90 seconds for each question. This means that you need to learn to move around the Reading Passage and the questions quickly. In the exam there is no time to 'study' the Reading Passages. In order to be as fast as possible there are three important strategies that you need to learn:

- scanning and skimming – these are reading skills that you need to employ at different times to answer various types of questions
- understanding the different questions types
- understanding when to leave questions you cannot do initially, move on and come back later.

Understanding True/False/Not Given statements

'True/False/Not Given' statements are used to check if statements agree with information in the Reading Passage.

Example:

Questions 22–26

Do the following statements agree with the information given in Reading Passage 2?

In boxes 22–26 on your answer sheet, write

TRUE   *if the statement agrees with the information*

FALSE   *if the statement contradicts the information*

NOT GIVEN *if there is no information on this*

What does 'false' mean here?

What is the difference between 'false' and 'not given'?

1 Read the extract on page 85 and do the exercises, which follow.

THE BRONZE AGE: XIA DYNASTY

The Bronze Age in China refers to the period between about 2000 and 771 BC, when bronze was produced on a massive scale for weapons and ritual objects used by the ruling elite.

Traditional Chinese histories, written in later centuries, speak of a series of ancient rulers who invented agriculture, writing, and the arts of government. The last of these legendary rulers, Yu, is credited with controlling floods and founding the Xia dynasty. Yu also cast nine sacred bronze vessels that became symbolic of the right to rule, and these were passed on to subsequent dynasties. While the account in the traditional histories is linear, with states following one another in a logical progression, the archaeological record reveals a more complicated picture of Bronze Age China.

Archaeological investigation has confirmed much of the legendary history of the dynasty following the Xia – the Shang – but the existence of Xia itself is still debated. Today Chinese scholars generally identify Xia with the Erlitou culture, but debate continues on whether Erlitou represents an early stage of the Shang dynasty, or whether it is entirely unique. In any event, new prototypes emerged at Erlitou – in architecture, bronze vessels, tomb structures, and weapons – that greatly influenced material culture in the Shang and subsequent Zhou dynasties.

2   Work in pairs. Use **a–k** to help you analyse the 'True/False/Not Given' statements in sentences **1–9** on page 86. Underline the relevant words in each sentence.

  a verbs to do with cause and effect, for example, *lead to, bring about, result in/from*

  b restricting/excluding words, for example, *only*

  c quantities, for example, *all, majority/ most/ little/a little*

  d adjectives that qualify, for example, *particular, inevitable, mistaken, higher*

  e adverbs that qualify, for example, *largely, slightly*

  f numbers

  g 'negative' verbs, for example, *ignore, fail*

  h verbs/phrases that indicate doubt, for example, *suggest: It is suggested …*

  i comparisons

  j verbs to do with linking, for example, *connect, link, associate*, but not cause and effect

  k time relationships

Example:

The Bronze Age in China lasted more than a thousand years.

Comparison (*more than*) and length of time (*a thousand years*): **i/k** .

1 Bronze was used more for weapons than for ritual objects.

2 According to later Chinese histories, ancient rulers were only interested in the administrative side of leadership.

3 Yu is said to have established the Xia dynasty.

4 Ten sacred vessels were made by Yu.

5 The sacred vessels were destroyed at the end of each dynasty.

6 The Chinese Bronze Age was a simpler period than discoveries show.

7 All of the legendary history of the Xia has been substantiated by archaeology.

8 The Xia are connected with the Erlitou culture.

9 The Erlitou culture had an impact on the Zhou.

3 Scan the text to locate the information in statements **1–9** and decide whether they are 'True', 'False' or 'Not Given'.

Understanding 'Yes/No/Not Given' statements

'Yes/No/Not Given' statements are used to check if statements agree with the claims or views of the writer in the Reading Passage – i.e. does the writer make a judgement about information in the Reading Passage?

Checking claims is similar to checking information. Look at the 'True/False/Not Given' statements above. All of the statements can be classed as claims, but only statement **7** could be classed as an opinion or view. For example, statement **1** cannot be an opinion because it is either a statement of fact or a claim. The same applies to statement **2** and so on. You can put *It is a fact that* or *I claim that* in front of all these statements, but you cannot say *I believe that* before the statements, because it is not a matter of opinion. Can you say: *I believe that water boils at 100 degrees centigrade?* It is a claim until it is proven.

1 Work in pairs. Look at the extract and statements **1–7** on page 87. The words <u>underlined</u> highlight the views expressed in the statements. These words can occur in statements checking the views of the writer. Decide what the function of the words <u>underlined</u> is in each sentence.

Active cities

Many cities over the years have actively contributed to making their residents less physically active, as there is now less need for the public to walk anywhere. Yet, the health and economic benefits gained from financial investment in making cities active places for residents are clear for everyone to see.

Active cities can provide their residents with a range of opportunities that encourage people to have a more active lifestyle and improve their health. An active city is one that has, for example, open spaces and parks which can enhance the lives of workers or local people enormously by providing places for relaxation like walking, running or just sitting in the open air. Further, if open spaces such as the urban greenway* in London, are joined up, this then enables people to walk long distances through green trails, away from traffic and noise. It is, therefore, important for more open spaces to be created to benefit the general public health-wise, from which cities should then gain from more active and productive citizens.

Another key feature of an active city is good urban design. Such design makes the streets safe with good lighting and also inviting with street furniture like benches, micro-gardens and trees. As such simple changes clearly add to people's quality of life, they are a vital ingredient of active cities, and should be implemented everywhere.

* A cycleway and footpath in east London.

1 People in cities now <u>tend to</u> be less active.

2 <u>The best way</u> to ensure the health benefits from active cities is through investment.

3 Open spaces in an active city are of <u>little</u> use to workers.

4 City dwellers <u>should</u> make more use of the open spaces.

5 <u>It is easier</u> for people in London than those in other cities to make use of open spaces.

6 <u>It is likely that</u> cities will benefit from having more open spaces.

7 Having good street design is an <u>effective</u> way to improve the quality of life of the public.

2 Scan the text to locate the information in statements **1–7** and decide whether the answer is 'Yes', 'No' or 'Not Given'.

Write:

YES　　　*if the statement agrees with the views of the writer*
NO　　　*if the statement contradicts the views of the writer*
NOT GIVEN　*if it is impossible to say what the writer thinks of this*

Paragraph/Section headings

1 The title of the whole Reading Passage is *The Impact of Coastal Erosion*. Predict which of the following you expect to find in the passage:

cause	effect	problem	solution	historical background

2 Match your answer in exercise 1 to words in the heading below.

Factors leading to coastal erosion

A There is little doubt that rates of coastal change will escalate with enhanced rates of sea level rise and increasing storminess, both of which are associated with global warming. These changes are likely to have a significant impact on coastal populations and infrastructure. Sea levels are expected to rise significantly over the next century, largely as a result of the melting of ice sheets and thermal expansion of the oceans. Global warming will also change ocean currents, world weather patterns, winds, coastal currents, waves and storms. The increase in the frequency and size of the latter, which have an enormous influence on coastal change and near-shore sediment transport, will have a major impact on the form of UK coasts.

3 Look at paragraph A above related to the heading.

<u>Underline</u> the words that relate to factors. Then ⃝circle⃝ words that relate to coastal erosion.

4 Look at paragraph B and decide whether it is about:

1 the effects of coastal change
2 the methods employed to check coastal change.

Which verb(s) and noun helped you make your decision?

> **B** Geological, archaeological and historical records are used to establish the nature of past coastal change. Monitoring of coastal change is also undertaken using a broad range of techniques including airborne laser ranging technology (LIDAR) and digital aerial photogrammetry. These techniques are used to determine coastal topography, coastal erosion, and shoreline position with high accuracy. The bathymetry of offshore areas is determined by several geophysical techniques including side-scan sonar or multi-beam surveys. In the UK geoscientists are widely involved in projects that address past coastal change and monitor how coasts are changing today. The principal aim of many of these studies is to understand the natural processes that govern coastal change in order to predict the patterns and rates of future coastal evolution.

5 Look at the list of headings below for the Reading Passage and circle the general nouns, e.g. *factors* and *methods*, in the headings.

List of Headings

i The complexity of making decisions about coastal defences

ii A contrast between engineered and natural defence techniques

iii The methods employed to check coastal change

iv The need for an integrated approach to coastal management

v Factors leading to coastal erosion

---

6 Underline the words that make the general nouns in the headings specific.

Summary completion

1 Work in groups. Look at paragraphs **C–E**. Read the summary below and use the questions in the coloured boxes to help you answer **Questions 10–13**.

C Currently about 44% of the English and Welsh coast is protected by some form of coastal defence. Difficult decisions will need to be made to determine how this percentage will change in response to the increased rates of coastal erosion caused by sea-level rise. These decisions cannot be made without widespread consultation and will need to balance the socio-economic needs of developers, landowners and residents with coastal protection and environmental groups. Furthermore, they will need to take aspects of European legislation (e.g. the Habitats Directive) that have been incorporated into British law, into consideration.

D Coastal managers have to consider not only which parts of the coast they should attempt to defend, but also which type of defence is most appropriate. Locally it will be best to defend coastal areas using traditional constructions, such as sea-walls, dykes, groynes and breakwaters. Such engineered 'hard' structures are expensive and may only result in enhanced coastal erosion on adjacent coasts. The alternative approach is to work with natural processes and create 'soft' engineered solutions, e.g. by encouraging accumulation of sediments in selected areas. For example, sediments accumulating in estuarine salt marshes protect the estuaries and associated human infrastructure from erosion, storm surges and coastal flooding.

E Whatever approach is used, no section of coast should be studied or managed in isolation. The whole picture must be understood, in regard to changes in the past, the present position and how any coastal management scheme will be affected by future changes. The best and most sustainable options probably lie in an integrated coastal zone management approach. These may contain multiple response strategies that can be modified for different socio-economic factors and environmental conditions, working with natural processes rather than against them. Geoscientists have a key role to play in providing the foundations for such management.

Question 10:

Is the answer a noun/noun phrase, etc ?

Is the answer connected with the word decision?

Is decision-making connected with discussing?

Does the latter part of the sentence give you a clue?

Question 11:

Is the answer a noun/noun phrase, etc?

Is there anything in the sentence that tells you the answer might be people or a body of people?

If so, which words?

Questions 10–13

*Complete the summary of paragraphs **C–E** below.*

*Choose **NO MORE THAN TWO WORDS** from the passage for each answer.*

Any decision on how much of the coastline will have some form of protection in years to come will not be easy. It will, however, need to be taken after **10** …………………….. , taking into account the needs of local people and agencies. **11** ……………............ need to look at the parts of the coast which they ought to try and protect and the most suitable defence. Local answers will involve the use of **12** ………………............ , from sea-walls to breakwaters, but these 'hard' structures may only lead to the erosion in nearby coastal areas. Alternatively, methods such as encouraging the build up of sediments in certain places may be the answer. In any case, no stretch of the coastline should be dealt with in **13** ……………….......... .

Question 12:

Is the answer a noun/noun phrase, etc?

Do the examples after the blank space help you?

Are these examples physical things?

What words do you associate with making physical things?

Question 13:

Is the answer a noun/noun phrase, etc?

Different solutions need to be thought of together. Is this important?

2 Compare your answers with another group.

Sentence completion

1 Work in groups. Look at the last paragraph E and make questions for examining the following sentence:

*Choose **NO MORE THAN TWO WORDS** from the passage for each answer.*

As well as examining the past and the present, management of the coast needs to take into account ………………............ .

The basis of an integrated management strategy can be created by ………………............ .

2 Compare your answers with another group.

3 Answer the question.

IELTS Reading checklist

1 Survey any headings, the text and questions in 5-10 seconds.

2 Skim the passage and questions quickly (in about two minutes) to get the gist of the whole passage.

3 Identify the questions which are easy and require less time.

4 Identify the questions which are difficult and require more time. Do not waste time on such questions. Come back to them later.

5 Use the nature of the passage to predict the organisation and structure of the text, e.g. *problem/solution*.

6 Use the questions to predict the organisation and structure of the text, e.g. *problem/solution*.

7 Use the questions and the predicted organisation to predict the possible location of answers in paragraphs and the text generally.

8 Predict where general information is likely to be in the whole text and in paragraphs, e.g. *is it likely to be at the beginning/end of text/paragraph?*

9 Predict where specific information is likely to be in the whole text and in paragraphs, e.g. *are examples likely to be in the middle of a sentence/paragraph?*

10 Use the title and repeated or related vocabulary such as words that relate to the environment to activate schemata.

11 Use the title and related nature of the text to predict the type of vocabulary and grammar that will occur in the text, e.g. *cause and effect, present simple and active passive*.

12 Check spelling in your answers.

13 Avoid leaving questions unanswered.

14 Answer global questions like paragraph and section headings first. (They help you find your way around the passage and help locate more specific questions.)

15 Use specific questions like sentence completion that follow global questions to check questions relating to headings are correct.

16 Locate the part of the text relating to questions quickly to give yourself time to analyse the questions closely.

17 Think carefully before you change answers. Your first instincts may be correct if you have read the text closely.

18 Do not be afraid of changing your mind.

19 Make sure your answers for a Reading Passage do not contradict each other, e.g. *paragraph headings and specific questions*.

20 If you panic, take a deep breath and continue.

The world of work and education

Vocabulary 1: Work

1 👥 With a partner, look at the photographs and describe what is happening in each.

2 Work in pairs. Match the words to the correct explanation below.

a	job	a profession or occupation over a period of time
b	work	what people gain at the end of a course, e.g. a degree
c	occupation	what work people do to earn money to live
d	profession	the job people follow, usually after gaining some kind of qualification
e	career	the job or profession people have
f	livelihood	paid work people do on a regular basis
g	qualifications	what people do or the place they do something to achieve some kind of result

3   Work in pairs. Choose a noun from exercise 2 to complete the sentences below. More than one answer may be possible.

   1   I want to be independent, so I'd like to earn my _____ running my own business.

   2   The _____ ethic varies from country to country and from one profession to another.

   3   I would really like to have a good _____ which allows me to achieve my aims.

   4   The second interview was successful and I got the _____ .

   5   Do you think it is important to have a good _____–life balance?

   6   I am a teacher by _____ .

   7   In order to improve their _____ prospects, and thus to climb the _____ ladder, students need to study hard.

   8   Being up to date is essential; otherwise, it is possible to miss out on the best _____ opportunities.

4   Work in pairs. Decide which three skills are the most important for your work and personal life. Use the items below and your own ideas. Give examples and reasons for your choices.

   • using mobile technology and laptops

   • numeracy

   • touch typing

   • socialising

   • being organised

Speaking
Part 3

1   Work in pairs. Look at three questions on goals and career below. Decide what an examiner might expect you to say in your answers, using the items in the bubbles. Then explain how you would answer the questions.

Don't forget!

• Make sure you support your answers by giving examples and reasons.

• Develop ideas using cause and effect.

• Talk about abstract details and avoid personal examples.

> **Goals and career**
>
> Do you think having aims and goals in life is useful for young people's careers? Why/Why not?
> Are there any benefits to society of young people achieving success in their career? Why do you think this is?
> Do you think that having a career in itself is a sign of success? Why/Why not?

evaluation   reasons   opinion   arguments to persuade

positive impact   examples   negative impact

2   Change partners. Take turns asking and answering the Part 3 questions above. When your partner has finished speaking, give him/her feedback using the checklist on page 181.

Reading
Questions 1–13

1 Work in groups. Decide which of the following features are the most important in a work environment. Add your own features if you want.

- a relaxed atmosphere
- a supportive environment
- a strong boss/leader
- working when and where you want

Don't forget!

- Look at the title and think about the kind of information that will be in the passage.
- Decide whether the passage is likely to be factual or presenting an argument about something.

READING PASSAGE

*You should spend about 20 minutes on **Questions 1–13**, which are based on the Reading Passage below.*

Why people thrive in coworking spaces

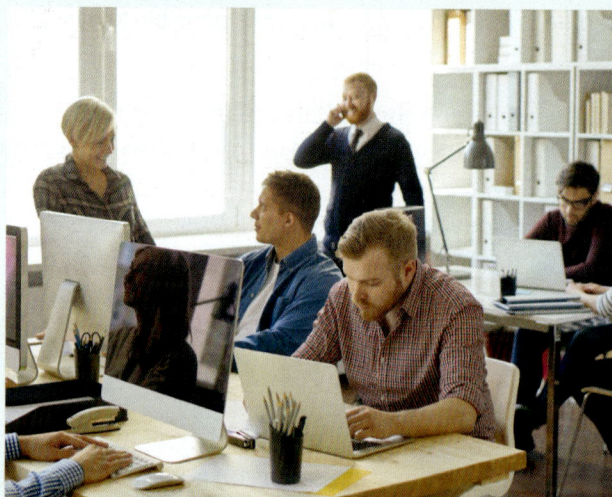

There seems to be something special about coworking spaces. What makes such spaces – defined as membership-based workspaces where diverse groups of freelancers, remote workers, and other independent professionals work together in a shared, communal setting – so effective? And are there lessons for more traditional offices?

People who use coworking spaces see their work as meaningful. First, unlike a traditional office, coworking spaces consist of members who work for a range of different companies, ventures, and projects. Because there is little direct competition or internal politics, they don't feel they have to put on a work persona to fit in. Working amidst people doing different kinds of work can also make one's own work identity stronger.

Second, meaning may also come from working in a culture where it is the norm to help each other out, and there are many opportunities to do so. Lastly, meaning may also be derived from a more concrete source: the social mission inherent in the Coworking Manifesto, an online document signed by members of more than 1,700 working spaces. It clearly articulates the values that the coworking movement aspires to, including community, collaboration, learning, and sustainability.

So in many cases, it's not simply the case that a person is going to work; they're also part of a social movement. They have more job control. Coworking spaces are normally accessible 24/7. People can decide whether to put in a long day when they have a deadline or want to show progress, or can decide to take a long break in the middle of the day to go to the gym. They can choose whether they want to work in a quiet space so they can focus, or in a more collaborative space with shared tables where interaction is encouraged.

Coworkers feel part of a community. Connections with others are a big reason why people pay to work in a communal space, as opposed to working from home for free or renting a nondescript office. Each coworking space has its own vibe, and the managers of each space go to great lengths to cultivate a unique experience that meets the needs of their respective members. Grind, for example, is a growing network of coworking spaces in New York and Chicago. Anthony Marinos, who oversees Grind's marketing, community management, and member services, shared with us, "When it comes to cultivating our community at Grind, we're all about the human element. We consider ourselves as much a hospitality company as we do a workspace provider. Our staff knows all of our members by name and profession, and we're constantly facilitating introductions between Grindists."

So what are the implications for traditional companies? Even though the coworking movement has its origins among freelancers, entrepreneurs, and the tech industry, it's increasingly relevant for a broader range of people and organizations. In fact, coworking can become part of your company's strategy, and it can help your people and your business thrive. An increasing number of companies are incorporating coworking into their business strategies in two ways.

First, they're being used as an alternative place for people to work. Michael Kenny, Managing Partner of San Diego-based Co-Merge, told us, "In the past year and a half, we've seen a dramatic increase in the use of the space by enterprise employees. We have seen teams come in to use various on-demand meeting rooms. We have users from global companies of size ranging from several hundred to several thousand employees who use the space not only to allow their distributed workers to get productive work done, but also to attract employees who demand flexible workplace and work time."

Grind is also witnessing growth in the number of remote workers who are becoming members. "We haven't had to reach out to larger organizations, they actually tend to just come to us," Anthony Marinos says. "We've had employees from Visa, journalists from the Chicago Tribune, and even people affiliated with large financial institutions all work out of Grind."

Spending time away from the office at a coworking space can also spark new ideas. Rebecca Brian Pan, the founder of COVO and former chief operating officer of NextSpace, explained how the innovation team of Ricoh, a multinational company, worked out of NextSpace Santa Cruz for several months to observe how people work and where they hit pain points. Based on member insight and feedback, and their own observations, the Ricoh team explored several new products that could help members in their daily work and chose the most highly rated product to pursue.

Second, the lessons of coworking spaces can be applied to corporate offices. Just as it's important to encourage flexibility and support your mobile workforce, there is an equally important reality of creating the right kind of work environment inside your own walls. But this doesn't just mean creating open plan layouts or adding a coffee bar.

In reality, people need to be able to craft their work in ways that give them purpose and meaning. They should be given control and flexibility in their work environment. The combination of a well-designed work environment and a well-curated work experience are part of the reason people who cowork demonstrate higher levels of thriving than their office-based counterparts.

Questions 1–7

Complete the notes below.

Choose **NO MORE THAN TWO WORDS** *from the passage for each answer.*

Coworking spaces and their benefits

Definition

- Workspaces with various workers sharing a **1** ………………………………………

Benefits

- Different from a **2** ……………………………………… : people linked to various enterprises
- People don't have to adopt a **3** ……………………………………… in their job
- Working with different professionals – strengthens people's **4** ………………………………………

Meaning given to coworking

- Helping coworkers is regarded as the **5** ………………………………………
- Possibly coming from a concrete **6** ……………………………………… : mission in the Coworking Manifesto
- Coworkers seen as a part of social **7** ………………………………………

How to go about it

For **Questions 8–12**

- Circle the names of the people in the Reading Passage. This will help you find the answers quicker.
- Note the names are usually in the order they occur in the passage.
- Read and underline words or phrases in the statement that will help you match statements and people in the Reading Passage.
- Note the rubric says you can use any letter more than once.
- Note **D** *None of the above* at the end of the list of names.

Questions 8–12

*Look at the following statements (**Questions 8–12**) and the list of people below.*

*Match each statement with the correct person, **A–D**.*

NB You may use any letter more than once.

8 The traditional office needs substantial training input for workers.

9 Research was conducted by one institution on various products.

10 Coworking spaces attract employees from international firms wanting greater flexibility.

11 There is no need to do anything to attract custom from bigger institutions.

12 The focus of the development of the coworking community is on the people.

> **List of people**
> **A** Anthony Marinos
> **B** Michael Kenny
> **C** Rebecca Brian Pan
> **D** None of the above

Question 13

*Choose the correct letter **A**, **B**, **C** or **D**.*

Which of the following observations is made by the writer about corporate offices?

A Care needs to be taken to develop and support a mobile workforce.
B The advantages of coworking spaces on professionals is underestimated.
C Coworking spaces have a role to play in offices in corporations.
D Open plan offices are a major step towards developing coworking spaces.

2 Do you think that coworking spaces are a good idea? Gives reasons and examples. If you were able to create your ideal work environment, what would it be like?

Vocabulary 2: Collocations

1 Work in pairs. For **1–10** below, decide which words collocate with the noun.

1 considerable / enjoy / make / derive / accrue	benefit
2 huge / education / gain / outweigh / take	advantage
3 once-in-a-lifetime / silver / career / seize / waste	opportunity
4 enormous / large / achieve / guarantee / depends on	success
5 excellent / get / offer / boost / career	prospects
6 distinct / obvious / suffer / have / enjoy	disadvantage
7 total / achieve / result in / ensue	failure
8 outstanding / accrue / impressive / represent / a lack of	achievement
9 huge / show / make / take up / room	improvement
10 good / deserve / throw away / possess / arise	chance

2 Complete the gaps in **1–8** below with a word or phrase from exercise 1. There may be more than one possible answer.

1 Achieving _____ in life depends on many factors like qualifications, but it cannot always be _____ by having them.

2 Even if an academic career ends in _____ , it does not mean that someone's long-term career _____ are seriously damaged.

3 Everyone _____ a fair _____ at succeeding in life, but all too often people waste the opportunity.

4 I made a huge _____ in my last years at school, but looking back there was certainly _____ for more.

5 A person who has a vocational education in plumbing or engineering does not suffer any _____ in life. On the contrary, having such an education is a/an _____ .

6 The financial _____ that _____ from acquiring training and skills means that one can enjoy the fruits of one's labours.

7 Finding my first job _____ the proudest _____ in my life so far.

8 Going to university in my country is a _____ _____ that needs to be _____ if it comes along.

3 👥 Do you think failure is ever beneficial for a person? Can you think of examples from your own experiences?

Listening
Section 3

1 👥 Work in pairs. Make a list of points that you need to consider when you are doing a presentation. Then discuss which would be the most important for you and why.

Don't forget!

• Skim the questions to see what the topic is about.

• Underline words that will help you listen for the answers.

🎧 12 **SECTION 3** *Questions 21–30*

Questions 21–25

Choose **FIVE** *letters,* **A–H**.

Which **FIVE** improvements does Francesca suggest about the presentation?

A test the equipment

B reduce the delivery speed

C add more data

D distribute the handouts

E lengthen the talk

F improve the organisation

G shorten the talk

H check the chair layout

Questions 26–28

Complete the sentences below.

Write **ONE WORD ONLY** *for each answer.*

JACK'S FEEDBACK

26 He thinks that he used too much ………………………................ in his talk.

27 He was frightened that they would appear ………………………............... .

28 He feels the main thing for him is to control his ………………………............... .

Questions 29 and 30

Answer the questions below.

Write **ONE WORD ONLY** *for each answer.*

29 What did the other students say the presentation was? ....

30 What is the tutor going to photocopy for them to take away? ....

2 👥 Have you ever seen or given a presentation? What kind of presentation was it?

Did you feel it went well? Why/Why not? What would you do differently if you had to do it again?

Language focus: Conditionals 1

1 Look at the statements below from the Listening on page 232. Identify the tenses and number the boxes as follows:

1 1st conditional

2 2nd conditional

3 3rd conditional

☐ *If we had given ourselves more time, it would have flowed better.*

☐ *… but if I had to do it all over again, I'd change a few things.*

☐ *If I do it again, I'll definitely spend more time practising to make it run more smoothly.*

☐ *… unless time is devoted to practising, it'll not be possible to give a good performance.*

G Read more about conditionals in the Grammar reference on page 223.

2 For sentences **1–7** below, put the verbs in brackets into the correct tense.

1 Going to university _____ (turn out) to be an enjoyable experience if students balance studying time with making new friends.

2 If people pursued their goals, they _____ (succeed) whatever happens.

3 Unless governments invest money in education, they _____ (find) it difficult to tackle unemployment.

4 I would not have achieved the results I did unless I _____ (work) hard.

5 If time and effort _____ (devote) to team-building in the company, the team would have bonded more closely by now.

6 If people _____ (give) opportunities to prepare for the changes affecting the world, finding a job will prove easier for them in the future.

7 Many people would love to turn the clock back and lead the same life again if they _____ (have) the chance.

3 👥 Work in pairs. Choose one of the statements in exercise 2. Discuss the statement by explaining why you agree or disagree with it. Give reasons and examples.

4 For **1–6** below, decide which word is missing in each sentence.

1 The educational process for children is free of unnecessary stress, they won't develop properly.

2 Had there been a better opportunity in a different company, I would not have left my old job.

3 If my father had not migrated to Australia, I have been born in Japan.

4 If people did have qualifications, it would be more difficult to assess their suitability for a job.

5 Some adults had better literacy and numeracy skills, they would access the job market more easily.

6 Had universities permitted to expand faster, there would have been a more skilled workforce by now.

5 Complete sentences **1–6** below with your own words.

1 Were the government to take more responsibility for people's training needs, then …

2 Had I been able to choose …

3 If the change in the pace of life continues at its current rate, …

4 If people are not adaptable and prepared to change jobs, then …

5 It is important for everyone nowadays to aim to have some kind of profession; otherwise, …

6 Unless my parents had been prepared to sacrifice a lot to educate me, …

6 👥 Work in pairs. Take turns asking and answering the questions below about your future, using the following:

What would happen if … ?

What would have happened if … ?/If you had another chance … ?

Speaking
Part 2

1   Choose one of the Task Cards **A** or **B** and check how the plans relate to each part of the Card. Make **brief** notes for each part of the frame using no more than 10 to 12 words. Use words and phrases from Vocabulary 2 on page 96.

A

Describe an achievement that you will never forget.
You should say:
  what the achievement is
  how long ago you had this achievement
  why you will never forget this achievement
and explain how the achievement has affected your life.

B

Describe a job that you would like to have.
You should say:
  what the job is
  how long you have wanted to have this job
  what the job would involve
and explain why you would like to do the job.

Frame A

What I'd like to talk about is _____

It took place/occurred/happened _____

The reason why I'll never forget this achievement _____

It's also very memorable, because _____

and also I'll always remember it because _____

It would mean that _____

It would also be _____

Frame B

The job I'd like to have _____

I first decided I'd like to do the job _____

The job would involve/include/mean/entail _____

I think I'd like it, because it would be _____

It would mean that _____

It would also be _____

It would help me _____

---

2   Compare your notes with someone who chose the same Task Card. With another partner, take turns talking about the topic. When your partner has finished speaking, give him/her feedback using the checklist on page 181.

99

Writing
Task 2

1   Work in groups. Discuss the structure and content of the answer required for the following Task 2 question. Then answer questions **1–3** below.

WRITING TASK 2

You should spend about 40 minutes on this task.

Write about the following topic:

> *Some people believe that children at secondary school should be streamed, i.e. taught in classes according to ability, rather than being taught in mixed-ability classes.*
>
> *Do you think the advantages of streaming children at secondary school outweigh the disadvantages?*

Give reasons for your answer and include any relevant examples from your own knowledge and experience.

Write at least 250 words.

---

1   What is the general context of the task?

2   What two specific areas do you have to compare?

3   Does the rubric ask you to give your opinion?

2   The text below is part of an answer to the Task 2 question above. Insert the following items into the correct place in paragraph 2 and explain their purpose in the paragraph.

a   it is easier to teach a class who are all of the same ability level.

b   everything is aimed at the pupils in the middle-ability range.

c   pupils are struggling with a chemistry lesson, the teacher can go at a slower pace and vice versa for higher-level pupils.

Grouping children at secondary level according to ability is favoured by some people over classes with different ability levels. While there may be some advantages to this approach, I personally think that the drawbacks of streaming outweigh the benefits.

The main benefit of streaming is that pupils of all abilities will benefit through being taught at a pace that suits their level. If, for example, **1** _____ Some people also argue that mixed-ability classes disadvantage students at both extremes of ability, as **2** _____ From the teacher's point of view, **3** _____ .

Having said that however, I feel that streaming children at secondary level is harmful. The main drawback is that if children are not taught in mixed-ability classes, it does not prepare them for the real world they will encounter in the future. This could then hold them back and reduce their career opportunities considerably.

Streaming can also disadvantage children, because it is possible that children will be labelled wrongly and their potential not realised. Unless there is some competition in the classroom as in mixed-ability classrooms, the children will not be stretched. This can then have a negative impact on children's attitude to learning and to school in general, resulting in a decline in pupils' attainment.

As we have seen, there are both advantages and disadvantages involved in streaming pupils at secondary level, but, in my opinion, the latter outweigh the former.

3   Look at paragraph 3 in the model answer and find the following features:

    1 a topic sentence

    2 a disadvantage

    3 an opinion

    4 an adjective of evaluation

    5 three results

4   Work in groups. Look at paragraph 4 and using your answers to exercises 2 and 3, explain the development of the paragraph in your own words.

5   Work in groups. Explain how the conclusion relates to each of the topic sentences in the three body paragraphs, the introduction and the Task 2 question.

6   Now skim the model answer opposite and decide which is the correct outline below, **A** or **B**.

    A

    1 introduction with opinion

    2 advantages of streaming

    3 disadvantages of streaming/advantages of mixed-ability

    4 disadvantages of streaming/advantages of mixed-ability

    5 conclusion

    B

    1 introduction with opinion

    2 advantages and disadvantages of streaming

    3 advantages of mixed ability

    4 advantages of mixed ability

    5 conclusion

7   Write your own answer for the Task 2 question on page 210. When you have finished, check your answer using the checklist on page 139.

Vocabulary 1: Work

1 In each space below, add a suitable singular or plural noun related to work. You may use each noun once only.

The _____ that my friends want to go into are varied. Some want to find a permanent _____ in banking or business, while others want to go into the medical or legal _____ . It is possible to find _____ in the former without specific _____ and considerable _____ , but for medicine and law the first of these is essential in order to find something where it is possible to have a good _____ a successful _____ .

Vocabulary 2: Collocations

1 Combine the two items to make five complete sentences. You may use each item once only.

What do you think people nowadays can do to boost

Example: →

their job prospects?

Do you think it's possible to achieve

can lead to failure.

Some people think that technology has made

achievement so far?

Do you think the advantages of working part-time

huge improvements in the workplace. To what extent do you agree or disagree?

What do you think is your most impressive

success without qualifications?

I think giving up rather than the lack of ability

outweigh the disadvantages?

Language focus: Conditionals 1

1   Add the words *if, unless, otherwise* or *nothing* to the first gap in the sentences below. In the second gap put the verbs in brackets into the correct tense.

   1   _____ I hadn't passed my exams at university, I _____ (not be) able to follow the profession I wanted.

   2   People in today's world should have both qualifications and experience; _____ , finding a job _____ (become) slightly harder.

   3   _____ I don't learn to drive, it _____ (limit) my job opportunities.

   4   _____ more money is invested in the education system, the workforce _____ (be) less well-trained.

   5   _____ people did some kind of volunteering, it _____ (help) them when they started looking for a job.

   6   _____ I _____ (not work) as hard as I did in the past, I wouldn't be as successful as I am now.

   7   _____ people _____ (focus) on achieving a good work-life balance, their working lives would be less stressful.

   8   _____ I hadn't had the chance to change my career, I _____ (not do) it.

2   Rewrite sentences in exercise 1 using the words below. Make any necessary changes.

   Example:

   Had

   Had I not passed my exams at university, I would not be able to follow the profession I wanted.

had	unless	unless	if	were	had	were	otherwise

Accuracy in IELTS

1   Find the spelling mistakes in the words below.

achievement	profesional	success	occasions	prospects
improvment	career	disatisfied	excellense	scenes
oportunity	livlihood	aspirations	guaranteing	impressive

2   In the text below, (circle) and correct the seven words that are misspelled.

> An efficient workplace is one where the work enviroment encourages people to be succesful, to develop their proffessional skills and acheive their aspirations. If people are denied the chanc to develop in this way, then their own and the company's success is limited. Furthermore, if everyone has the same opportunites at school and at work, there is a good chance their careir prospects will be improved dramatically and the economy will benefit from a happier and, subsequently, a more productive workforce.

Mapping the world

Vocabulary: Nouns relating to places

1 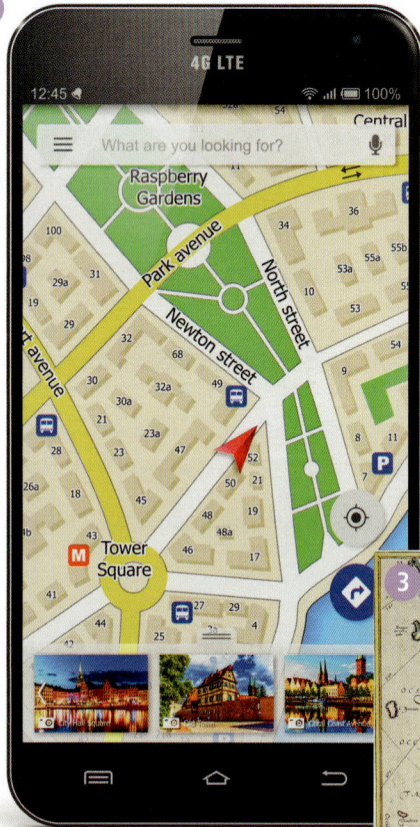 Work in groups. What do the images show? Describe the similarities and the differences between the maps. Then discuss the questions below.

- What do you think the purpose of each map is?
- When was the last time you consulted a map? Why did you use it?
- Do you think maps on smartphones are always helpful?
- Do you think satellite maps or phones that track location invade people's privacy?

---

2 Look at the first photograph and answer the following questions:

1 Is the area shown in the photograph urban or rural?

2 How many residential neighbourhoods can you identify?

3 Where do you think the quietest spot is?

3 Decide which of the nouns in brackets go in each gap. Use each noun only once to complete the sentences and use the plural where appropriate. Make any necessary changes.

1 Yes, I had a favourite _____ I liked to visit, but it has become a real tourist _____ , so I don't go there anymore. (place/spot)

2 The park in the business _____ is surrounded by a pedestrian _____ , which makes it a real haven of peace. (area/district)

3 My family home is in a magnificent _____ overlooking the sea. It's a _____ famed for its views. (region/location)

4 The _____ I now live in is quite built-up, but it still has quite a lot of big open _____ . (area/space)

5 There have been a few burglaries in the _____ recently, but by and large it is a very safe _____ . (vicinity/neighbourhood)

6 India has some beautiful _____ to visit, especially in the northern _____ of the country, where you can avoid most of the tourist hot _____ . (region/spot/place)

7 The house was built in a beautiful _____ on a hillside with a stream and surrounded by trees. This whole _____ is spectacular at any time of the year but especially in the autumn. (region/setting)

4 Work in pairs. You can build up a description of a place by adding phrases after the noun. Decide which phrases **1–10** you associate most with phrases **a–j**. There may be more than one possible answer.

1 in a lively district	**a** surrounded by trees
2 in a beautiful setting	**b** overlooking the sea
3 a wooded hillside	**c** with no houses, just open fields
4 an open space	**d** covered with trees
5 an empty desert	**e** with lots of cars and people
6 a noisy neighbourhood	**f** full of shops and cafés
7 a temperate zone	**g** located near a lake
8 a sandy beach	**h** with huge sand dunes and no people
9 a secluded spot	**i** full of wildlife
10 a rugged mountain	**j** stretching into the distance

5 For **1–4** below, put the words in *italics* into the correct order.

1 I live in a block of flats, *small a overlooking garden*. It's in a really beautiful and quiet *old buildings neighbourhood with*. And though it's in the heart of the city, it is a peaceful area, *full of park large near located a flowers and plants*.

2 My family home is on a beach *seashore miles along the stretching for*. It's an ideal place for sports enthusiasts *opportunity of boating with for lots of plenty and swimming*. The house, though *two built years ago hundred*, is still in good condition.

3 My family come from a village *by mountains beautiful surrounded*. In summer the mountainside, *purple its with flowers*, is a blaze of colour.

4 My dream home would be a secluded lake with *forest full a by wildlife surrounded of* or even on a hillside *with covered views out but with looking trees* over the countryside.

6 Work in pairs. Think of a place in the countryside or in a town you are familiar with and describe it to your partner.

1 Work in pairs. As quickly as you can, find words or phrases in the Reading Passage which have the same meaning as words **1–8** below.

1 advanced   **2** natural to   **3** makes up   **4** main

5 showing   **6** linked   **7** system   **8** development

2 Work in groups. Bring together the information you have about the Reading Passage so far.

READING PASSAGE

*You should spend about 20 minutes on **Questions 1–13**, which are based on the Reading Passage below.*

Cartography

Cartography, from the Greek word *khartes* meaning 'map' and *graphein* meaning 'write', , is a science that is at its simplest level the study and practice of making maps. At a more sophisticated level, it is not just a science, but an art that seeks to give in a simple and beautiful form, to the spatial information in the human environment. Cartography, along with science and aesthetics, obviously involves technical expertise, which has been developing over millennia.

Historically, maps have sought to utilise the complex knowledge of the environment, innate in the majority of the human race, to suit the needs of people who seek to use them. Communities living in small groups and not travelling very far have little need of complex maps, while urban dwellers, seafarers or traders operating in a much more complex and/or wider environment need something more sophisticated, either to delineate boundaries and define ownership, or to travel routes beyond the immediate confines of their communities. As humanity's needs have changed and the world they encountered has changed, so have the maps they need to shape or navigate that world.

What exactly constitutes a map has made the identification of the first maps not easy. Early dot maps of the night sky from the 17,000 BC have been found in caves at Lascaux in France, but even earlier representations of mountains and routes dated to 25,000 BC have been identified in the Czech Republic. At present-day Catalhuyuk in Anatolia, an aerial map-like plan of the town has been dated to about 7,000 years BC, while at Valcamonica in the Italian Alps, examples of images date to the 4th millennium BC.

The primary function of the creation of maps is to locate the place of humanity in their world and to guide. Drawings of totemic ancestors, such as crocodiles or birds, and their actions, have been made on bark and cave walls by Australian Aboriginals, as well as through songs and rituals, to act as maps to help guide souls through the world in Dream Time. In the Marshall Islands in the Pacific Ocean are found stick charts, which give an idea of what maps in ancient times might have looked like. The charts are memory aids showing the swells of the ocean that were studied and learnt prior to a sea voyage. They recorded different features from today's maps, but nonetheless their contribution to cartography is not insignificant.

In Mesopotamia, in modern day Iraq, ancient clay tablets dating back as far as the 3rd Century BC have been found depicting estates and, at times, cities such as Nippur, south of Babylon, with marking for irrigation channels, a river and estate boundaries. These tablets are title deeds for an urbanising world. A clay tablet dated about 600 BC has a world map with Babylon and the Euphrates near its centre. The Nazca lines in Peru in South America have also been variously associated with irrigation and celestial maps. By contrast, there are few maps from Ancient Egypt with those that are relating to the maintenance of the boundaries of properties after the annual Nile floods. However, the Turin papyrus map dating from about the 12th Century BC was used for those on quarrying expeditions and contains topographical features such as mountains, wells and road networks.

At a much later date, in The Middle Ages, remarkably accurate sea charts, called portolans, were used with the magnetic compass, which was not invented in Europe until the latter part of the 12th century. These sea charts were all created in in the same way from vellum from goats or sheep skin. Further, they were rectangular in shape with the neck skin of the animal still attached. They also all had line drawings in coloured ink. The charts basically consisted of a network of line drawings, with the cartographer drawing a hidden circle around a central point and then vertical and horizontal lines through the centre. A series of other circles were drawn with similar lines. Depending on the direction, these lines were then drawn in different colours. Another characteristic of the maps was the enlarged headlands because they were important for seafarers. Names going clockwise around the Mediterranean Sea were written perpendicular to the coastline to avoid obscuring the coastline.

With three-dimensional and digital maps, modern-day cartographers have very sophisticated digital tools at their disposal to make sense, shape and refine our place in the world and to guide us. As in the past, cartography as a science is still having a huge impact on human progress.

How to go about it

For **Questions 1–5**:
- Read the sentence beginnings and then the endings.
- Check for beginnings and endings that don't fit together.
- Scan the Reading Passage for words or paraphrases of words in the sentence beginnings. Put a (circle) around the words in the text to help you refer to them.
- Match the endings to the words you located in the text.

Questions 1–5

Complete each sentence with the correct ending, **A–G**, below.

1 At a basic level, cartography is a subject that
2 Cartography also
3 A complex map
4 The identification of what a map is
5 The main purpose of cartography

A teaches us about politics and commerce.
B indicates the main human settlements in late antiquity.
C is connected with studying and making maps.
D is for guidance and location of people.
E includes art and technical know-how.
F is of little use to people in small communities.
G is a difficult process.

Questions 6–11

Complete the table below.

*Choose **NO MORE THAN TWO WORDS** from the passage for each answer.*

Maps among different peoples

People	Artefacts	Purpose	Other notes
Australian Aboriginals	6 .... and .... drawings of animals	to guide souls in 7	contained representations of totemic ancestors
Marshall Islanders	stick chart	memory 8 .... for navigators at sea	huge contribution to cartography map
Mesopotamians	9	10 .... for a more urban society	containing details of ownership of land/ mainly from 1st millennium BC
Ancient Egyptians	Turin papyrus	used on 11 .... to quarry stones	contains drawings of mountains, wells and roads

Questions 12 and 13

*Choose **TWO** letters, A–E.*

Which **TWO** features of the creating of sea charts are mentioned by the writer in the passage?

A A wide range of animal skins were used in their production.

B Coloured lines were used on the maps to indicate direction.

C The lines differed depending on where the sea charts were made.

D The features on all the sea charts were to scale and not distorted.

E The process of making the maps is apparently identical in each case.

3 Do you think using interactive maps on smart phones and GPS is making life easier or reducing spatial awareness in people? Give reasons and examples.

Language focus: Referring in a text

1 Read the following extracts from the Reading Passage on page 106. Look at the words in bold in the first sentence of each extract. Decide which word or phrase in the second sentence refers back to them.

Cartography, from the Greek word *khartes* meaning 'map' and *graphein* meaning 'write', is a science that is at its simplest level the study and practice of making maps. At a more sophisticated level, it is not just a science …

In the Marshall Islands in the Pacific Ocean are found **stick charts**, which give an idea of what maps in ancient times might have looked like. The charts are memory aids …

In Mesopotamia, in modern day Iraq, **ancient clay tablets** dating back as far as the 3rd Century BC have been found depicting estates … These tablets are title deeds for an urbanising world.

2 Look at sentences **1–3** below. What does the word in bold refer to in each sentence?

1 The neighbourhood is very noisy because **it** is full of shops and restaurants.

2 As the region is full of large farms, **it** is very rich.

3 The cost of farming has increased dramatically over the period. **This** (rise) has led to inflation.

3 Is it possible to use *this* instead of *it* in sentences **1** and **2**? Why/Why not?

4 Is it possible to use *it* instead of *this* in sentence **3**? Can you leave out the word *rise* in the second sentence? Why/Why not?

G Read more about referring in a text in the Grammar reference on page 223.

5 Underline the correct alternative in *italics* in **1–8** below.

1 The neighbourhood where I live now was very different a few years ago. *The neighbourhood/It/This* used to be much more pleasant then.

2 The region is full of many places to see. This is what makes *this/it/that* such a fantastic place to live.

3 The location for the new airport has been changed to somewhere completely different. *This new development/Those/They* will cost a lot of money.

4 When I first discovered the woodland *it/this/that* was not known by many people, but now *it/this/that* is visited by dozens of people every day.

5 The area has been transformed by the building of new factories and a business park. *This/It/They* has unfortunately made the place less attractive.

6 Various industrial sites are for sale at the moment, but *they/it/these* are too expensive. *This/That/It* will stop the area from developing.

7 The neighbourhoods here in the south of the city are industrialised, while *these/they/those* in the north are more residential.

8 More people have moved away from the city centre to the suburbs. As a result, *those/they/these* areas are becoming more crowded and expensive.

6 For **1–7** below, remove the repetition in each sentence by using a suitable reference.

1 The price of property in this region is increasing, and the increase in the price of property in this region is set to continue.

2 The neighbourhood was poor once but the neighbourhood is rich now.

3 I like visiting the seaside when nobody is around; visiting the seaside when nobody is around is very relaxing.

4 If people make an effort to clean up after themselves when people visit parks, then parks will be much more inviting for the public in general.

5 My friend suggested I should go away for a few days for a break. The suggestion I should go away for a few days was a good idea, but the suggestion I should go away for a few days might be expensive.

6 The government should pass laws to protect more areas of great natural beauty. Passing laws to protect more areas of great natural beauty would benefit all of us.

7 Change in the local area cannot be stopped. Change in the local area is inevitable, even if the change in the local area is very slow and the change stops altogether for a while. But change stopping altogether for a while is unlikely to happen.

7 Work in groups. Discuss the idea in sentence **7** in exercise 6. To what extent do you agree or disagree?

Listening
Section 4

1 Work in pairs. Look at the headings in bold and predict what the notes are about.

2 Read the notes in **Questions 31–40** below and decide what type of information is missing (nouns, etc) and which words indicate the answer is about to be mentioned.

---

13 **SECTION 4** *Questions 31–40*

Questions 31–40

Complete the notes below.

*Write **NO MORE THAN THREE WORDS AND/OR A NUMBER** for each answer.*

Migration of early humans

- Movements of people – common occurrence through history

- First significant migration: from Africa about **31** .... years ago

- Early pioneers did not survive

- Earth experienced changes in **32** ....

- About 70,000 years ago, departure of modern humans from Africa

Areas of colonisation

- China about 50,000 years ago

- Europe about **33** .... years ago

- Open steppes of Siberia some 40,000 years ago

- Roughly 20,000 years ago arrival in Japan, then linked to the main **34** ....

- Australia reached across the sea on **35** .... 50,000 years ago

- America via Alaska some time between 15 and 13,000 years ago

Migration within Africa

Bantu occupation of around **36** .... of the African continent by 1,000 AD

Stimulus for the Bantu migration: perhaps the farming of the **37** ....

Population expansion led to movement into sparsely populated surrounding areas

Introduction of iron production from **38** ....

Use of iron tools by the Bantu to fell trees, clear forests and **39** ....

Iron gave the Bantu a **40** .... over their neighbours

---

3 Work in pairs. Do you think people will always move around the world? Give reasons and examples.

1 Work in pairs. Match each sentence beginning **1–7** with an ending **a–g**. There may be more than one possible answer

1 The town centre	**a** replaced the old hospital.
2 Several old buildings	**b** was completely transformed over the period.
3 A new school	**c** were turned into flats.
4 The old houses	**d** was built in place of the old meeting house.
5 Some old derelict factories	**e** was chopped down to widen the road.
6 A line of old trees	**f** was converted into a restaurant and a cinema.
7 The bank	**g** were knocked down/demolished to make way for a new supermarket.

2 Underline the verbs used to describe change in each sentence in exercise 1.

3 Underline the most suitable verb in *italics* in sentences **1–8** below. Then put it into the correct tense.

1 The railway *extend/expand* to the centre of town, and three new stations were built.

2 As the town *extend/expand*, all the open spaces were used up for housing.

3 An airport *construct/become* on a green field site on the edge of the town.

4 The neighbourhood completely *change/demolish* with the building of new apartments.

5 The area around the town *turn into/become* more built-up.

6 A number of dramatic developments *take place/convert*, which *alter/expand* the character of the town completely.

7 The area *turn into/become* less rural and leafy with the building of new offices.

8 The empty space near the university *develop/become* into a park.

4 Decide which verbs in exercise 3 can be turned into nouns with the following endings: *-ation, -ition, -sion, -tion, -ment*.

5 🗣 Work in pairs. Describe an area you know that has changed in recent years, using the nouns in exercise 4 where possible.

6 Look at the two maps in the Task 1 question on page 112. Describe the map of Wetherby in 2000 in your own words. Use the following expressions:

in the north/south/east/west of …

north/south/east/west of …

to the north/south/east/west of …

there is … ,

… lies, is situated, is sited, is located

stands, runs

Example:

In the north west of Wetherby there is some farmland.
Main Street runs west to east through the middle of Wetherby.

WRITING TASK 1

You should spend about 20 minutes on this task.

> The maps below show the changes experienced by the town of Wetherby at the beginning of the 21st Century.
>
> Summarise the information by selecting and reporting the main features, and make comparisons where necessary.

Write at least 150 words.

Wetherby 2000

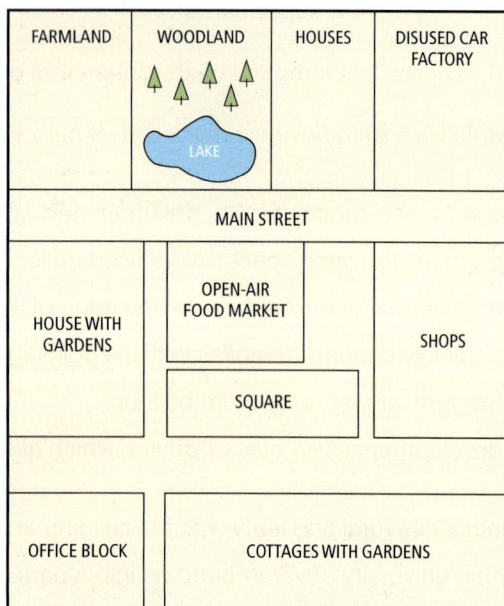

Wetherby 2016

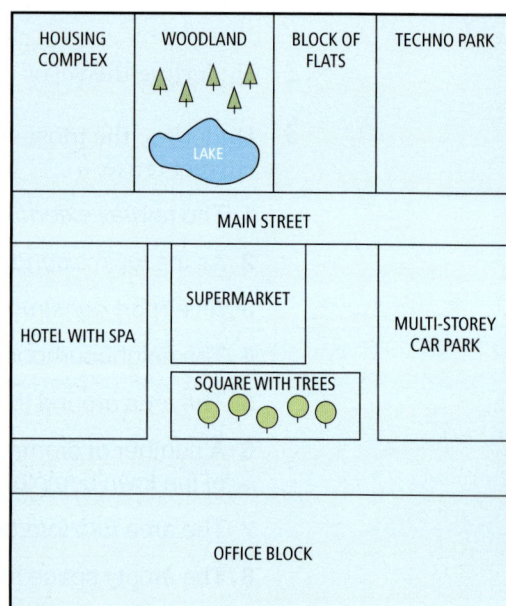

7 Describe the changes to the maps in exercise 6 using the following words and phrases:

1 build in place of
2 give way to
3 build on the site of
4 not change
5 turn into
6 give over to
7 become
8 reconstruct to become
9 replace/build
10 urban transformation

8 Work in pairs. Underline the adverbs of location in each phrase **a–g** below which relate to the maps in exercise 6. Decide if the adverbs are correct and make any necessary changes.

a the shops in the north-east of the area

b the square south of the open-air market

c the woodland with the lake to the north of the farmland

d the disused car factory in the north-east

e the farmland in the north-east of Wetherby

f South of Main Street, the area witnessed even greater change

g the office block west of the house in 2016 was extended

9   Look at the model. Insert items **a–g** from exercise 8 into the correct spaces **1–7**.

> The maps illustrate the changes that took place in Wetherby between 2000 and 2016. Overall, it is clear that the town underwent a complete transformation with the conversion of some areas and the replacement of others.
>
> Over the period, the neighbourhood north of Main Street, experienced a significant change. For example, **1** _____ was turned into a housing complex, while **2** _____ remained the same. **3** _____ was converted into a techno park with the houses to the west being replaced with blocks of flats. **4** _____ . The house with gardens in the northwest of the area became a hotel with a spa. Moreover, by 2016 **5** _____ , replacing all the cottages. The open-air market had given way to a supermarket and **6** _____ had become a multi-storey car park. Trees had also been added to **7** _____ .

10 Identify the verbs only in each sentence. Decide which tense is used and give reasons.

11 Identify the overview in the model in exercise 9 and rewrite it in your own words.

Don't forget!

You need to write an overview.
- Avoid listing the information.
- You cannot summarise trends, but you can summarise overall changes.

12 Work in pairs.

Student A: Look at the map of Sandring in 2016 on page 208, which has the names of places **1–10** missing. Listen to Student B's description and write the name of each place.

Student B: Look at the map of Sandring in 2016 on page 210, which has the names of the places marked. Describe to Student A where each place is. When you have finished, show Student A your map to check their answers.

13 Write your own answer for the Task 1 question on page 208. When you have finished, check your answer using the checklist on page 139.

Speaking
Parts 2 and 3

Don't forget!

Time yourselves. You should speak for up to two minutes.

1   Work in pairs. Take turns to ask each other questions about the Part 2 Task Card below.

> **Describe a neighbourbood you know that has changed.**
>
> You should say:
>   where the neighbourbood is
>   when you first visited the neighbourbood
>   what the neighbourbood looks like
> and explain how the neighbourhood has changed.

2   Use words and phrases from your answers in exercise 1 to make notes for the Task Card. With a different partner, take turns to talk about the topic. Give him/her feedback using the checklist on page 181.

3   Work in pairs. Decide what you might talk about in your answers to the Part 3 questions below. Then take turns asking each other the questions and give feedback using the checklist on page 181.

> **Social interaction with neighbours**
>
> How much time do people spend interacting socially with their neighbours in your country? Do you think this is the same worldwide?
> How important do you think social interaction in local neighbourhoods is for building happy communities? Why?
> Has the development of blocks of flats had a positive or negative social effect in local communities? Why do you think that is?

8 Review

Vocabulary: Nouns relating to places

1 Use each noun in brackets once only to complete the sentences.

1 I live in a quiet _____ with attractive houses, but my friends are staying in a(n) _____ of the city, which is really noisy as there are many clubs and restaurants in the immediate _____ . (area/neighbourhood/vicinity)

2 When I first visited the _____ just along the coast from the city, we found a secluded _____ on a beach far away from the crowds, but when we went back we didn't recognise the _____ at all. (area/place/spot)

3 The shop is in the pedestrian _____ next to the business _____ . You can't miss it as it's got a huge open _____ in front of it with some trees. (district/space/zone)

4 My family home is in a great _____ on a hilltop in one of the most popular _____ of the country. It is a fantastic _____ to live. (location/place/regions)

5 I'd like to live somewhere rural far from city life. The _____ is tranquil and beautiful as it's in the heart of the countryside with no other buildings of any kind in the immediate _____ . It is so different from the _____ that I live in. (place/setting/vicinity)

Language focus: Referring in a text

1 Decide which of the two <u>underlined</u> sections the word in bold refers to.

1 <u>The ruined castle</u> is on a <u>cliff top overlooking the North Sea</u>. **It** is in a remote, but very romantic location.

2 <u>New schools</u> are now spreading into <u>residential areas in the city</u>, so now **they** are becoming even more desirable.

3 While <u>holidays</u> to warmer <u>climates</u> have always been very popular, **those** to other colder places are just as desirable.

2 Complete the sentences with the correct alternatives in brackets.

1 A park was created from the derelict land. _____ is a good use of the land, as _____ will benefit the local community. (it/this)

2 Last year the government suggested covering the canals in the area with roads, but people knew _____ wouldn't work at all, as _____ would destroy the area! (it/that)

3 The city is full of many places to see. _____ is what makes _____ such an attractive tourist destination. (it/this)

4 The beach is stunning and quiet, but _____ is difficult to get to and _____ is what makes _____ attractive. (it/that/it)

5 The Sahara desert is vast, but _____ is not as empty as places like _____ seem at first sight. (it/this)

6 The renovation of the streets around the station are taking a long time, but _____ will be magnificent when _____ is all finished. (it/they)

7 The location for the new airport has been changed to somewhere completely different. At _____ stage, such a change will involve more expense than _____ in charge think. (this/those)

Verbs relating to changes in places

1 Make nouns from the verbs below.

construct   convert   demolish   replace   transform   renovate

2 The verbs highlighted in **1–8** below are in the wrong sentences. Rewrite each sentence with the correct verb.

1 The old houses were **transformed** to make way for a block of flats.

2 The area was completely **demolished** with new houses and shops.

3 A supermarket was **chopped down** to make way for a wider road.

4 A line of trees was **renovated and converted** and houses were constructed in their place.

5 The bank was **knocked down** into a restaurant.

6 The main street **replaced** a small pedestrian area.

7 A new bridge was **turned into** the tunnel.

8 The offices were **pulled down** and rebuilt again.

3 Rewrite the first two sentences using nouns.

Accuracy in IELTS

1 Remove any extra words in the sentences below.

1 The tramline was extended to the suburbs and three new stations were added.

2 As the town expanded, the fields were used up for housing.

3 A retail complex was constructed on a greenfield site on the edge of the town.

4 The neighbourhood was completely transformed with the building of a huge apartment blocks.

5 The area in the north west of the town was became more built-up.

6 A number of dramatic developments took place, which was altered the character of the town considerably.

7 The neighbourhood to the northwest of the town centre became less rural and leafy with the building of new offices.

8 The empty space to the west of the university campus was turned into a technology development centre.

9 What is beauty?

Vocabulary: Beauty

1 👥 Work in groups. Describe the buildings in each of the photographs. Name them if you can. Then discuss the questions below.

- What is your reaction to the buildings in the photographs? Do you think they are beautiful? Why/Why not?
- What is your favourite building or monument in the world?
- Is it important to live in beautiful surroundings? Why/Why not?

2 👥 In groups, evaluate each of the buildings in the photographs in exercise 1. Rank the buildings according to how beautiful you think they are: 1 = the most beautiful, 5 = the least beautiful. Give reasons.

3　For **1–6** below, complete the gaps with a building from exercise 1 so that the statement is true for you. Then complete the statement using your own ideas.

Example:

I think building _____ is breathtaking, as …

I think the building in the first photo is breathtaking because it is very elegant and attractive for a modern skyscraper.

1　I find building _____ very old-fashioned, because …

2　Building means _____ nothing to me at all, because …

3　Building _____ is not as beautiful as _____ , because …

4　Buildings such as _____ leave me cold, as they …

5　Building _____ made little impression on me, but building _____ fills me with excitement; it makes me want to …

6　When I look at the photograph of building _____ it makes me feel nostalgic, because …

4　Work in pairs. When you evaluate a building you can: **A** describe it physically; **B** say what effect it has on you. Look at the adjectives in the box below and decide which category they fit in, **A** or **B**.

evocative	tall	melancholic	thoughtful	ancient	spacious
dazzling	humbling	magnificent	impressive	overwhelmed	
emotional	ecstatic	stone	nostalgic	majestic	

5　Complete the gaps in **1–5** below with the correct form of a word from exercise 4.

Example:

When I saw the Taj Mahal for the first time it made a huge _impression_ on me.

1　Standing next to the Sphinx made me feel very _____ .

2　I was filled with _____ at the sight of the Himalayas. I was taken aback by their majesty.

3　Thinking of places that I love sometimes fills me with _____ , but this is not a negative feeling.

4　When I look at photographs of my home country they _____ so many memories and usually make me feel homesick.

5　The sight of the old people wandering through the ruins made me _____ about life and how things can change very suddenly.

6　Transform at least three sentences from exercise 5 by changing the word you added into a noun, verb or adjective where possible. Make any other necessary changes.

Example:

When I saw the Taj Mahal for the first time it made a huge impression on me.
When I saw the Taj Mahal for the first time it impressed me enormously.

7　Work in pairs. Choose three monuments that you think represent important times in your country's development or are symbolic of your country. Describe them to your partner and explain why they are important. Try to use the vocabulary from this section.

117

Speaking
Part 2

Don't forget!
● In the exam you will only have one minute to prepare.

1 You can emphasise your own opinion by contrasting it using linking words such as *but, though, although, however, nevertheless, even so, even though*, etc.

Even though the building leaves some people cold, I have a sentimental attachment to it.

Think of at least two buildings that are important, or have been important, in your life. Write sentences about them using at least five of the words and phrases **1–6** below and the linking words above.

Example:

Even though the building where I went to secondary school leaves some people cold, I have a sentimental attachment to it.

1 leave me cold

2 bring back memories

3 bleak but beautiful

4 ugly/unattractive/unsightly/unpleasant

5 in a rundown area

6 beautiful to see/to look at/to visit

2 With a partner, explain the effect these buildings have had on you. Use the sentences in exercise 1.

Useful expressions

What made (the building) important to me is …

The reason I chose (the building) is …

(The building) makes me …

When I see (the building) or photographs of (the building), it makes me feel …

(The building) is underrated, but …

3 Look at the following Part 2 Task Card. Choose ten verbs and/or adjectives from this unit so far, which will help you explain why the building is important to you. Write a note for each heading on the Task Card. Then narrow your verbs and adjectives down to three or four. Use the useful expressions in the box to help organise your answer.

> Describe a building or monument that you find impressive.
> You should say:
>   what the building or monument is
>   where the building or monument is located
>   what the building is like
> and explain why the building or monument impresses you.

4 Work in pairs. Take turns talking about the topic. Use your notes to guide you. You should speak for up to two minutes. Time each other using a stopwatch. When you have finished, give each other feedback using the checklist on page 181.

Reading
Questions 1–13

1 Work in groups. Look quickly at the title of the Reading Passage and skim the passage and the questions. Close your books and share as much information about the passage as possible.

2 In your groups, make a list of three or four things that you would expect to read in a passage about an architect.

3 Scan the passage and find words and phrases that have the opposite meaning to **1–7**.

1 separated   **5** revealing

2 alien/strange   **6** talentless

3 hated   **7** final

4 attacked

READING PASSAGE

*You should spend about 20 minutes on **Questions 1–13**, which are based on the Reading Passage below.*

Giles Gilbert Scott

A A bastion of the architectural establishment in early 20th-century Britain, Giles Gilbert Scott (1880–1960) fused tradition with modernity by applying historic styles to industrial structures in his designs from the Battersea and Bankside power stations in London, to Liverpool Anglican Cathedral, and to the K2 telephone kiosk.

B At the top of the splendid Portland stone tomb of the 19th-century architect John Soane and his wife and son, in St Pancras Old Church Gardens, north London, is a dome in a surprisingly familiar shape. Designed by Soane in 1815 as a monument to his beloved wife, the tomb is one of his most romantic designs, ornate in form and decorated by stone carvings of snakes and pineapples. It is familiar not because of its association with Soane's family tomb, but because of its influence on the design of the red K2 telephone kiosks, which were once a common sight throughout Britain.

C The architect who designed the K2, Giles Gilbert Scott, admired Soane's work and had recently become a trustee of the Sir John Soane Museum in London when invited in 1924 to enter a competition to design a public telephone kiosk. The shape of his design was inspired by the central domed structure of Soane's tomb. By rooting his design in Britain's architectural heritage, Scott transformed the telephone kiosk from what was then seen as an intimidating symbol of modernity into something that seemed reassuringly familiar. When the wooden models of the competing designs were exhibited outside the National Gallery, Giles Gilbert Scott's was chosen as the winner.

D Scott continued to package modernity in British traditionalism throughout his career. In his inaugural address as president of the Royal Institute of British Architects in 1933, when Britain was finally succumbing to modernism and the architectural profession was split by battling 'trads v. rads', he advocated a 'middle line' of both embracing technological progress and the human qualities of architecture. The 'middle line' was illustrated by Scott's best known London buildings, the power stations at Battersea (1929–1935) and Bankside (1947–1960), where he disguised their industrial purpose behind Gothic facades. Battersea, in particular, became a popular London landmark. Yet in an age when progressive architects such as Le Corbusier and Jean Prouvé romanticised technology, Scott's attempts to popularise industrial buildings by obfuscating their function seemed, at best, conservative.

E In 1923, Giles Gilbert Scott was commissioned to design Memorial Court, a hall of residence at Clare College, Cambridge (begun in 1923), which he completed in a Georgian-inspired style. The following year he won the telephone kiosk competition. Traditional though his kiosk was in style, functionally it was very advanced. An ingenious ventilation system was installed using perforations in the dome, and the glass was divided into small panels for speedy replacement in case of breakages. Scott's original proposal was for a mild steel structure, but the Post Office insisted on changing it to cast iron. It also insisted on painting the kiosks bright red for maximum visibility in emergencies rather than Scott's suggested shade of duck egg blue. Following protests in rural areas, where people complained that the bright red kiosks looked overbearing in the open countryside, the Post Office agreed to repaint them in green.

F Despite the rural complaints, the K2 kiosk was a popular success, and Scott was invited by the Post Office to modify his design in 1930 for the concrete K3, intended principally for country use. He was recalled again to design the K6 in 1935 to commemorate King George V's silver jubilee. This became the most widely used version of the kiosk with thousands being installed.

G As well as these landmark commissions, Scott designed dozens of churches throughout his career, as well as more understated public projects such as monuments and extensions to existing buildings. One of his most conspicuous commissions was as a consultant, rather than an architect, to Battersea Power Station in south London. Charged with making the enormous electricity generating station more appealing, Scott suggested brick as the main material for the central structure and turned the four chimneys – one on each corner – into reassuringly familiar neo-classical columns. The result is surprisingly engaging for such a vast structure, but with the showiness of the Art Deco cinemas then being constructed across Britain.

H His most significant post-war commission came in 1947 when Scott was invited to design a second London power station at Bankside beside the Thames in Southwark. More austere in style than Battersea, Bankside did not match its popularity until its conversion in 2000 by the Swiss architects Herzog and De Meuron into the Tate Modern museum. Yet formally and functionally it is the more sophisticated of the two buildings, not least as Scott combined all of Bankside's chimneys into a single central tower.

Questions 1–4

Complete the sentences below.

Choose **NO MORE THAN TWO WORDS** from the passage for each answer.

1 Scott combined .... and .... in the buildings he designed.

2 Scott's efforts to make industrial buildings more popular appeared ....

3 Despite not being innovative style-wise, from a practical point of view Scott's telephone box was ....

4 Although people objected to the K2 phone boxes, they were generally a ....

Questions 5–9

Classify the following events as occurring in Scott's life.

   A between 1920 and 1930

   B between 1930 and 1940

   C after 1940

5 a modification in telephone box design to mark a special occasion

6 a power station that much later became a museum

7 success in the contest to design a telephone box

8 an invitation to design accommodation for students

9 Scott's support for architectural progress that appeals to people

Questions 10–13

The Reading Passage has eight paragraphs, **A–H**.

Which paragraph contains the following information?

10 a comparison of the features of two buildings which Scott was associated with

11 the place where the designs for the K2 were put on public display

12 the reason given for the colour change to the K2

13 a reference to the fact that a tomb decoration is remarkably recognisable

> **Don't forget!**
>
> Questions **5–9**
> • Circle dates in the passage.

4 🗨 Do architects have more influence on our lives than we realise? Should there be more or less control over the work of architects? Give reasons and examples.

Word building: Prefixes *under-* and *over-*

1   Scan the Reading Passage on page 119 and find examples of adjectives with the prefix *under-* or *over-*. What is the meaning of the prefixes *under-* and *over-* here?

2   Complete sentences **1–10** below. Make a suitable word for each gap by using the correct form of a verb from the box and the prefix *under-* and *over-*.

overpriced	fund	value	run	state	come
estimate	awe	rate (x 2)	take		

Example:

However stunning the tourist attraction is, the entrance fee is definitely <u>overpriced</u> .

1   Many scientists have _____ the importance of early archaeological discoveries. They are much more significant than was once thought.

2   The monuments were totally _____ by people. I couldn't take any pictures.

3   The museum is really _____ . It's a very boring building.

4   Artefacts from a long time ago are frequently _____ . At auctions they may only sell for a fraction of the price of modern art.

5   Some people are completely _____ with emotion when they visit Florence. It's a syndrome called the Stendhal effect.

6   The museum _____ the theme park as the most popular attraction last year.

7   Many buildings and monuments of international significance are crumbling, because government repair schemes are _____ .

8   The ruins of Greater Zimbabwe are seriously _____ . I think they are more important than they are thought to be.

9   The architecture of the building is very _____ . It is this simplicity which makes it magnificent.

10 I was completely _____ by the carvings. I've never seen anything like them.

3   👥 Write two sentences about a place, country monument or film you know. Use at least one of the words from exercise 2. Then read and explain them to a partner.

Example:

I was overawed the first time I went into the Sahara. The sand dunes stretched as far as I could see in every direction.

Listening
Section 3

Don't forget!

• Underline the words in the questions that show you that the answer is about to be given.

1 You are going to listen to a conversation between a tutor and a student about a film project. Look at **Questions 21–30** below and decide what the project is about.

2 Work in pairs. You will hear words **1–9** below during the conversation. Check the meaning of the words.

1 perception	**2** collage	**3** grandeur	**4** digital stills	**5** narrow down
6 discipline	**7** fade	**8** access	**9** click	

🎧 14 **SECTION 3** *Questions 21–30*

Questions 21–25

Write **NO MORE THAN TWO WORDS AND/OR A NUMBER** *for each answer.*

21 Malcolm feels the topic he's chosen may be ....

22 Malcolm was .... by his visit to India.

23 Malcolm comments that his pictures of various locations were ....

24 The tutor suggests Malcolm should restrict the image selection to ....

25 Malcolm intends to make a film that is similar to a ....

Questions 26–30

What comments does the tutor make about the submission of the film project?

Choose **FIVE** *answers from the box.*

```
                    Comments

        A  prepare handouts

        B  follow the website instructions

        C  send in DVD format

        D  use a memory stick

        E  remember people's attention span

        F  provide background information

        G  focus on simplicity
```

Submission

26 end product   ....
27 audience   ....
28 submission process   ....
29 accompanying form   ....
30 film format   ....

3 👥 Would you like to make a film about a place you have visited? Which place would you choose? Why?

Language focus: Modal verbs for evaluating

In addition to using adjectives and verbs to give evaluations, we can also use modal verbs. Look at the following statement from the Listening on page 233.

I should have been halfway through by now.

Malcolm is criticising himself for something he hasn't done. He is reflecting on and evaluating his own actions.

G Read more about using modal verbs for evaluating in the Grammar reference on page 224.

1 Work in pairs. Think of three things that you did last weekend which you shouldn't have done, or you should have done but didn't. Tell your partner about the events.

2 For **1–9** below, underline the correct items in *italics*.

1 They *should/shouldn't* have knocked that building down ages ago; it was rather hideous.

2 The government *could have dealt/must have dealt* with this more diplomatically.

3 He *might have/should have* told me; I'm not sure.

4 She *might/couldn't* have told me! I really wish she had.

5 Something *must/should* have happened, because suddenly everyone seems happier.

6 Fines *could be/must have been* imposed on those who throw litter in public.

7 With the involvement of UNESCO, more and more places of great natural beauty *should be/shouldn't have been* protected in future.

8 Local people *ought to/might* play a greater part in plans for new buildings in their area.

9 The car *could/must* be incredibly expensive, because it's stunning to look at.

3 Which of the sentences **1–9** in exercise 2 show that something 'didn't happen' in the past?

4 Which of the sentences **1–9** in exercise 2 express the following:
- a conclusion
- a regret
- a suggestion
- a criticism
- an expectation
- a possibility/weak suggestion
- a possibility

5 Work in groups. You have been asked by the local council to come up with ways to make the city or town you live or study in more attractive for the general public. Make a list of the following things in order to improve the area. Use other modal verbs where appropriate and the words from the Vocabulary and Word building sections in this unit.

Things that should not have been done.

Things that should have been done.

Things that should be done.

Speaking
Part 3

1 Work in pairs. Spend several minutes thinking about the following questions. Take turns asking and answering the questions. Try to include the verbs and adjectives that you have used in this unit so far.

Don't forget!

- Use adjectives to evaluate. Then give reasons and examples.
- Use linking words like *but, although, however,* etc.
- Keep your ideas abstract.

Beautiful buildings

Do people need to have beautiful surroundings such as buildings and monuments? Why/Why not?

Can living and working in attractive buildings have a positive effect on people's moods? How?

Which is more important, the design or the function of a building? In what way?

Buildings and traditions

Do you think buildings such as housing and public buildings should reflect the traditions of a country? In what way?

Some people feel that modern architecture worldwide is having a detrimental effect on the appearance of towns and cities. To what extent do you agree or disagree?

Do the advantages of preserving traditional buildings outweigh the cost of preserving them?

Writing
Task 2

1 Work in pairs. Discuss the task below and decide what kind of statement is given in the task beginning 'Some people think … '.

WRITING TASK 2

You should spend about 40 minutes on this task.

Write about the following topic:

> *Some people think it is important to keep and maintain old buildings rather than replacing them with modern buildings.*
> *To what extent do you agree or disagree?*

Give reasons for your answer and include any relevant examples from your own knowledge or experience.

Write at least 250 words.

---

2 Work in pairs. Make a list of ideas about keeping and maintaining old buildings and about replacing them with modern buildings. If necessary, use the ideas in the box below. When you have finished, change partners and discuss.

> built/natural environment   educate in general about the past
>
> respect buildings/property   appreciate beauty
>
> pride in one's heritage   protect environment   helps relaxation
>
> promote mental/physical health

3 Work in groups. Write an outline of the essay with an introduction, a topic sentence for each body paragraph and a conclusion.

4 You can use particular words and phrases to show the effects or consequences of something, for example, *affect, make, produce, lead to, have an effect/impact on, result in*. To describe effects and consequences you can also use adjectives from previous units, for example, *exciting, exhilarating, interesting*.

Work in pairs. For **1–6** below, decide the order of **a** and **b** so that they make sense.

1 a and so urban neighbourhoods where people live are being made more appealing

b everything in the physical world makes an impression on us directly or indirectly

2 a people are able to see and appreciate different buildings in cities all around the world

b thanks to cheap travel and the internet

3 a some countries are now showcasing their national heritage by renovating old buildings

b leading to pride in their national standing

4 a for example a park could be opened and trees could be planted

b and then the health of the people in that district of the city would be improved

5 a the lack of space in many towns and cities has saved many old buildings

b with planners turning to renovation rather than erecting something new

6 a people are happier and are now more productive in many urban areas

b as a result of turning old ruins into gardens

5 For **1–6** in exercise 4:

   a decide which part of the text, **a** or **b**, describes the 'cause', and which describes the 'effect'.

   b <u>underline</u> the words and phrases which indicate 'cause'. Then (circle) the words and phrases which indicate 'effect'.

   c decide if there are any sentences where no linking words are used to indicate a cause or effect.

   d decide if any of the linking words can be removed without affecting the connection.

6 Work in pairs. For **1–5** below, complete the gaps with one phrase from box **A** and one phrase from box **B**. There may be more than one possible answer. Each phrase can be used more than once.

A	with	there are, as a result,	which in turn	thanks to

B	has a positive effect	shouldn't have relaxed	are focusing on
	now lighten up	should be attractive	

   1 For example, the government _____ the restrictions on building in green spaces in the city. _____ very few places for people to relax.

   2 The built environment in modern cities _____ to the people that live there, but often it is overwhelming _____ skyscrapers, which shut out the light.

   3 _____ new construction techniques and materials, modern buildings _____ cities and make them attractive.

   4 It is obvious that beauty _____ on people's well-being, _____ increases their happiness and productivity.

   5 _____ increased awareness of the impact that healthy environments have on employees, more and more architects _____ design now and not just function.

7 Work in pairs. Make notes for the Task 2 question on page 210. Make a list of ideas about the built environment and the natural environment. If necessary, use the ideas in the box on page 124. When you have finished, change partners and explain your ideas.

8 Write your answer to the Task 2 question on page 210. When you have finished, check your answer using the checklist on page 139.

Vocabulary: Beauty

1 Decide which adjective each sentence relates to. There may be more than one possible answer.

Example:

The size of the statues impressed me enormously.
Adjective: impressive

   1 When I first saw the city it took my breath away.

   2 The palace looked really grand and regal.

   3 The rooms in the palace were really enormous.

   4 Old films bring back memories of the past, and I love how they make me feel.

   5 When so many people came to say goodbye to me at the party, I was so overcome by their kindness I was speechless.

   6 The sight of the building made me reflect on many things.

   7 The tour made me feel sad but only for a short time.

   8 The archaeological site was certainly very old.

   9 I was overcome with excitement when we went on the tour of castles of the Loire.

2 Use the adjectives in the first five sentences to give an evaluation.

Example:

The size of the statues impressed me enormously.
I found the size of the statues very impressive.

Word building: Prefixes *under-* and *over-*

1 Complete the word in *italics* in each sentence.

   1 Early inventions are often *under_____* because we are in awe of modern technology.

   2 The care of old buildings which are of great architectural interest is often *under_____* .

   3 In my opinion, the attractiveness of modern buildings is *over_____* .

   4 I think the entrance fee to the museum exhibitions is *under_____* .

   5 He was *over_____* with emotion at the sight of his childhood home.

   6 The documentary showed that some ancient items are often *under_____* because people do not realise how old and precious they are.

   7 The art gallery was *over_____* by the modern art museum in the race to become the most popular art venue last year.

   8 The organisers *under_____* the popularity of the exhibition, which drew large crowds.

Language focus: Modal verbs for evaluating

1 Give your own evaluation in each case below. Use the notes to help you.

Example:
The building's not there any more.
Conclusion: They <u>must have knocked</u> it down.

1 The shop is not there any more.

Conclusion: They _____ closed it.

2 The neighbourhood has been improved with trees and new street furniture.

Expectation: People _____ happy.

3 Everyone's here earlier than usual.

Conclusion: The transport _____ on time.

4 In the past, the government didn't invest money preserving old buildings.

Mild criticism: The government _____ invested money earlier.

5 She didn't phone me!

Criticism: She _____ phoned me!

6 The town is not very pretty.

Suggestion: _____ made more attractive.

7 The house is certainly magnificent and very impressive.

Conclusion: It _____ money.

8 The building is being knocked down and is not being renovated.

Weak Suggestion: The building _____ rather than being knocked down.

9 The new park was opened to the public today.

Expectation: _____ the environment more pleasant.

Accuracy in IELTS

1 Find the five mistakes in the paragraph below. Then categorise the type of mistake, e.g. *a missing word, wrong tense/word,* etc.

> The main reason is that a beautiful environment has a positive impact in people's mood, which in turn should increase the health status of the general population. As result, the economic health of the nation should also have improved with fewer days off work and increased productivity. For example, local neighbourhoods could given funds to improve their surroundings by creating mini-gardens and decorating buildings. This must definitely have a beneficial effect on people's mood.

2 Check the organisation of the paragraph in exercise 1 by:

1 underlining the topic sentence/phrase

2 ticking three expectations in the paragraph

3 double ticking a mild suggestion

4 circling a cause

Introduction

The IELTS Academic Writing module lasts one hour and there are two tasks. You are advised to spend 20 minutes on Task 1 and asked to write at least 150 words. For Task 2 you are advised to spend 40 minutes and asked to write at least 250 words.

In both tasks, you are assessed on your ability to write in a style that is suitable.

Task 1

In Task 1 you are asked to describe data, presented as a graph, chart or table, or a diagram such as a map, plan or process, using your own words.

1 Name the charts below.

Example: 1 (stacked) bar chart

1

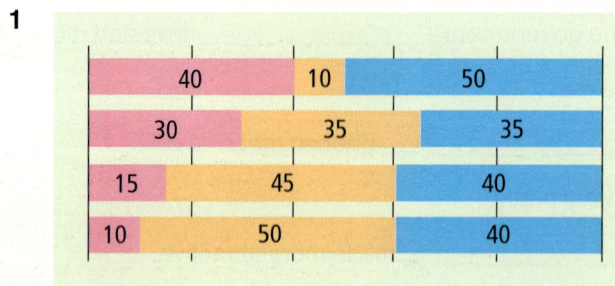

2

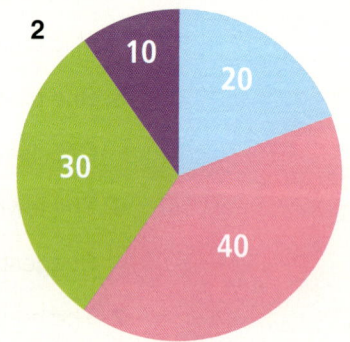

3

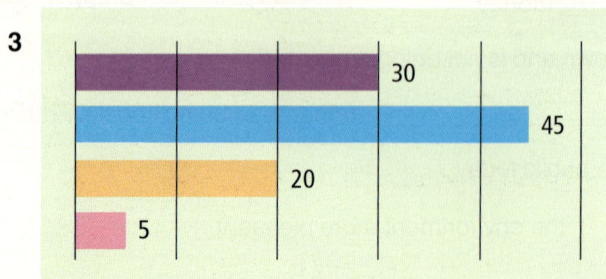

4

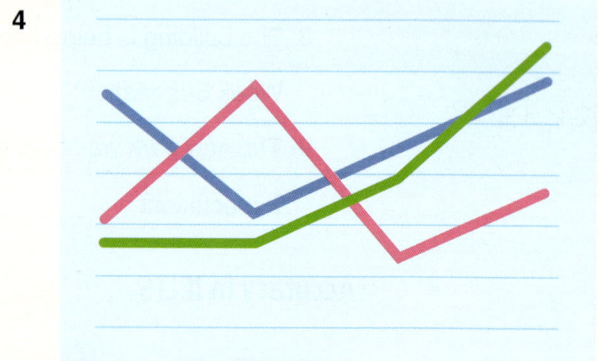

5	Years	2005	2010	2015
	Shop A	3,679	4,881	8,889
	Shop B	22,765	15,006	7,009

2 Look at the charts again and decide whether the statements below are 'true' or 'false'.

1 Only line graphs show trends.

2 Pie charts normally present proportions in percentages, but they can also present numbers.

3 Bar charts sometimes don't have years.

4 Stacked bar charts like 1 above present information in the same way as pie charts.

5 Tables should be read mainly from left to right but at the same time from top to bottom for the headings in the rows.

Graph

1 Look at the Task 1 question and model text below. In the model answer, find:

   1 the overview

   2 examples of complex sentences

   3 examples of language of comparison

   4 sentences where high access and high equipment costs are described.

WRITING TASK 1

You should spend about 20 minutes on this task.

> *The graph below shows the percentage of households not having internet access by reason in Great Britain between 2008 and 2014.*
>
> *Summarise the information by selecting and reporting the main features, and make comparisons where relevant.*

Write at least 150 words.

Percentage of households not having internet access by reason in Great Britain

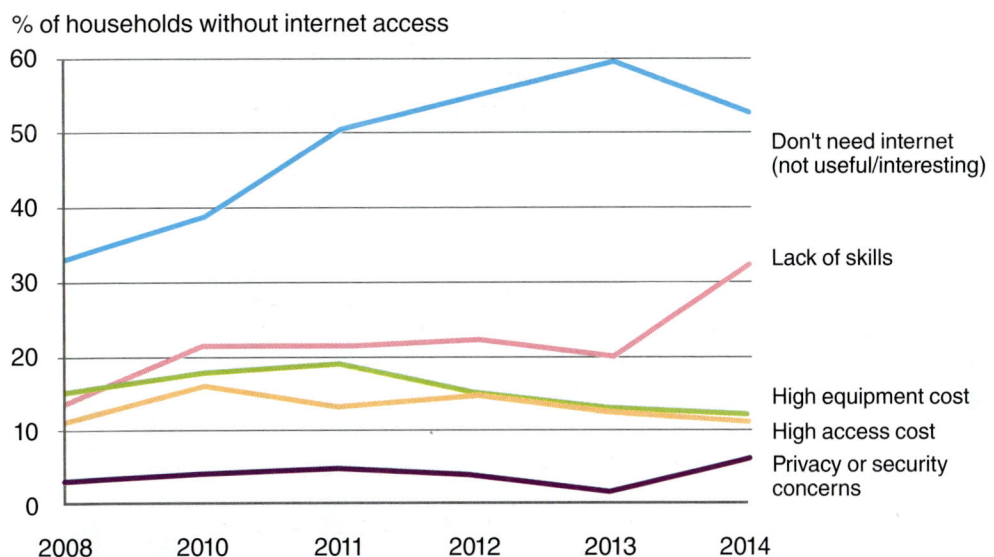

% of households without internet access

The chart compares various reasons why households in Great Britain lack internet access between 2008 and 2014.

Overall, it is clear that regarding the two main reasons, not needing the internet and a lack of skills, the trend was upwards throughout the period, while that for the other reasons was fairly flat. For example, approximately one third (about 34%) of households did not need internet access in 2008 compared to more than a half (approximately 54%) in 2014.

By contrast, while there was a rise in the proportion of households without internet access because of lack of skills, from about 15% in 2008 to just over 30% in 2014, the trend in the proportion for high equipment costs was slightly downwards, 10% compared to 13% in 2000 and 2014 respectively. As regards high access cost, the trend was flat with a peak of about 15% in 2010 from 11% in 2008, but privacy and security was less of a concern with the proportion giving this reason, however, doubling between 2008 and 2014, from approximately 3% to 6%.

Bar chart

1 Look at the Task 1 question and the model answer below. Complete the model answer by inserting the following data into the gaps.

    a just under 25%

    b 33% in 2008 in comparison with about 58% in 2012

    c from just over 40% to about 60%

    d (just over 60% in 2008)

    e about 35% to about 55% in 2012 with a peak of about 58% in 2011.

WRITING TASK 1

You should spend about 20 minutes on this task.

> *The chart below shows the proportion of businesses making e-commerce purchases by industry in Great Britain between 2008 and 2012.*
>
> *Summarise the information by selecting and reporting the main features, and make comparisons where relevant.*

Write at least 150 words.

Proportion of businesses making e-commerce purchases in industry in Great Britain between 2008 and 2012

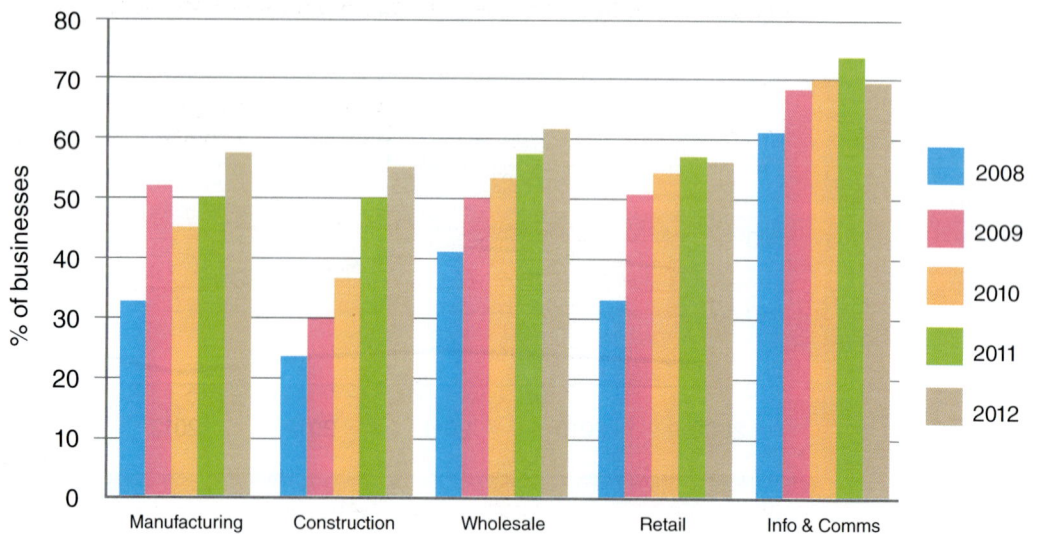

The bar chart provides information about the proportion of businesses purchasing items online according to industry in Great Britain between 2008 in 2012.

Generally speaking, the proportion of businesses involved in e-commerce purchases across the years and sectors varied with the practice being most common in the information and communications industry. In this sector, there was a greater proportion of businesses involved **1** _____ than the other sectors with a rise to just under 70% in 2012, including a peak to about 75% in 2011. The proportion of businesses involved in purchases online in the retail sector followed a similar pattern, increasing from **2** _____ .

3 _____ of construction businesses used online purchasing in 2008 compared to more than a half in 2012, whereas in the wholesale industry the rise was much smaller 4 _____ .

As regards manufacturing, there was a near 100% increase in the proportion of businesses purchasing online from about 5 _____ .

Pie charts

1   Study the Writing Task 1 and the model frame below. Complete the model answer using your own words.

WRITING TASK 1

You should spend about 20 minutes on this task.

The pie charts below compare the hours worked by employees and self-employed homeworkers in 2014 in the UK.

Summarise the information by selecting and reporting the main features, and make comparisons where relevant.

Write at least 150 words.

Average working hours for employees and self-employed

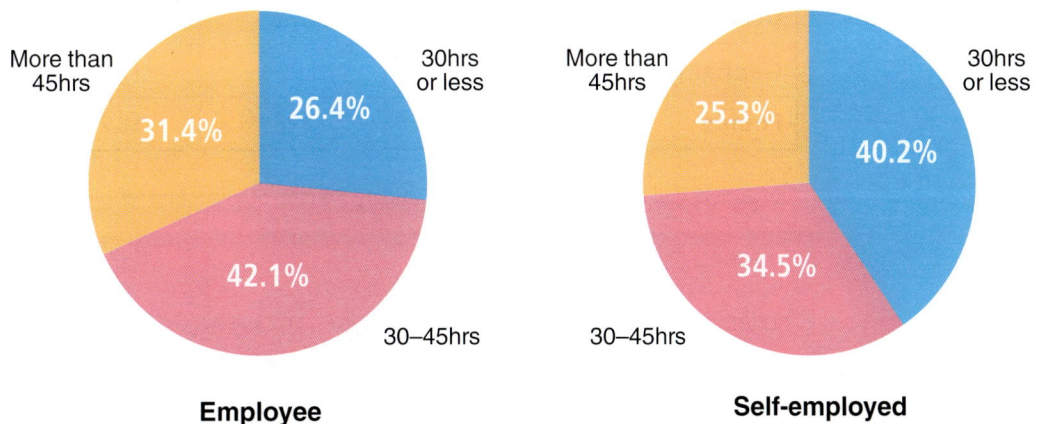

More than 45hrs — 31.4%
30hrs or less — 26.4%
30–45hrs — 42.1%

Employee

More than 45hrs — 25.3%
30hrs or less — 40.2%
30–45hrs — 34.5%

Self-employed

The pie charts show the number of hours worked by two categories of people, homeworkers who are self-employed and employees, in the UK in 2014.

Generally speaking, it is clear that homeworkers who are self-employed work fewer hours on average than employees with 1 _____ . For example, a greater proportion of employees (31.4%) worked 2 _____ _____ . Likewise, while just over a third of self-employed workers (34.5%) work between 30 and 45 hours,

3 _____ . By contrast, there is a marked difference between the two groups when it comes to working 30 hours or less.

In this category, 4 _____ .

Table

1   Study the Writing Task 1 and the model answer below. <u>Underline</u> all the examples of comparison in the model. Decide what types of comparison are used, e.g., comparative adjectives or adverbs, conjunctions, or other.

WRITING TASK 1

You should spend about 20 minutes on this task.

> *The table below provides a breakdown of the amount of different cereals produced by several countries in Europe in 2000.*
>
> *Summarise the information by selecting and reporting the main features, and make comparisons where relevant.*

Write at least 150 words.

Production of cereals by country in 2000

	Common wheat and spelt *	Rye and maslin **	Barley
Belgium	1,919	–	400
Bulgaria	5,319	28	851
Czech Republic	5,442	130	1,967
Denmark	5,153	678	3,548
Germany	27,711	3,854	11,563
France	37,501	128	11,775

* an ancient grain that is a sub-species of wheat   ** a crop of wheat and rye grown together

---

The table shows the volume of various types of cereals that were produced in a selection of European countries in 2000. Overall, it is clear that France and Germany produce the largest amounts of the cereal crops with Belgium producing the least.

The volume of common wheat and spelt*, for example, produced in Germany was 27,711 tons compared to 37,501 for France and 5,153, 5,442, 5,319 and 1,919 for Denmark, the Czech Republic, Bulgaria and Belgium respectively. By contrast, France produced only 128 tons of rye and maslin as opposed to 3,854 tons in Germany, with no data available for Belgium. Likewise, Denmark produced 678 tons in contrast to 130 tons in the Czech Republic and only 28 tons in Bulgaria.

The largest producer of barley was France with 11,775 tons followed closely by Germany with 11,563 tons. By comparison, Denmark produced more barley than the Czech Republic, Bulgaria and Belgium together, 3,548 tons against 1,967 tons, 851 tons and 400 tons, respectively.

Plan A

1 Look at the Task 1 question and the overview in the model answer. Find three nouns in the overview that relate to type of changes that are then described in the model.

2 Find examples of each noun in the model answer and paraphrase the overview.

WRITING TASK 1

You should spend about 20 minutes on this task.

> The diagrams below show the changes in the ground floor plan of an office between 2010 and 2016.
>
> Summarise the information by selecting and reporting the main features, and make comparisons where relevant.

Write at least 150 words.

Floor plan

2010

Reception desk | Stairs | Office for 10 workers | Office for 10 workers | Office for 10 workers

Lifts | Boardroom

Entrance

Kitchen and staff lounge

Office for 10 workers | Office for 10 workers

2016

Stairs | Open-plan office for 45 workers

Seating | ← Electronic turnstile

Entrance | Lifts | Boardroom

Seating | Meeting rooms

Electronic database | Open-plan office for 30 workers

Reception desk

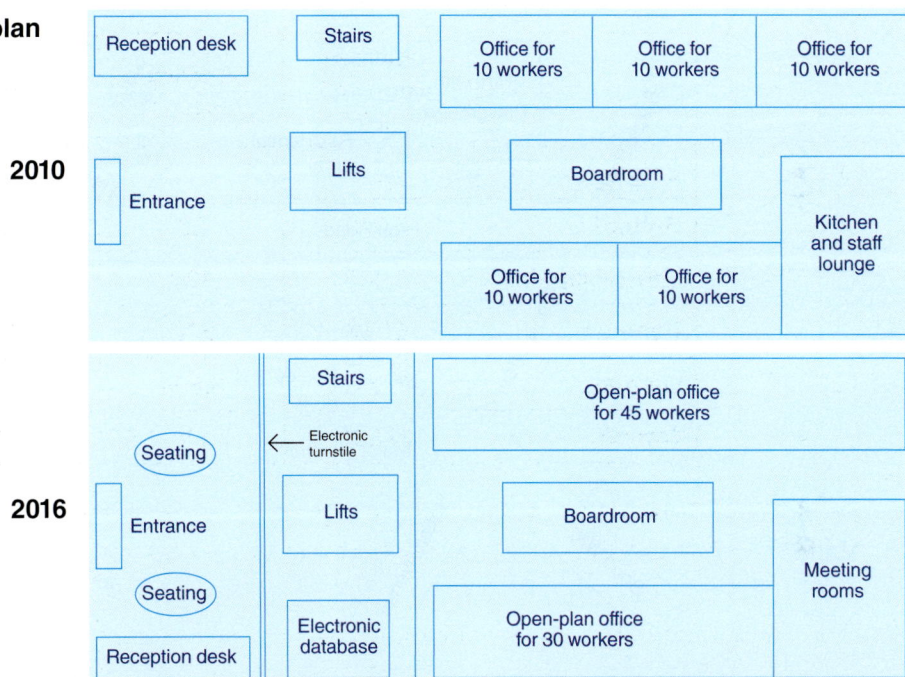

The plans illustrate how the ground floor of an office was modified from 2010 to 2016.

Overall, it is clear the ground floor of the office underwent a complete transformation between the six years with the relocation, addition and the replacement of various facilities. First all, between 2010 and 2016, the reception was moved to the right hand side of the entrance. New seating areas were also introduced to the left and right of the entrance with a new electronic turnstile being added just between the reception area and the lift and stairs. Another addition was the electronic databank to the right of the lifts.

By 2016, the three offices for 10 workers each on the left hand side had been turned into an open plan office for 45 workers. Moreover, the kitchen and staff lounge at the back had been replaced with meeting rooms. Similarly, the two offices for 10 workers on the right had been turned into an office for 30 workers. Meanwhile, the boardroom remained the same.

Plan B

1 Look at the Task 1 question and model answer. Add words and phrases from the diagrams to complete the model answer.

WRITING TASK 1

You should spend about 20 minutes on this task.

The street plans below show a residential area with a park and playground in 2016 and the proposed changes for 2025 to make it safer for families and children.

Summarise the information by selecting and reporting the main features, and make comparisons where relevant.

Write at least 150 words.

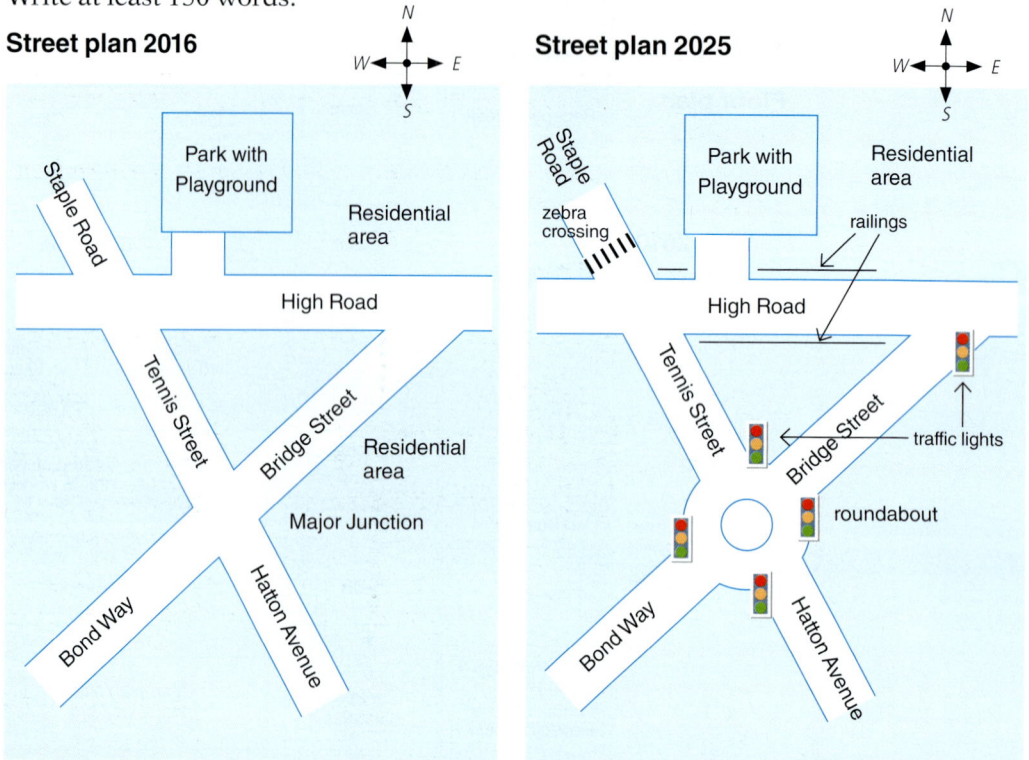

The plans illustrate the layout of the streets in a residential area with a park and playground in 2016, along with plans for modifications for 2025 to ensure the safety of families and children in the area.

Generally speaking, it is clear that various measures to prevent children running on to the road and to slow down the traffic, such as the safety **1** _____ , traffic lights and a zebra crossing will be introduced. For example, there is a proposal to introduce railings on both sides of the **2** _____ at the entrance to the **3** _____ with the playground. In addition, a **4** _____ will be added just before the junction of **5** _____ , west of the park and the High Road.

Another plan is to turn the **6** _____ of the four main roads, Tennis Street, Bridge Street, Bond Way and Hatton Avenue into a **7** _____ with a set of **8** _____ at the junction of each street with the roundabout.

Process

1 Study the Task 1 question and the model answer below. Find:

   1 the overview

   2 the steps in the process

   3 examples of linking devices

   4 examples of intransitive verbs

   5 examples of complex sentences.

2 Estimate the length of the text. Does it follow the word limit?

WRITING TASK 1

You should spend about 20 minutes on this task.

> *The diagrams below show the process of electricity generation using an artificial lagoon and tidal power.*
>
> *Summarise the information by selecting and reporting the main features, and make comparisons where relevant.*

Write at least 150 words.

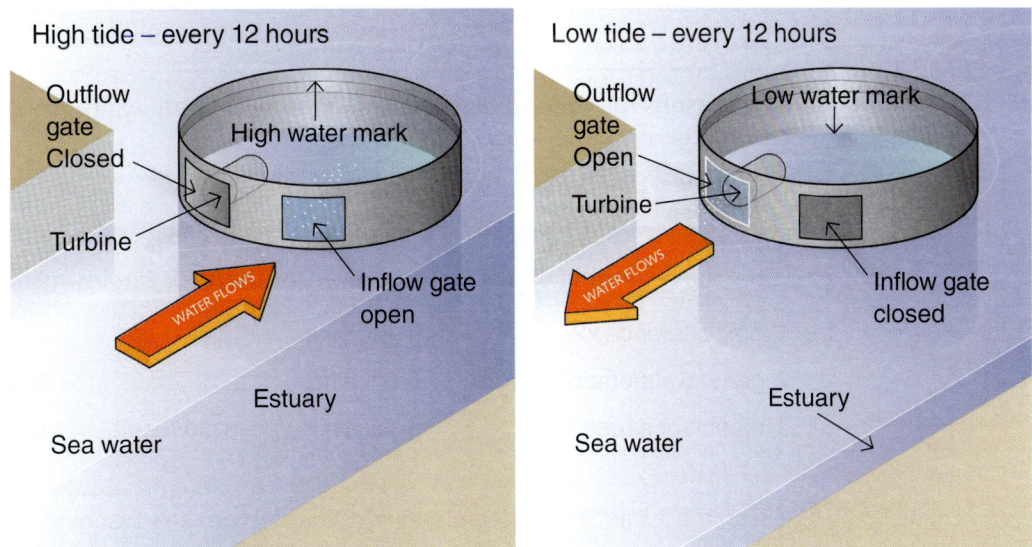

High tide – every 12 hours: Outflow gate Closed, High water mark, Turbine, Inflow gate open, WATER FLOWS, Estuary, Sea water

Low tide – every 12 hours: Outflow gate Open, Low water mark, Turbine, Inflow gate closed, WATER FLOWS, Estuary, Sea water

---

The diagrams show how tidal power is used to generate electricity in an artificial lagoon.

Overall, the production of the energy from tidal power using the artificial circular lagoon involves several stages relating to the opening and closing of the inflow and outflow gates in the lagoon. The tide around the artificial lagoon falls and rises twice a day. First of all, before the high tide comes into the estuary, the inflow gate is opened to allow the water to flow into the lagoon and at the same time the outflow gate is closed to prevent the water escaping again. Then, when the tide is at its highest, the lagoon is full of water.

Subsequently, as soon as the tide turns and it is at its lowest level, the inflow gate is closed and the outflow gate, to which a turbine is attached, is opened and the water flows out of the lagoon, generating electricity.

The whole process repeats itself twice a day every 12 hours.

Task 2

In Task 2 you are given a point of view, argument or problem. Assessment for Task 2 is based on your ability to:

- present and support your opinion
- compare and contrast evidence and opinions
- write a solution to a problem
- evaluate and challenge ideas, evidence or arguments
- write in an appropriate style.

1 Analyse the Task 2 question below using the following:

- the suggested time limit
- the statement in the topic to be discussed
- the specific questions relating to the topic
- the minimum number of words (and think of the maximum)
- the possible organisation of your answer
- the standard/generic rubric
- possible ideas
- the general nouns in the questions

WRITING TASK 2

You should spend about 40 minutes on this task.

Write about the following topic:

> *Health experts say that walking is a good way to improve the health of the general public, but nowadays people are walking less than ever before.*
> *What are the causes? What measures could be effective?*

Give reasons for your answer and include any relevant examples from your own knowledge and experience.

Write at least 250 words.

---

2 Label the beginning of a possible answer for the Task 2 below using the following items:

1 topic sentence x2	4 example	7 reason or cause 2
2 general statement or hook	5 condition	8 a result
3 reason or cause 1	6 possibility/possible result	9 a solution

With the advances in technology, people's lifestyles are changing and are becoming much more sedentary. As a result, people are walking less. There are many factors behinds this development, but there are many approaches that can be taken to deal with the situation. The main factor behind the decrease in walking among the general population is the modern lifestyle that is much more sedentary, especially for people working in offices. For example, if people are sitting at a desk in an office for long periods of time rather than doing manual work on the land, this can reduce the time for people to do simple activities like walking. Moreover people are more inclined to travel by car or bus so there is less need for people to walk. In many cases people do not walk for more than a few minutes each day. The main solution is to encourage people through advertising to become more physically active. Such encouragement should start in...

3 List the perspectives you can use to collect ideas for one or more of the Task 2 questions below, e.g. for 1, educational, technological, mental, physical, future, employment, etc. Are any of the perspectives you chose relevant to other tasks below?

4 Compare the organisation of two of the four Tasks 2 questions below.

---

1 **WRITING TASK 2**

You should spend about 40 minutes on this task.

Write about the following topic:

> *Some people believe that software programming should be taught at primary school. Others think that the focus at this level should be on playing.*
> *Discuss both these views and give your own opinion.*

Give reasons for your answer and include any relevant examples from your own knowledge and experience.

Write at least 250 words.

---

2 **WRITING TASK 2**

You should spend about 40 minutes on this task.

Write about the following topic:

> *Nowadays more and more museums and art galleries around the world are putting their material contents online. Do you think this is a positive or negative development?*

Give reasons for your answer and include any relevant examples from your own knowledge and experience.

Write at least 250 words.

---

3 **WRITING TASK 2**

You should spend about 40 minutes on this task.

Write about the following topic:

> *The best way for employers to make their workforce happy is allow them more flexible working hours.*
> *To what extent do you agree? What other measures could be effective?*

Give reasons for your answer and include any relevant examples from your own knowledge and experience.

Write at least 250 words.

---

4 **WRITING TASK 2**

You should spend about 40 minutes on this task.

Write about the following topic:

> *In the modern world, many employees lack soft skills such as communication and working in teams.*
> *What are the main causes of this problem? What are the effects of the lack of such skills?*

Give reasons for your answer and include any relevant examples from your own knowledge and experience.

Write at least 250 words.

---

5 Look at the introduction, topic sentences and the conclusion for the first Task 2 question on page 137. Paraphrase the introduction and the third topic sentence.

> At primary school, the curriculum is constantly changing to keep pace with the modern world. While it is argued software programming should now be part of the curriculum at this level, others feel that the focus should be on play. I feel that children need to play more at this stage rather than being bombarded by more technology.
>
> On the one hand, software is considered as important for primary school children.
>
> On the other hand, playing is much more important at this level.
>
> Having examined both these views, I am more inclined to agree with the latter view, but I also feel that the focus in the modern world on technology is an important skill for children to learn.
>
> Software programming and playing are both important for the development of children, but I personally feel that play is more important in a child's development at the primary level.

6 Write an introduction for the second Task 2 question on page 137.

> Introduction: _____
>
> There is no denying that having museum art gallery content available on the internet might encourage people not to visit them.
>
> Personally, however, I feel that it is a major step in the right direction for educational reasons. Another reason, in my opinion, is that it brings artifacts to the attention of people who might not otherwise be able to see them.
>
> As we have seen, despite there being some sound arguments against the development of museums and art galleries making their contents available for public viewing online, this is in the main a positive development.

7 Add the following phrases to the introduction, topic sentences and the conclusion of the third Task 2 on page 137:

a another strategy is to make sure that

b is certainly a sound way of making workers happier

c while I feel that this is a good approach

d there is no doubt that this is an effective approach

> Employers are always considering different methods to make their workforce happy, such as permitting them to work in a more flexible way. **1** _____ , there are others which could be equally or more successful. Giving workers the opportunity to be flexible as regards their working hours **2** _____ .
>
> **3** _____ , but another more effective way would be to ensure that workers are paid properly.
>
> **4** _____ the work environment is suitable for all workers. In conclusion, despite the approach allowing employees to work more flexibly being a sound approach, paying workers and making the work environment more comfortable are equally important strategies.

8 Write an introduction, topic sentences and the conclusion for the fourth Task 2 question.

9 Complete your own answer to the fourth Task 2 question on page 137.

IELTS Writing checklists

IELTS Writing Task 1

Assessment for Task 1 is based on your ability to:
- summarise, organise and compare data where possible
- describe the stages of a process
- describe an object or event or explain how something works
- write accurately and coherently
- use a range of vocabulary
- use a range of grammatical structures.

Checklist

1 Have you paraphrased the rubric in your introduction or just copied it?
2 Have you written a clear overview?
3 Have you summarised the information and not just listed every piece of data?
4 Have you included any information that is not in the data?
5 Have you left any important data out?
6 Have you just listed information or have you compared it?
7 Have you divided your answer into clear paragraphs?
8 Have you mentioned any striking features?
9 Have you avoided repetition of words and structures?
10 Have you used a range of grammar, vocabulary and complex structures?
11 Have you used the correct tenses and verb form?
12 Have you used appropriate linking devices such as adverbs and conjunctions?
12 Have you checked your writing for mistakes?
13 Have you completed the task according to the rubric?
14 Have you written at least 150 words?
15 Have you written *too many* words?
   You aren't penalised for writing too much, but you may be penalised for *not summarising*. You don't need to write more than about 185 words.

IELTS Writing Task 2

In Task 2 you are given a point of view, an argument or a problem. Assessment for Task 2 is based on your ability to:
- present and support your opinion
- compare and contrast evidence and opinions
- write a solution to a problem
- evaluate and challenge ideas, evidence or arguments
- write in an appropriate style.

Checklist

1 Have you paraphrased the question in your introduction?
2 Have you given a clear indication of the organisation of your answer in the introduction?
3 Have you given a clear statement of your stance/opinion/position in the introduction?
4 Have you given a clear statement about the content of each paragraph?
5 Have you given reasons and examples as requested in the rubric?
6 Have you also developed your ideas by expressing contrasts, causes, effects, purposes and conclusions?
7 Have you written a conclusion? Do all the paragraphs now fit together well?
8 Is your answer abstract as required? Or does it contain personal examples?
9 Have you divided your answer into clear paragraphs? Have you written 4/5 paragraphs?
10 Have you included any irrelevant ideas?
11 Have you avoided the repetition of words and structures?
12 Have you used a range of grammar, vocabulary and complex structures?
13 Have you checked your writing for mistakes?
14 Have you completed the task according to the rubric?
15 Have you written at least 250 words?

10 Is it art?

Vocabulary: Art

1 👥 Work in groups. Decide what art form is represented in each photograph and share your opinions about each of them.

2 Choose your favourite art form and give reasons and examples for your choice.

3 Work in groups. For **1–7** below, write as many people you associate with each word as you can.

1 play *actor, director, producer, designer, make-up artist* _____

2 exhibition _____

3 musical _____

4 book _____

5 sculpture _____

6 video game _____

7 film _____

4 Work in pairs. In each bubble below, find two words that go together and explain why. There may be more than one answer.

1
draw   design   play
direct   artist   video game
clothes   programmer

2
drama   perform
musical   sing   plot
writer   novels   ballet

3
construct   act
soap opera   symphony
compose   art installation

5 For **1–7** below, complete the gaps with the correct form of the words in the box below.

exhibit   sculpt   scene   criticise (x2)   vision   collect

1 The _____ cost a lot of money to visit and was a waste of time; it was full of avant-garde work I couldn't understand.

2 The bronze _____ were displayed in the garden and the galleries.

3 My _____ is purely subjective I know, but I think the paintings were not just childlike, but childish.

4 The new extension where the sculptures are on show is more stunning than the _____ itself.

5 His works have been hailed as masterpieces by _____ , but I honestly can't see anything in them.

6 The _____ in the play was a work of art in itself. The artist who painted the panels must be a genius.

7 I prefer the performing arts to the _____ arts; paintings are so boring!

141

6   Work in pairs. Discuss the similarities and differences between two different art forms, e.g. *performing arts* and *visual arts*.

7   Look at the possible responses to Part 3 questions on the arts. <u>Underline</u> the correct words in *italics*.

1   First of all, if children study *drama/plays/acts* at secondary level, they can learn different skills such as social or organisational skills, which can help them later in their working life. They can also learn about different technical aspects of work in the theatre like arranging all the props and *scenes/scenery/backgrounds* … and if they are really lucky they might have a drama teacher who *shows/produces/composes* a *theatre/play/stage* or musical each year. Such performances don't have to be very *highbrow/lowbrow* art, but they are very useful if they give young people practical experience.

2   As the arts improve society generally, I think organisations and individuals promoting the arts should be subsidised by the taxpayer. But many people don't agree. For instance, they attack *today/modern/these*-day art, basically because they don't *appreciate/see/realise* it. If people look at it a little more closely, they will be less *unfavourable/critical/approving* of it. And they might support the arts in general more.

3   I think the main way is installing more real *working/works/bits* of art in public spaces like parks and squares, which could play a major role in making people more aware of art. *Figure/Extract/Abstract* art with boxes and colours in many modern *exhibitions/rooms/shows* can be very difficult for people to understand, but *classical/established/orthodox* paintings are sometimes just as difficult. So if vibrant art is brought to the public, it might entice people to visit museums and art galleries, or even to take up art themselves.

Speaking
Part 3

1   In groups, match the three texts in exercise 7 above to the Part 3 questions below.

Don't forget!

- Develop your ideas by giving reasons and examples.
- Use abstract not personal ideas.
- Speak fluently, but not quickly.

The arts

What are the advantages of making some form of the arts compulsory at secondary school?

In what ways do you think an interest in the arts can be used to help to improve the lives of all people in society? Give reasons and examples.

How do you think institutions involved in the arts such as museums and art schools should be funded? Should it be from public funds or private donations?

2   Discuss one or more of the Part 3 questions above. Choose someone to write down the ideas as you discuss them. When you have finished, discuss as a whole class.

3   Work in groups of three. Take turns performing the following roles using the questions in exercise 1: the candidate, the examiner and the monitor. The monitor prompts the candidate and makes notes about the candidate's performance using the checklist on page 181 and gives feedback when they have finished speaking.

Reading
Questions 1–13

1 👥 Work in groups. Discuss the statement below.

'Installation art is a legitimate and exciting art form.'

2 Work in groups. The following words and phrases **1–10** all appear in the Reading Passage below. Match the words to meanings **a–j**.

1 commission		**a** speed up
2 parameters		**b** beaten by hammering
3 wing		**c** slight
4 endorsed		**d** job
5 expedite		**e** limits
6 congruent		**f** evocative
7 tenuous		**g** corresponding
8 wrought		**h** agreed
9 reminiscent		**i** annex
10 palette		**j** colour scheme

3 Scan the Reading Passage for the words from exercise 2.

READING PASSAGE

*You should spend about 20 minutes on **Questions 1–13**, which are based on the Reading Passage below.*

Fern Garden — an art installation

At the beginning of 1996 Mary Eagle, then the National Gallery's Senior Curator of Australian Art, approached Fiona Hall to consider a commission for a work to be placed in the Sculpture Garden. The artist proposed instead that she would create a discrete garden on a site at the eastern side of the building, outside the parameters of the Sculpture Garden. This formerly out-of-sight and unused 'courtyard' space, approximately 20 metres square, bounded by the Gallery's 23-metre high bush-hammered concrete walls on three sides, and its planned temporary exhibitions wing on the fourth, was to become exposed to the public gaze and re-defined through the window wall of the foyer of the new galleries looking onto the space.

The commission was endorsed at the December 1996 meeting of the National Gallery Council and made possible by funding from the Painting and Sculpture budget of the Department of Australian Art along with a generous donation from the Friends of Tamsin and Deuchar Davy. Council members were able to actually observe the design intent through a detailed model that the artist produced to expedite planning for the commission.

During 1997 Hall refined the design and made drawings describing specific features within the garden. The logistical challenges were many. The design involved a planting of 58 mature *Dicksonia Antarctica* tree ferns 2.6 metres tall, with a system of paths, water channels, grates, fountains, seating and a fence and gate. Expert horticultural, engineering, hydraulic and lighting advice was sought to confirm the mechanical requirements and ensure the congruent relationship between the elements comprising the design.

Construction began in January 1998. After initial preparatory excavation and concreting, Fiona Hall and two assistants decorated the main 1.5-metre wide, 55-metre long pathway and fountains with white silica and quartz pebbles quarried from a streambed at nearby Collector in New South Wales. Pebbles of the required size were sorted from a stockpile

and laid into a base of dry mortar which was watered to make the cement set. The ferns were planted to a strict grid, and work continued at a pace to be completed by the beginning of March to coincide with the opening of the new Exhibitions Wing. Botanical references and particularly humankind's tenuous relationship with nature have been central to Fiona Hall's expression and illustrated through works such as her *Genesis* series of 1984, *Paradisus Terrestris* 1989–90, *Historia Non-natural/s* 1991 and *Paradisus Terrestris entitled* 1997.

The garden, based on the spiral form of the fern frond, a symbol of healing and rejuvenation, is the artist's first opportunity to realise a major permanent installation.

The *Dicksonia Antarctica* tree fern is found in Tasmania and along the east coast of Australia. Those planted in the garden, estimated to be at least two hundred years old, have stood witness to the arrival of the settlers in Australia and the gradual disappearance of the Aboriginal peoples and their culture. The scant number of extant Aboriginal languages recognising the word for the *Dicksonia Antarctica* are represented on tombstone-like plaques embedded in the main path. The artist approached the local Ngunnawal people for approval to construct the garden.

There is a wrought steel gate at the entry to the Fern Garden. The main path is decorated in vortex patterns much like the movement of the eddying stream from which the pebbles originated. The path unfolds in the shape of a frond, and curves down a gentle ramp to the central fountain. There is space to walk around the fountain, which is set below the surrounding ground level, or to sit on the ledge while a circle of 101 thin jets of water is projected upward and falls in a parabolic pattern similar to the fronds of the *Dicksonia Antarctica*. Surrounding the edge of the fountain, there is a copper membrane. Auxiliary pathways formed in plain white concrete provide options for navigating the garden and lead to seats of austral verde granite with wrought steel spiral bases, or to the central recessed area. The water from three smaller fountains is channelled inwards towards the main fountain in a manner reminiscent of Islamic garden design.

The palette for the garden is refined and austere. The hard surfaces are rendered homogeneous with the surrounding architecture – white concrete and pebbles/white bush-hammered concrete walls. The fibrous dark brown trunks of the ferns and the tanbark mulch are almost indistinguishable, while the frond canopy imbues the garden with a verdant green cast. Viewed from above, from the galleries of Australian art or the foyer of the Exhibitions Wing, the Fern Garden is all curves and a resolute foil to the straight linear geometry of the surrounding architecture

Questions 1–9

Complete the summary using the list of words, A–Q, below.

The Fern Garden was created in an open space 20 metres square, which would be 1 .... to visitors to the proposed galleries for 2 .... The Commission for the garden was 3 .... by the National Gallery Council and was funded by money from 4 .... The 5 .... for the garden, which was refined in 1997, 6 .... planting 58 mature fern trees that were several metres tall and it contained 7 .... including paths and water features. 8 .... were consulted to ensure the whole design would 9 .... together.

A government bodies	B different sources	C experts from different fields
D temporary exhibitions	E various officials	F avoided
G show	H fit	I design
J various elements	K operated	L detectable
M rejected	N painters	O visible
P included	Q approved	

Questions 10–13

Label the diagram below.

*Choose **NO MORE THAN TWO WORDS** from the passage for each answer.*

Central fountain below ground level

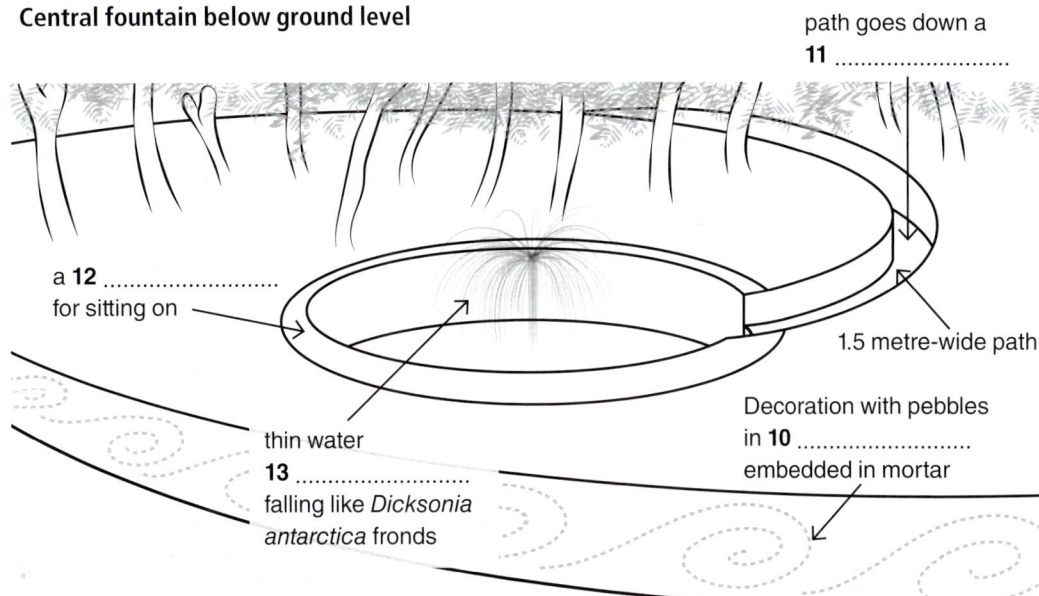

path goes down a
11 ....

a **12** ....
for sitting on

1.5 metre-wide path

Decoration with pebbles
in **10** ....
embedded in mortar

thin water
13 ....
falling like *Dicksonia
antarctica* fronds

4 ⊕ Do you think cities and towns would benefit from having more public art
such as statues, installation art for each answer and murals or wall paintings?
Give reasons and examples.

Language focus: Defining and non-defining relative clauses

1 Defining relative clauses provide information which cannot
be left out, as they identify what is being referred to. They do
not have commas at the beginning and end of the clause.

*Council members were able to actually observe the design intent
through a detailed model that the artist produced to expedite
planning for the commission.*

Non-defining relative clauses provide additional information,
which can be left out. They have commas at the beginning
and the end.

*There is space to walk around the fountain, which is set below the
surrounding ground level, or …*

2 Scan the Reading Passage and find other examples of relative
clauses.

Ⓖ Read more about defining and non-defining relative
clauses in the Grammar reference on page 224.

3 Work in groups. For each pair of sentences **1–5** below,
underline the relative clauses. Explain in your own words
what effect using a defining and non-defining clause has on
the meaning of the sentence.

  1 a A new play by Shakespeare, which the playwright
wrote when he was young, has just been discovered.

    b The play that he wrote at the age of 21 has just won a
major prize.

2 a Part of the soundtrack in the film, which is taken from
Beethoven's 9th symphony, is my favourite piece of
music.

   b A pop song that I heard on the car radio yesterday was
very familiar.

3 a The artist that I would like to talk about is Kandinsky.

   b The artist, who is still alive, has influenced my own
paintings.

4 a A museum I go to regularly has my favourite café on
its roof.

   b Modern museums, which often have interactive
displays, attract many children.

5 a The arts subjects that need to be taught at school are
painting and drama.

   b The arts, which include painting and drama, need to be
taught at school.

4 Work in pairs. Complete each gap with a suitable relative
pronoun where necessary. More than one pronoun may be
possible.

1 The book _____ he gave me as a present was
really exciting.

2 The actor, _____ name I have forgotten now, was
in the shop this morning.

3 Art classes, _____ often need expensive materials, can cost a lot to run.

4 I think literature, _____ is essential for the development of children, should have more time devoted to it in the school curriculum.

5 The painting _____ he bought for $50 000 was a fake; the other one was genuine.

6 The sister _____ is the dancer got married, not the singer.

7 Films _____ contain special effects do not always have good reviews.

8 This is the TV programme _____ I am going to talk about.

5 For **1–7** below, complete the gaps with a clause **a–g**. Add any necessary punctuation.

1 My uncle's flat _____ is empty for the next two weeks, so I'm staying there.

2 The friend _____ got me into the film preview.

3 One of my sculptures _____ has just won an art prize.

4 The film _____ starts in a few minutes.

5 I like literature _____ .

6 Is that the folk concert _____ ?

7 The culture tour _____ was dazzling.

a that you were praising last night because of the quality of the singer

b which I made when I started the art course

c which overlooks the opera house

d whose father is the film director

e which was incredibly expensive for the length of the trip

f which has some breathtaking locations

g that is not dumbed down in any way

6 Complete one or more of sentences **1–6** below so that they are true for you. Then explain your sentences to a partner, giving reasons and examples.

1 I like literature (which/that) I …

2 I don't like films (which/that) I …

3 I'm really mad about music (which/that) I …

4 I want to go to an exhibition (which/that) I …

5 I dislike (operas/rock concerts) most of all, which I have never liked …

6 I have seen loads of films, which is a hobby of mine …

Listening
Section 2

1 Work in groups. Look at **Questions 11–20** below and discuss the topic of the listening test.

'What opinions might people have about an art exhibition?'

2 Work in groups. Look at **Questions 11–14** below and decide which words will paraphrase the words *proposals* and *aims*.

3 For **Questions 15–20**, <u>underline</u> the words that warn you that the answer is coming soon.

4 When you have answered the questions below, check if your predictions for exercises **1–3** were correct.

15   **SECTION 2**   *Questions 11–20*

Questions 11 and 12

*Choose **TWO** letters, **A–E**.*

Which **TWO** proposals about the art exhibition are mentioned?

A It needs more public money.

B It should be permanent.

C More sculptures could be used.

D Local artists could be exhibited.

E More information would be helpful.

Questions 13 and 14

*Choose **TWO** letters, **A–E**.*

Which **TWO** aims for the Public Art project are mentioned?

    A more recognition for the city

    B an increase in investment

    C greater number of sculptures

    D a happier city

    E increased awareness about art

Questions 15–17

*Choose the correct letter, **A**, **B** or **C**.*

15 The public didn't go to the art institutions because of the

    A expense.

    B crowds.

    C time.

16 The website survey showed a majority

    A for free admission.

    B for more exhibitions.

    C unsure about the museum extension.

17 According to Jenny Driver, people in the art world are concerned about the

    A timing of the introduction of support.

    B level of financial support from the state.

    C loss of jobs in the sector.

Questions 18–20

Complete the sentences below.

*Write **NO MORE THAN TWO WORDS AND/OR A NUMBER** for each answer.*

18 The radio show will have two reporters on ………………..................………… .

19 The purpose of the outside broadcasts is to check …………………..................……… to the idea of museum charges.

20 The second reporter will be outside the …………………..................……… in the shopping centre.

5 What do you think about public art? Do people notice it or care about it? Why/Why not?

Speaking
Part 2

1 Work in pairs. Look at the Task Card and the beginning of a candidate's response. <u>Underline</u> the relative clauses and explain why they are used.

> Describe the art form, such as visual or performing arts, that you find exciting.
>
> You should say:
>   what the art form is
>   how you first became interested in this art form
>   how often you participate in it
> and explain why you find this art form exciting.

> The art form I'm going to describe is part of the performing arts …
> dancing, which to me is exciting and inspiring. I'm actually interested in
> all forms of dance, but I find modern dance particularly inspiring. The first
> time that I became attracted to it was when my parents took me to see a
> dance show, which was very noisy and energetic. After that, I was hooked
> and joined a dance class after school, and I've been involved in dancing,
> both participating and watching, at least once per week ever since. I think
> dancing is really exciting, because …

2 Look at the following reasons and purposes for participating in dancing and choose the three most important. Give reasons and examples for your choice.

to develop coordination	*as a form of entertainment*
to meet new people	*to improve my physical fitness*
to reduce stress	*to build confidence*

3 Work in pairs. Add some more information about one of the purposes you chose in exercise 2.

Example:

… to develop coordination, which is very important in perfecting physical skills such as those needed in any mechanical work.

4 In the example, what is the purpose of the <u>underlined</u> text?

Example:

… to develop coordination, which is very important in perfecting physical skills such as those needed in any mechanical work, <u>which, in turn, can improve your chances of finding a good job, and hence of earning a living.</u>

5 Work in pairs and choose another purpose and develop it in the same way as in exercises 3 and 4.

6 Make notes to prepare your own answer for the topic in exercise 1. With a partner, take turns talking about the topic, using your notes to guide you. When your partner has finished speaking, give him/her feedback using the checklist on page 181.

Writing
Task 2

1 Work in groups. Explain the statement and the question in the task below in your own words.

WRITING TASK 2

You should spend about 40 minutes on this task.

Write about the following topic:

> *Nowadays, there is a greater focus at all levels in education on science and business studies rather than the arts.*
> *Do you think this is a positive or negative development?*

Give reasons for your answer and include any relevant examples from your own knowledge or experience.

Write at least 250 words.

2 Is it possible to replace the question in the task with the following question:

To what extent do you agree or disagree?

Give reasons for your answer.

3 Read the description of someone describing a possible plan for the task. Decide whether the writer is planning **a** a positive, **b** a negative or **c** a negative and positive answer.

> I'm going to write an introduction saying that it is a negative development. My second paragraph will discuss the positive aspect(s) of the sciences and business studies. Then, I'm going to contrast this with two paragraphs showing the negative side of studying the arts, followed by a conclusion.

4 Describe how to plan the answer where the focus on science and business studies is

1 a positive development.
2 both positive and negative.

5 Work in groups. Explain how the introduction and three topic sentences below match the plan described in exercise 3.

> Science and business studies and the arts are all important for progress in society in general. However, I think the current emphasis in education on science and business studies is a negative trend.
>
> There is no doubt that science and business studies are invaluable in today's world.
>
> The study of the arts, however, plays a key role in the development of society.
>
> Another reason is that training in the arts can open up many career opportunities for young people.

6 Work in groups. Write an introduction, topic sentences and a conclusion supporting the development in the statement in the writing task in exercise 1 opposite and then present them to another group.

7 The text below is an extract from an answer to the Task 2 question on page 148. For **1–10**, complete the gaps with a suitable word. The first letter of each word is given.

> Science, business studies and the **1** a_____ are integral to the development of society. However, I think the current emphasis in the **2** f_____ of education on science and business studies is a positive **3** t_____ .
>
> There is no doubt that **4** p_____ in the arts is useful for the development of the individual and society generally. **5** T_____ drama, for example. Drama, which requires lots of activity, is obviously good for **6** p_____ and mental health as it improves **7** c_____ , which is a skill that is missing in education today. **8** L_____ , painting and pottery also help in this regard. For others, the purpose of involvement in the arts is to help them relax, even if it is only going to see an **9** e_____ at an art **10** g_____ .
>
> Having said this however, I feel ...

8 Find **1–5** below in the text in exercise 7:

1 examples of the writer's opinion/position
2 examples of non-defining relative clauses, if they exist
3 examples of defining relative clauses, if they exist
4 an example of a purpose
5 an example.

9 Write your answer to the Task 2 question on page 210. When you have finished, check your answer using the checklist on page 139.

10 Review

Vocabulary: Art

1 In **1–8** below, there is one word missing. Decide which word is missing in each sentence.

  1 Actors and actresses act in plays or films. Sometimes some of them become famous because they star in soap.

  2 He the symphony and conducted the orchestra at the performance.

  3 She has written many fantasy novels but people still do not think that she is a great, but there are many children and adults who would disagree.

  4 As a playwright, he wrote many and even directed some of his works in well-known theatres, appearing from time to time on the stage himself.

  5 Is a newspaper journalist an? Many would like to think they have artistic qualities.

  6 He was a great and painter, having carved many famous statues and painted many of the world's greatest paintings.

  7 The producer got on well with the actors and in the film, but he didn't always like the way the director directed it.

  8 The choreographer arranged the ballet very carefully, but some of the found it very difficult to perform.

2 For texts **1–3** below, underline the correct word in *italics*.

1 Studying *drama/play* at secondary school is a very good way to be introduced to acting. Many schools have their own *stages/theatres* at the front of the gym with *scenery/background*. *Drama/Actor* teachers are in great demand to *produce/compose theatres/plays* each year. It isn't very *highbrow/drama*, but everyone enjoys it so I think it's good for drama to be taught at school.

2 For some people I think graffiti can cause problems, because it can make urban areas seem quite threatening. But is it an act of vandalism? I personally don't think so. It is in many ways like primitive art. The problem, I think, is that *extract/abstract* art, like a lot of graffiti, isn't easy for people to understand, but then how much do people these days understand about paintings by *classical/orthodox* artists? Who for instance can unravel the *allusions/illusions/delusions* in early works of art. And I think there are places where graffiti can be a work of *art/artists*.

3 Yes. It's far from easy for people to be able to *appreciate/see/realise* modern art. But if they look at it in greater depth, they will see it in a more *favourable/critical/approving* way.

Language focus: Defining and non-defining relative clauses

1 <u>Underline</u> the defining clause in each sentence.

1 Although I have a large number of books, which I've collected over many years, the book that has influenced me the most is *Crime and Punishment* by Dostoyevsky.

2 The sculpture (that) I want to talk about is one I saw recently in Libya, which has many beautiful works of art.

3 Watching plays, which is a relaxing leisure activity, should be an art form that is free for all schoolchildren.

4 The artist I admire the most is Frida Kahlo, who created some amazing works.

5 An extension, which incidentally I think is impressive, has been built onto the museum that is close to my flat.

6 Is the café you usually go to, which I think you said is closed today, near the market?

7 A teacher at school, who taught me maths for a while, won the art prize that was announced last night on TV.

8 Someone that you know very well left this present, which looks rather magnificent.

2 Decide which of the following statements are true about non-defining clauses.

1 They help to identify something or someone.

2 They give background information that can be removed without disturbing the grammar of the rest of the sentence.

3 You need to use commas before and after the non-defining clause.

4 You can leave out the relative pronoun when you use non-defining clauses.

5 They help to give fuller explanations and hence provide more context for speaking and writing.

Accuracy in IELTS

1 In some sentences below a word has an extra letter *s* in each sentence. Find and correct.

1 Exhibitions that entertain childrens of school age are very useful.

2 The main arts form that I like is the theatre, but I do go the cinema occasionally.

3 Public art such as installation arts is becoming more and more popular among the general public, which is a good development.

4 The arts deserve to be funded as much as the sciences as they are integral to the development of any society.

5 Extra-curricular activities such as trips to museums and art galleries are essential for young peoples of all ages.

6 The gallery sells only modern arts of the last twenty years.

7 Literature is central to the development of schoolchildrens.

Vocabulary: The family

1 👥 Work in groups. Describe the relationships between the people in the photographs.

2 Work in pairs. Answer questions **1–10** below. Then check your answers with another pair.

    1 What is the collective word for mother and father?

    2 What is the collective word for grandmother and grandfather?

    3 What is the collective word for brothers and sisters?

    4 What is the name for a diagram showing the organisation of a family?

    5 What is a widow or widower?

    6 What is the plural word for people you are related to by blood or marriage?

    7 What is the word for a person in your family who lived before you?

    8 What is the word for you in relation to your mother or father's brother or sister?

    9 What is the word for the group consisting of parents and children?

   10 What is the word for the people who live in a house, flat or other accommodation, when they are considered as a single unit?

3 Work in pairs. Match a sentence beginning **1–7** with an ending **a–g**.

1 I am an only child,

a only me, my brother and my parents.

2 Both my parents come from large families,

b so I have no siblings.

3 My brother has two children,

c but I am sure it was no different in the past.

4 There are not many people in our household;

d they had seven children in total.

5 People often criticise today's young generation,

e so I have many relatives.

6 My grandparents had a really big family;

f my niece is called Anne and my nephew is called Thomas.

7 Our family tree can be traced to the last century,

g so I know the names of my ancestors going back four generations.

4 Work in pairs. Write at least two sentences about yourself using the ideas in exercise 3. Then write three questions you would like your partner to ask you relating to the sentences. Take turns asking questions and explaining the sentences you wrote.

Useful expressions

Tell me about your (siblings/ grandparents).

Can you describe your (household/ family/relatives)?

What do you know about your (family history)?

Reading
Questions 1–14

1 Work in pairs. Find the words below in the first paragraph of the Reading Passage and decide what you think the Reading Passage is about.

socialize   relatives   kinship   networks

2 Skim the passage and underline the main words and phrases in each paragraph that show you what the paragraph is about.

READING PASSAGE

*You should spend about 20 minutes on **Questions 1–14**, which are based on the Reading Passage below.*

It takes a village to raise a child

A It takes an African village to bring up and socialize the child into the community. Nothing illustrates this more than the fact that children are sometimes allowed to spend holidays with relatives such as aunts, uncles or grandparents who live far away from home. The children are shown in a practical way the nature of kinship and the extent of familial and kinship relations. They get to know that they are part of a wide network of relatives, who are as important as the immediate family of father, mother and siblings. Such networks are useful in case of calamities when a child loses one or both parents and is forced to relocate to live with relatives who will be responsible for his or her upbringing. The parents exhibit less of the possessiveness over children that characterizes Western society.

B That adolescence brings with it challenges that ought to be handled carefully is appreciated by the society. Indeed, the initiation ceremonies that mark the transition from childhood to adulthood are primarily meant to address some of these challenges. Instructions during initiation focus on conduct and behaviour as well as duties and responsibilities on the part of the initiate for his/her own good and for the interests of the entire community.

C Kinship and family interests take precedence over individual interests. Young people who go through the process of initiation from childhood to adulthood are taught that life is worth living because the society is there for them in good and bad times. They bond together as members of the same age-grade. They have come of age as a group, been taught the historical information about the cultural group and its rituals, and been united by the rite that they have all gone through. In due course, they are supposed to marry and start raising a family. With the passage of time they in turn will become elders, taking over from the generation that preceded them in the initiation ceremony. Kinship networks are still a significant factor in the contemporary economy and politics. Waged employment is heavily influenced by familial and kinship ties.

D Seniority in age is respected and admired because old age is associated with wisdom. Senior citizens therefore are accorded due respect in the light of the fact that they are custodians of societal values. Their counsel is usually sought during times of crisis. They should not be argued with because their curse could ruin one's future. However, the respect and admiration also comes with certain responsibilities. As an elder an individual is supposed to be unemotional, sober and focused during a crisis or stressful times. As an arbiter an elder has to be candid and sincere in providing counsel. Also, as either father and grandfather, or mother and grandmother, the elder is supposed to be above partisan differences for his word and counsel to be accorded due respect and recognition. He is not supposed to engage in gossip. Thus while in general seniority is synonymous with honour, respect, admiration and wisdom, it is one's ability to manifest these qualities in old age that gives an individual elevated status in society.

E Families strive to take good care of senior citizens because it sets a good example for young children. By treating their elders well, parents send a message to their children that they too would like to be accorded that honour, respect and good treatment in old age. Indeed, one of the important reasons for procreation in traditional society was to have somebody to look after you in old age. Children brought up well were considered an asset. It was considered rude for a young man to sit down while an old person was standing. The young person was supposed to give up a seat for the old person as a sign of respect. The parents themselves must set a good example by respecting and taking care of their own parents. When children see that their grandparents are treated well, they learn by example that they too are expected to take care of their parents in old age.

F The elder is the pillar of both the nuclear and the extended family. Being the eldest living male descendant of the eldest son of the founder of the lineage, he is the link between the living and ancestors. He is supposed to unite the family so that the unity survives his death. He reinforces kinship ideology, maintains peace and presides over family gatherings, during which period he keeps members within bounds by insisting on customs, laws and traditional observances. He helps to socialize members of the family, immediate and extended, into the ways of the group. He represents the family whenever there are communal lineage meetings. In this way elders unite family and kinship members. In their oral will, in the presence of other elders, they provide guidance on how land will be parcelled out among family members, appeal for unity among family and kinship members and pass the baton of leadership to the next patriarch of the family. Thus, all members of the society take socialization seriously. That role transcends age and gender. This is because socialization contributes to cohesion.

Don't forget!

For questions **1–5**:
- Check the word limit. <u>Underline</u> key words. Do not write words from the questions as part of your answer.

Questions 1–5

Complete the sentences below.

Choose **NO MORE THAN TWO WORDS** *from the passage for each answer.*

1 One characteristic of _____ is possessiveness over children.

2 Familial and kinship well-being comes before personal _____ .

3 In African society, older people are respected because they are the guardians of _____ .

4 Despite the many positive associations connected with old age, it has particular _____ attached to it.

5 When counselling, an elder has to be _____ and _____ .

Don't forget!

or questions **6–9**:
• Check the rubric
  to see if you can
  use any letter more
  than once.

Questions 6–9

The Reading Passage has six paragraphs, **A–F**.

Which paragraph contains the following information?

NB You may use any letter more than once.

6 a series of steps involved in developing kinship ties throughout life

7 the reason behind endeavours to look after older members of society

8 the role played by the wider family in the event of misfortune

9 the fact that well-raised children were considered beneficial in traditional society

Questions 10–14

*Choose **FIVE** letters, **A–H**.*

Which **FIVE** of the following statements are true of the male elder within a family?

A He gives advice on how land is distributed among family members.

B He is responsible for increasing the wealth of the family.

C He hands over control to the next head of the family.

D He advises family members on career choices.

E He connects the living with their ancestors.

F He makes sure family members follow customs.

G He trains family members in the ways of the society.

H He assigns roles to the various family members according to ability.

3 Does what is described in the passage reflect the family and the society you come from? Give reasons and examples.

Do you think that attitudes to the family are undergoing change in many societies around the world? Is this change an inevitable part of progress?

Word building: Suffixes *-hood* and *-ship*

The suffixes *-hood* and *-ship* are used to express the following:

1 a state *membership/partnership*

2 an office or position *leadership/apprenticeship*

3 a skill *craftsmanship/musicianship*

4 a period of time *childhood/boyhood*

5 a group *neighbourhood/brotherhood*

1 Find examples of words with the suffixes *-hood* and *-ship* in the Reading Passage on page 153. Then decide which of the five meanings above they express.

2 Work in pairs. In sentences **1–10** below, add the suffix *-hood* and *-ship* to the words in brackets to complete the sentences.

    1 It is said that Britain has a special (relation) with America.

    2 Some people think it is important to develop good behaviour in (child).

    3 My grandparents live in a quiet (neighbour) on the edge of the town.

    4 (Parent) brings responsibilities as well as happiness.

    5 Club (member) is one way for people to socialise and develop their circle of friends.

    6 Before people reach (adult), they generally need to have some idea of the career they want.

7 Developing a lasting (partner) with international companies is essential for the development of trade.

8 Establishing a national (apprentice) scheme in the technical industries can build a strong economy.

9 Improvement of young people's prospects can be achieved through (sponsor) by private enterprise and the government.

10 (Leader) qualities need to be identified clearly at job interviews and nurtured.

3 Work in pairs. For sentences **1–7** below, replace the <u>underlined</u> words with a noun with the suffix *-hood* or *-ship*. If necessary, use the nouns in the box below to help you. Make any necessary changes to the word order.

nation	parent	child	leader	relation	sponsor	hard

1 Seeing people overcome a <u>period of great difficulty</u> in life can inspire others to succeed.

2 When the country achieved <u>the state of being an independent nation</u>, there was widespread celebration.

3 He had <u>qualities that showed he would make a good leader</u>, and therefore he received enormous backing from the public.

4 I have such happy memories of my <u>life as a child</u> in New Zealand.

5 <u>Being a mother or father</u> is an enormous responsibility.

6 Government and businesses could set up a <u>scheme to provide money</u> to enable young people to visit other countries.

7 The aim of the organisation is to encourage <u>good relations</u> between nations.

4 Work in pairs. For sentences **1–7**, complete each sentence with a noun that you made in exercise 3 and a verb from the box below. Make any necessary changes to the verb.

withdraw	reach	cultivate	face	spend	show	prepare

1 Over the years, the prime minister _____ a close _____ with the ambassadors of neighbouring countries.

2 The government _____ _____ from the social programme, but the organisers managed to attract more funds from alternative sources.

3 Despite_____ appalling _____ during the journey, the explorers survived.

4 I _____ such a happy_____ with my grandparents, of whom I have fond memories.

5 When _____ was _____ , there were wild celebrations throughout the country.

6 He _____ outstanding _____ during the crisis.

7 Having children changes people's lives, but more information is available today to help _____ for _____ .

5 👥 The words below can be used when describing the different stages in a person's life. Choose two or more of the stages that are relevant to your life and think of a relationship that was important to you in each of them. Tell a partner which relationship you have chosen and why it was important in this period.

childhood   adolescence   adulthood   father/motherhood

1 Look at the Part 2 Task Cards **A–D** and match one of them to the possible answer below.

A

Describe the time in your life that you have enjoyed the most so far.

You should say:

when the time was

where you were during this time

what happened during this time

and explain why you enjoyed it.

B

Describe a club membership that is/ was beneficial to you.

You should say:

where the club is located

when your club membership began

what kind of activities are/were involved at the club

and explain why club membership is/ was beneficial to you.

C

Describe a friendship that is/was important to you.

You should say:

who the friendship is/was with

when you first met your friend

what you and your friend do/did together

and explain why this friendship is/was important to you.

D

Describe a family relationship which is important to you.

You should say:

how this person is related to you

what this person looks like

what this person's personality is like

and explain why this person is important to you.

I'm going to talk about a friendship that I had when I was in my early years of secondary school. It was with my best friend at the time, Jane, ... whom I met when I first went to secondary school. I can remember very well the first day we actually ran into each other. I think we knew immediately that we were going to become very good friends. We were in the same class throughout our secondary school years, and we would sit next to each other in most classes, play the same games together — we were just like sisters ... The friendship was very important to both of us ... firstly, because we gave each other support at a time when we were both nervous about being in a new place. And secondly, where we grew up we both had a happy childhood, but neither of us had any siblings, so it was nice to have the companionship of someone at school ... And I suppose I felt that I was leaving childhood behind, and it was, in fact, the first friendship of my adolescence. We're still friends and I sometimes think that even if we hadn't met at school, we would've been friends, somehow.

2 Underline the parts of the answer that address each prompt on the relevant Task Card.

3 Look at the answer in exercise 1 again. Decide which 10/12 words you think the candidate wrote in his/her notes.

4 Work in pairs. Look at the part of the text in exercise 1 which relates to the final prompt on the Task Card. Describe the reasons given in your own words. Decide whether they are good reasons and explain why.

5 Work in pairs. Choose one topic for your partner to talk about and make notes.

6 Choose at least two points from the speaking checklist on page 181 that you would like your partner to check as you speak. Take turns talking about the topic, using your notes to guide you. When your partner has finished speaking, give him/her feedback on the points they chose from the checklist.

1 Work in pairs. You will hear a conversation between a parent and an administrator at an agency for host families for international students. Look at **Questions 1–10** below and discuss what you think they will talk about.

Don't forget!

- Skim the questions to identify the types of words in the answers.
- Check the maximum number of words/numbers.

🎧 **16** **SECTION 1** *Questions 1–10*

Complete the notes below.

Write **NO MORE THAN TWO WORDS AND/OR A NUMBER** *for each answer.*

Host Family Registration

> *Example*
> Name of caller's friend: Mrs ...Dalton...

Host family registration process

Initial home visit for **1** ....

Purpose: to go through registration details

Background checks

And at least **2** .... required from professionals

Length of process: normally a couple of **3** ....

Aim to place students with families in the month of **4** ....

Number of students

Family aims to take: **5** .... students

Things to be checked:

Distance from school, library access, wi-fi access, transport and the **6** ....

Preliminary meeting:

On **7** ....

House number: **8** ....

Mobile number: **9** ....

Email address: **10** ....@maltby.co.uk

2 👥 When you were at school did you go on school trips? Where to? For how long? What do you think students learn from school trips?

Language focus: Conditionals 2

1 Look at the following examples of conditional sentences from the Listening on page 235.

We'd only do these if you made a definite commitment to proceed.

… provided we're then both happy after the preliminary chat, we usually begin the registration process there and then.

What tenses are used in each of the clauses in the two sentences? Can you use the simple future to replace any of the tenses? If yes, does this change the meaning?

G Read more about conditionals in the Grammar reference on page 225.

2 For **1–7** below, decide if sentence **b** is a paraphase of sentence **a**. Rewrite the sentences in **b** that are not paraphrases of **a**.

Example:

a If only I had studied psychotherapy, I would be able to find a job now.

b I did study psychotherapy and now I regret it.

b is not a paraphrase of a. 'I didn't study psychotherapy and now I regret it.' is a paraphrase of a.

1 a Even if the course is expensive, I'll pay for it.
   b If the course is expensive, I'll still pay for it.

2 a I'll do the psychology option on the course, unless all the places are taken.
   b I won't do the psychology option on the course even if there are free places.

3 a If the government should happen to address social issues like crime and poverty, we'll see big changes.
   b There's a possibility the government will address social issues like crime and poverty.

4 a Supposing future generations are even more highly trained than they are now, will their lives be better?
   b Future generations will be even more highly trained than they are now, but will their lives be better?

5 a People need to be psychologically well adapted to the changing face of the workplace; otherwise, they'll find it difficult to keep up with the times.
   b If people are psychologically well adapted to the changing face of the workplace, they'll find it difficult to keep up with the times.

6 a If it were not for the support of my teacher, I wouldn't have got such a good grade in the exam.
   b I got such a good grade in the exam due to the support of my teacher.

7 a If economic growth wasn't slowing down, more money would be available for spending and investment.
   b Economic growth is slowing down, and so less money is now available for spending and investment.

3 Work in pairs. For **1–6** below, underline the correct word or phrase in *italics*.

1 *Unless/If/Otherwise* socialisation takes place at home and at school, society will face the consequences.

2 *If only/Provided/Even if* I had met you sooner, we could have got married long ago.

3 *Supposing/If/Even if* communities are disrupted by the high incidence of crime, they always triumph in the end.

4 *Unless/If only/Provided* you are prepared psychologically for the interview, you'll get the job.

5 *Unless/If only/If* the company hadn't planned for the future properly, they would be in trouble now.

6 *Unless/Supposing/Provided* you were offered a very well paid job abroad, would you take it?

4 Work in pairs. Decide which conditional clauses in exercise 3 describe actions or situations that have already happened.

5 For **1–6** below, make one sentence from the two sentences given using the word in brackets. Make any necessary changes.

Example:

Children will grow up to be unruly adults. Parents need to take an interest in social behaviour. (unless)

Unless parents take an interest in social behaviour, children will grow up to be unruly adults.

1 Families can help to make society a better place. The government needs to give them support. (provided)

2 The government may fund more community centres. This will provide a place for people to meet. (if/would)

3 Globalisation occurred. Now there are social and cultural problems around the world. (hadn't/would be fewer)

4 Volunteer workers helped people deal with the psychological aspect of change. Without them the situation would have been worse. (if not for)

5 Today trade between different countries is increasing. Still there are sometimes big differences between various business cultures. (even though)

6 Social intelligence isn't taught in schools. If it were, would it be beneficial? (supposing)

6 With a partner, discuss your past, present and future, and the things you have done, haven't done and have yet to do. Before you start, spend two or three minutes making notes.

Writing
Task 2

1 Work in groups. Make a list of ideas for one of the topics below and compare your list with another group.

1

You should spend about 40 minutes on this task.

Write about the following topic:

> *Some people think that the world is now one large village and we are all responsible for each other.*
> *To what extent do you agree or disagree?*

Give reasons for your answer and include any relevant examples from your own knowledge and experience.

Write at least 250 words.

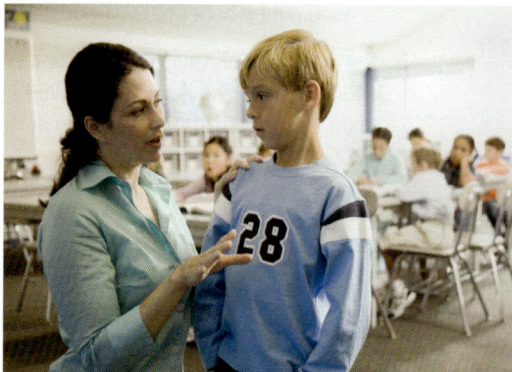

2

You should spend about 40 minutes on this task.

Write about the following topic:

> *Taking up some kind of sport is the best way for people to improve their social and psychological well-being.*
> *To what extent do you agree or disagree?*
> *What other measures do you think might be effective?*

Give reasons for your answer and include any relevant examples from your own knowledge and experience.

Write at least 250 words.

3

You should spend about 40 minutes on this task.

Write about the following topic:

> *Some people think only parents are responsible for teaching children how to behave. Others think the main responsibility lies with schools and the government.*
> *Discuss both these views and give your own opinion.*

Give reasons for your answer and include any relevant examples from your own knowledge and experience.

Write at least 250 words.

2   Work in groups. Match the possible conclusions below to the Task 2 questions in exercise 1. Give reasons for your choice and decide what the structure of the answer to one of the Task 2 questions would be.

   a   As we have seen, while adopting some kind of sporting activity is effective for improving people's social and psychological health, there are definitely other more effective strategies.

   b   As we have seen, although some argue that parents bear the sole responsibility for the behaviour of their children and others that schools and the government are mainly accountable, I think all three groups should share equal responsibility.

   c   In conclusion, there may be some strong arguments for countries concentrating their resources on their own citizens, but there is no doubt that in the modern world we are responsible for helping each other.

3   Work in groups. Discuss whether the conclusions match your own views on the topics.

4   Work in pairs. Look at the extracts below from answers to the Task 2 questions in exercise 1. Decide which question each extract relates to and explain why.

Extract 1

Helping each other no matter where people are is a natural human instinct. So this characteristic should be harnessed as it leads to the betterment of people's lives. In times of hardship and natural calamities like earthquakes and floods, people from different parts of the world always pull together. Unfortunately, it sometimes takes something bad to happen before people act together. As the world becomes smaller and smaller, it is important for different countries to live and work together without being encouraged to do so by tragedies.

Extract 2

Other more effective ways for people to improve their well-being exist, in my opinion, such as doing volunteer work or joining clubs or taking up a hobby. For instance, people could volunteer just one day a week to help others, such as young people at a youth club or families at a community centre, doing admin work or providing technical support. This would provide them with opportunities to meet other people, to share their skills and to develop friendships. Membership of a club or enrolment on a course learning a new skill like pottery can also help enhance people's lives by helping them relax.

---

5   In the extracts in exercise 4, underline the text you can replace with the conditional sentences below.

   For example, if people volunteered to help young people at a youth club or at a community centre doing admin work or providing technical support, this would provide them with opportunities to meet other people.

   Provided this characteristic were harnessed, the lives of many people around the world would be made better.

6   Work in pairs. Discuss whether you think the sentences in exercise 5 improve the paragraphs and how they do so.

7   Write your own answer for the Task 2 question on page 210. When you have finished, check your answer using the checklist on page 139.

11 Review

Vocabulary: The family

1 Complete the text below with a suitable singular or plural noun.

My family **1** _____ is very difficult to trace because both sets of my **2** _____ are from different countries, one from Egypt and one from Italy. My **3** _____ on my mother's side, who has been a **4** _____ now for 2 years, has told me many times that one of his **5** _____ was someone who was famous, but perhaps every **6** _____ has a **7** _____ who is famous. Our **8** _____ is small as I have no **9** _____ , but I have many **10** _____ as my mother and father both come from large families.

Word building: Suffixes *-hood* and *-ship*

1 Shorten each sentence by adding the suffixes *-hood* or *-ship* to a word in each sentence. Make any necessary changes in the sentence.

Example:

The cost of being a member of the club has increased.

The cost of club membership has increased.

1 He started working as an apprentice in electrical engineering last year.

2 He received money from sponsors to help pursue his dreams of being an athlete.

3 When I was a club member, I met many new friends.

4 I remember the time when I was a child with fondness.

5 Before people become adults, they are generally much more carefree.

6 My father and my uncle became partners in a business when they were very young.

7 The area and neighbours where I live now is generally very quiet.

Language focus: Conditionals 2

1 Add the phrase below to the appropriate places in the sentences.

a keep in touch

b If only apprenticeships

c we wouldn't have

d If I had to

e we will soon be able to

f If family bonds

g Unless people in local communities

1 _____ choose the time in my life that has been the most enjoyable, it would have to be my early teens.

2 Supposing you hadn't become a member of the swimming club, _____ become friends.

3 Even if young people move abroad, they can _____ more easily than in the past.

4 _____ have access to a range of facilities like parks and leisure centres, there is little opportunity for interaction.

5 _____ in engineering were more widely available, I might not have gone to university.

6 Provided communication software continues to develop, _____ send holograms to close friends and family.

7 _____ are strong, then the various members will stay in touch no matter how far apart they are.

2 Rewrite the sentences using the word in brackets. You can change the order of the information and there may be more than one answer.

1 Whatever the cost of the psychology course is, I'll pay for it. (expensive)

2 I will do the technology component of the course, if it's in the afternoon. (unless)

3 People can contribute to society with the support of the government. (provided).

4 The government can fund more crèches to enable more people to go to work. (if)

5 Parents and schools should both play a role in teaching good behaviour to children, otherwise they will not know right from wrong. (unless)

6 Private sponsorship of some university places is needed for people to develop their careers, otherwise the process will be harder. (if not)

7 It is essential that the socialisation of children takes place at home and school to ensure a healthy society. (if)

8 The world's present advanced state is due to the heavy investment in social and technological development programmes. (if not)

Accuracy in IELTS

1 Find and correct the seven mistakes below.

Some people think that the sole responsibility for bringing up children lies with parents, while others argued that schools also have an important role to play in this respect. Personally, I feel that both parents and schools should share the responsibility for a child's upbringing.

If we will look at the situation from the perspective of social skills, for example, it is clear that both parties should share the responsibility. Obviously, parents can teach children to form deep and meaningful relationships with friends and family at home. Schools could also have shown how to develop such relationships outside the home with their peer, while the same time picking up knowledge and information. If we as adults had not been introduced to the social norms of society, we would not know how to behave yourselves nor do we know how to pass on the skills essential to our children.

Vocabulary: Adjectives with multiple meanings

1 👥 Work in pairs. Decide what adjectives you could use to talk about the places in the photographs. Describe each photograph and answer the questions below.

> **1** Are these the sorts of places that you would like to visit? Which one appeals to you the most/least? Give reasons.
>
> **2** Have you ever visited anywhere that you would classify as pristine or completely unspoilt? Where?
>
> **3** Do you think people's desire to have novel experiences is actually destroying pristine environments? In what way(s)?

2 What does *novel* mean in question **3** in exercise 1? What other meanings does it have?

3 Work in pairs. For **1–9** below, <u>underline</u> the word that does not have the same meaning as the word on the left.

Example:

pristine	*new and untouched*	*clean*	<u>*different*</u>	
1 curious	apathetic	inquisitive	unusual	
2 alien	strange	native	extraterrestrial	
3 odd	unusual	irregular	different	new
4 foreign	from another country	unfamiliar	local	
5 different	dissimilar	diverse	unusual	similar
6 strange	unexpected	unfamiliar	uncomfortable	odd
7 fresh	new and different	cold and windy	odd	recently made
8 new	recently arrived	extra	inexperienced	replacing something
9 unique	treasured	only happening in one place	unlike anything else	

4 For **1–9** below, complete the gaps with an adjective from exercise 3 that makes sense in sentence **a** and **b**.

1 a I would like to live in a _____ area to where I am now.

   b Having _____ types of houses gives character to an area.

2 a The area was really _____ to me at first, but I soon got used to it.

   b I had this really _____ feeling that I had been inside the house before.

3 a Snowflakes have _____ shapes; no two flakes are alike.

   b With globalisation and the accessibility of travel, it is more difficult to find _____ travel experiences.

4 a The building has these _____ carvings over it, which none of us had ever come across.

   b He was _____ to know what the town looked like.

5 a Being in a _____ country is usually very exciting, especially when you're young.

   b The _____ minister met with the president and other ministers.

6 a It was mainly sunny, but we did have the _____ rain shower.

   b When I travelled into the Sahara for the first time I had this really _____ sensation.

7 a I was _____ to the job and didn't really know anything.

   b I bought a _____ set of clothes for the interview.

8 a The fruit we bought at the local market was very _____ .

   b Moving city and changing job was a _____ start for me.

9 a I found myself in the middle of an _____ landscape.

   b His ideas were completely _____ to mine.

5 Work in pairs. Check your answers to exercise 4 and decide what the noun is for each adjective you put in the gap.

6 Tell your partner about an experience you had recently, or an event that occurred recently. Use the adjectives from exercises 3 and 4.

Don't forget!

- Underline the words in the questions that show you that the answer will be given soon.

1 Work in groups. Read the questions and create a general description of the Listening.

🎧 17 **SECTION 2** *Questions 11–20*

Questions 11–15

*Choose the correct letter, **A**, **B** or **C**.*

11 The sources of information about the speaker's travels are

    A a book and a website.

    B a book and a blog.

    C a website and a blog.

12 According to the speaker, St Petersburg was

    A among his ten most popular holiday destinations.

    B his tenth favourite destination for a city break.

    C in the top five destinations in a recent survey.

13 The city of St Petersburg was memorable because of

    A the size of the river.

    B the weather.

    C the size of the museums.

14 The speaker says that visitors to the city will be struck by

    A the location of the city.

    B the size of the palaces.

    C St Petersburg's rich heritage.

15 The highlight of the trip to St Petersburg was

    A visiting the Hermitage Museum.

    B going round the Mariisnky theatre.

    C seeing the Bronze horseman.

Questions 16–20

Complete the sentences below.

*Write **NO MORE THAN TWO WORDS** for each answer.*

16 Apart from flying direct to St Petersburg, people can visit it as part of a .... of the Baltic Sea.

17 In the city outskirts, places to visit are magnificent .... and ....

18 Visitors should ensure they have time to .... beyond the city centre.

19 Holidays to destinations that are difficult to reach are more and more ....

20 For the speaker, the St Petersburg trip was a .... and a real adventure.

2 How do people feel when they travel abroad for the first time? If you have travelled to another country, what did you feel before you went, while you were there and after you came back?

Word building: Words related to memory

1 When people travel, they often bring back something to remind them of their trip. What is this thing called? With a partner, use a dictionary to find words with the root *mem-* that are related to *memory*.

2 Work in pairs. For **1–8** below, complete the gaps with a word made from the word *memory*. Make any necessary changes to the form of the word.

   1 I have many happy _____ from my time in the Caribbean. I can still picture the beaches and the surf.

   2 Do you _____ the last time you had a long holiday?

   3 She's writing her _____ now that she is no longer president. They should be interesting reading.

   4 Collecting cinema _____ is not particularly exciting. I'd rather collect holiday posters.

   5 We tried to _____ the route on the map so we would know it perfectly, but when we were going along the road through the forest we got lost.

   6 Would you say that your trip to Japan was a _____ experience or not?

   7 We visited the Taj Mahal in India. It's a _____ to the Mughal emperor Shah Jahan's wife, Mumtaz Mahal.

   8 It's always nice to have even a small _____ of a trip, even if it's only a card.

3 In the paragraph below the words in *italics* are in the wrong place. Decide the correct position **1–8** for each of the words.

I have really vivid **1** *memorabilia* of my holiday in Mexico last summer. I had a digital camera which takes excellent photographs. And as I am the sort of person who collects **2** *memories* of any kind, like concert tickets or theatre programmes, I came back with loads of **3** *memoirs* like little statues and trinkets. If I ever write my **4** *mementos*, I shall have lots of material to draw on. We visited a beautiful village, and I even bought a replica of a **5** *remember* to a famous heroine whom I don't really know, but the monument to her was very moving, which is what made it so **6** *remember*. Unfortunately, I am not sure I'd **7** *memorise* how to get there again as I didn't take much notice of the map. I didn't **8** *memorial* the name of the town.

4 Work in pairs. Write at least three questions each using the items below. Take turns asking and answering the questions.

Do you find it easy to memorise …
Are you the sort of person who collects … memorabilia?
What is your (most treasured/fond/vivid) memory of … ?
What details do you remember about … ?
What was your most memorable … ?

Speaking
Part 1

1   Look at the Part 1 questions below about travel where you live. Match each of the following ways to begin an answer to questions **1–4**.

   a   More and more people use …

   b   Most of the time I use …

   c   I think I'd …

   d   One problem they face is …

Travel

1   How do you prefer to travel abroad?
2   Has the way people travel abroad changed much in recent years?
3   What problems can people face when they travel nationally and/or internationally?
4   How would you improve long-distance travel?

---

2   Work in pairs. Think of at least two other suitable ways to begin the answer to the questions in exercise 1.

3   Take turns asking and answering the questions in exercise 1. Before you start, choose two points from the checklist on page 181 that you would like your partner to give you feedback on.

Speaking
Part 2

1   Work in groups. Discuss the questions below.

What synonyms do you know for the word *journey*?

What words do you associate with the word *journey*?

Don't forget!

- Write only 10/12 words for your notes.
- Glance at your notes as you speak to guide you.
- You have to speak for 1–2 minutes.

2   Look at the following Task Card and make lists in answer to questions **1–4** below.

Describe a journey you remember well.

You should say:
   where this journey was to
   when it was
   what you did on this journey
and explain why you remember this journey well.

---

   1   What adjectives do you associate with the word *journey*?

   2   What verbs do you associate with the word *journey*?

   3   What kinds of places do you associate with the word *journey*?

   4   What reasons are there for going on a *journey*?

3   Use the words in the lists to help you make notes for the topic above.

4   With a partner, take turns talking about the topic. Before you start, choose two points from the checklist on page 181 that you would like your partner to give you feedback on.

Reading
Questions 1–13

The Giant Stelae of Aksum

Machu Picchu

1 Work in groups. Decide whether the following statements are true or false.

1 World heritage sites around the world are designated by UNESCO.

2 The Grand Canyon is in the United States of America.

3 The Great Barrier Reef is off the coast of New Zealand.

4 The Inca ruins are in South America.

5 The Parthenon is in Rome in Italy.

6 The Giant Stelae of Aksum are in West Africa.

7 Mount Fuji is in Japan.

8 The Terracotta Army is in China.

9 The Hermitage museum is in Moscow.

10 The ruins of Persepolis are in Afghanistan.

The Grand Canyon

2 Work in groups. Look at the title of the Reading Passage on page 170. What facts do you already know about this topic? Share your information with the rest of your group.

3 Each of the following words from the Reading Passage has different meanings. Look at the words and their meanings and decide which is more likely in this passage.

1	*shelf*	a ledge (of rock or land)	a flat surface (for storing things on)
2	*maturity*	state of being fully developed	adulthood
3	*system*	scheme	organism
4	*range*	variety	scale
5	*list*	catalogue	slant
6	*vulnerable*	weak	in danger (of attack)
7	*breed*	reproduce	farm
8	*colony*	group (of animals)	settlement
9	*historic*	ancient	important
10	*sanctuary*	asylum	place of safety (for animals, etc)

4 Read the passage to check you have chosen the correct meaning. Explain your choices.

READING PASSAGE

You should spend about 20 minutes on **Questions 1–13**, *which are based on the Reading Passage below.*

The Great Barrier Reef

The Great Barrier Reef was one of Australia's first World Heritage Areas and is the world's largest World Heritage Area. The Great Barrier Reef was inscribed on the World Heritage List in 1981 and was one of 15 World Heritage places included in the National Heritage List on 21 May 2007. The Great Barrier Reef is the world's largest World Heritage property extending over 2,000 kilometres and covering 348,000 km² on the north-east continental shelf of Australia. Larger than Italy, it is one of the best known marine protected areas. The Great Barrier Reef's diversity reflects the maturity of the ecosystem which has evolved over many thousands of years. It is the world's most extensive coral reef and has some of the richest biological diversity found anywhere. The Great Barrier Reef contains extensive areas of seagrass, mangrove, sandy and muddy seabed communities, inter-reefal areas, deep oceanic waters and island communities. Contrary to popular belief, the Great Barrier Reef is not a continuous barrier, but a broken maze of around 2,900 individual reefs, of which 760 are fringing reefs along the mainland or around islands.

Some have coral cays. The reefs range in size from less than one hectare to over 1,000 km², and in shape from flat platform reefs to elongated ribbon reefs.

The Great Barrier Reef provides habitat for many diverse forms of marine life. There are an estimated 1,500 species of fish and over 360 species of hard, reef-building corals. More than 4,000 mollusc species and over 1,500 species of sponges have been identified.

Other well-represented animal groups include anemones, marine worms, crustaceans and echinoderms.

The extensive seagrass beds are an important feeding ground for the dugong, a mammal species internationally listed as vulnerable. The reef also supports a variety of fleshy algae that are heavily grazed by turtles, fish, sea urchins and molluscs.

The reef contains nesting grounds of world significance for the endangered loggerhead turtle, and for green, hawksbill and flatback turtles, which are all listed as vulnerable. It is also a breeding area for humpback whales that come from the Antarctic to give birth in the warm waters.

The islands and cays support around 215 bird species, many of which have breeding colonies there. Reef herons, osprey, pelicans, frigate birds, sea eagles and shearwaters are among the seabirds that have been recorded.

The Great Barrier Reef is also of cultural importance, containing many archaeological sites of Aboriginal or Torres Strait Islander origin, including fish traps, middens, rock quarries, story sites and rock art. Some notable examples occur on Lizard and Hinchinbrook Islands, and on Stanley, Cliff and Clack Islands where there are spectacular galleries of rock paintings. There are over 30 historic shipwrecks in the area, and on the islands are ruins, operating lighthouses and other sites that are of cultural and historical significance.

About 99.3 per cent of the World Heritage property is within the Great Barrier Reef Marine Park, with the remainder in Queensland waters and islands. Because of its status, many people think the entire Great Barrier Reef is a marine sanctuary or national park, and therefore protected equally throughout. However, the Great Barrier Reef Marine Park is a multiple-use area in which a wide range of activities and uses are allowed, including extractive industries.

This has been achieved using a comprehensive, multiple-use zoning system. Impacts and conflicts are minimized by providing high levels of protection for specific areas. A variety of other activities are allowed to continue in a managed way in certain zones (such as shipping, dredging, research, commercial fishing and recreational fishing). A new Zoning Plan for the entire Marine Park came into effect on 1 July 2004. The proportion of the Marine Park protected by no-take zones was increased from less than five per cent to over 33 per cent, and now protects representative examples of each of the 70 broad habitat types across the entire Marine Park. Two authorities are now responsible for the Great Barrier Reef: the Queensland Government and the Australian Government. The majority of the World Heritage property is still relatively pristine when compared with coral reef ecosystems elsewhere in the world. Guided by the principle of balancing conservation and sustainable use, the regulatory framework significantly enhances the resilience of the Great Barrier Reef.

The Australian and Queensland Governments have a cooperative and integrated approach to managing the Great Barrier Reef. The Great Barrier Reef Marine Park Authority (GBRMPA) is the Australian Government agency responsible for overall management, and the Queensland Government, particularly the Queensland Environmental Protection Agency, provides day-to-day management of the marine park for the Authority.

Questions 1–6

Complete the summary below.

*Choose **NO MORE THAN TWO WORDS** from the passage for each answer.*

The Great Barrier Reef, one of Australia's first sites to become a World Heritage area, is situated on the **1** .... off the north-eastern coast of Australia. The **2** .... of the reef is a result of the evolution of the **3** .... over a very long time. Being the biggest **4** .... of its kind, the reef is, from the **5** .... point of view, very varied. This vast area consists of disconnected reefs of different lengths and provides a habitat for a wide range of **6** .... from fish to coral and sponges and other creatures.

Questions 7–10

Do the following statements agree with the information given in the Reading Passage?
Write:

> **TRUE** *if the statement agrees with the information*
> **FALSE** *if the statement contradicts the information*
> **NOT GIVEN** *if there is no information on this*

7 The reef provides food for turtles.

8 No other World Heritage area contains as many culturally significant sites as the Great Barrier Reef.

9 There are plans to renovate some of the ruins on the islands.

10 All industrial activity is forbidden in the Great Barrier Reef Marine Park.

Questions 11–13

Answer the questions below.

*Choose **NO MORE THAN THREE WORDS** from the passage for each answer.*

11 What are kept low as a result of the high degree of protection for specific places?

12 What has a major impact on the Great Barrier Reef's capacity to flourish?

13 What is the Great Barrier Reef Marine Park Authority accountable for in respect of the reef?

5 🔁 Provided money were no object, would you like to visit the Great Barrier Reef? What aspect of the reef would appeal to you? Why?

Would you be concerned that carbon produced by travelling there could contribute to the destruction of the reef?

Language focus: Articles

1 In the extract below from the Reading Passage on page 170, underline examples of the following:

1 the definite article

2 the zero article

3 the indefinite article

Contrary to popular belief, the Great Barrier Reef is not a continuous barrier, but a broken maze of around 2,900 individual reefs, of which 760 are fringing reefs along the mainland or around islands.

G Read more about articles in the Grammar reference on page 225.

2 Work in pairs. Answer questions **1–9** below. Pay attention to the articles in your answers.

1 What gives us light during the day?

2 What objects do you see far away in the sky on a clear night?

3 Is the sun a star or a planet?

4 When can the sun be classified as a star?

5 Are there different solar systems?

6 What is the highest mountain in the world?

7 Which mountain range is it in?

8 What is the capital of Japan?

9 Are there different oceans on our planet? Name three.

3 Work in pairs. For sentences **a** and **b** in **1–8** below, decide which sentence requires an article and which does not. Explain why.

1 a I spent the day visiting _____ old monuments.

   b _____ monuments I visited were old.

2 a I like climbing _____ mountains.

   b I'd like to go climbing in _____ Himalayas.

3 a You shouldn't look at _____ sun directly.

   b _____ stars twinkle because they are far away.

4 a The Amazon flows through _____ various countries.

   b Rivers like _____ Nile bring life to desert regions.

5 a _____ capital city of Mexico is enormous.

   b _____ Mexico City is particularly big.

6 a _____ United Kingdom is usually just called the UK.

   b _____ kingdoms are ruled by monarchs.

7 a _____ prime minister runs the country.

   b _____ prime ministers are appointed by heads of state or parties.

8 a _____ heart sends blood around the body.

   b The body has _____ various organs.

4 In the following underline the articles that should not be there.

A trip I would like to describe is a journey I went on to the Brazil a few years back. I went with my family, two brothers but no the sisters, five people in all. We flew to the Rio de Janeiro which is an amazing city with many people and lots of entertainment. What I really like about the city is that it has the beaches and, of course, it's famous for its nightlife. We all had lots of the fun there with a sightseeing and parties, which we went to nearly every night. The cost of the living is cheap there and a meal in a restaurant is a real treat as everyone is very lively. I recommend Brazil as a place for the holidays and relaxing ...

Writing
Task 2

1 Work in groups. Explain the Task 2 question below in your own words. Then list what you need to do to complete all parts of the task.

WRITING TASK 2

You should spend about 40 minutes on this task.

Write about the following topic:

Some people think that the best way to broaden young people's understanding of the world is to encourage them to travel to other countries.

To what extent do you agree or disagree with this opinion?

What other measures do you think might be effective?

Give reasons for your answer and include any relevant examples from your own knowledge or experience.

Write at least 250 words.

2 Decide which of the ideas **1–7** below you think are the most relevant to the question. Then add your own ideas to the list.

   1 bad for the environment

   2 learn language and culture

   3 learn more while travelling

   4 travelling enjoyable experience

   5 waste of time when access to information elsewhwere

   6 online videos

   7 exposure to new ideas

3 For **1–6** below, decide whether the text in *italics* is relevant. Rewrite the text that is not relevant.

   1 Travel broadens people's minds by exposing them to new ideas and cultures. *For example, it allows them to experience a culture, which films or images cannot do.*

   2 Railway systems are being developed in many countries, as trains become faster and more comfortable. *At the moment, more people are travelling by coach.*

   3 Tourism can have a positive impact on travellers as well as on local culture *as people learn other languages and about culture.*

   4 Precious ecosystems around the world are in danger of being destroyed by the very tourists who most want to protect them, *so access to such sites needs to be restricted.*

   5 More people than ever, of all ages, are holidaying in other countries compared to previous generations. *This is surely because young people don't often stay in hotels.*

   6 Virtual tours and modern 3D TVs mean people can travel without leaving their living rooms. *Moreover, they will soon be able to immerse themselves in new places using virtual reality.*

4 Write sentences for at least two ideas in exercise 2, or about your own ideas.

5 Discuss the following Task 2 question. List three main ideas for each point of view and think of an example.

WRITING TASK 2

You should spend about 40 minutes on this task.

Write about the following topic:

> *Today, more people than ever are travelling around the world.*
> *Do you think this is a positive or negative development?*

Give reasons for your answer and include any relevant examples from your own knowledge or experience.

Write at least 250 words.

---

6 Write your own answer for the Task 2 question on page 210. When you have finished, check your answer using the checklist on page 139. Check your answers for correct use of articles.

Vocabulary: Adjectives with multiple meanings

1   Use the same word to replace the words and phrases in brackets in each pair of sentences below.

1 a It's always a good sign if children are (inquisitive) about the language when they travel to another country.

  b My grandfather's got an (unusual) way of fixing things, but it works.

2 a The graph shows the results of a survey on various modes of transport in (several) countries.

  b Visiting an area with (unusual) types of houses and shops is always interesting.

3 a People are always looking for (new and different) experiences, which is why the travel industry will always thrive.

  b Do you prefer to eat (recently made) food or ready-made meals?

4 a It was such a (new) experience for me to travel by helicopter for the first time.

  b I'm going to talk about a (long story) that I read when I was at school.

5 a The landscape was so (unfamiliar). It was like nothing I'd ever seen before.

  b Would we not be the (extra-terrestrial) on another planet?

6 a We're (recently arrived) here and don't know our way around yet.

  b What I'm going to describe is a time when I was (inexperienced) in a job, but still effective.

Word building: Words related to memory

1   Match the bubbles below to create five short dialogues.

Example:

Do you find it easy to memorise new words?

Yes, I don't remember them for long unless I use them more than once.

Is your memory good?

Where did this memento come from?

Do you collect historical memorabilia?

Mmm, I have so many vivid memories of my time there.

What was your most memorable experience in South America?

Don't you recognise it? It's from the famous memorial I visited in India.

Yes, but sometimes I leave memos for myself on the fridge to remind me to do things.

No, they don't interest me. But I love reading the memoirs of famous historical figures.

Language focus: Articles

1 Use each of the following, *a/an*, *the* and *the zero article*, once only to complete each sentence below. Change the punctuation as necessary.

1 _____ trains, some of which are very luxurious, are _____ good way to travel around _____ world.

2 _____ Abu Dhabi is _____ state in _____ UAE.

3 I have _____ fond memories of my stay in _____ Netherlands, even though I was there for _____ relatively short time.

4 _____ universe is made up of billions of _____ galaxies where _____ star like the sun in our solar system might exist.

5 Antarctica is _____ enormous expanse of _____ ice where _____ temperatures can drop to less than -90°C.

6 Some people like travelling by _____ plane, as it is _____ quick way of travelling for those going to _____ other side of the world.

7 Trips giving people unique experiences are in _____ great demand across _____ age spectrum and are not restricted to _____ single group of people.

8 _____ river like _____ Amazon supports _____ wildlife as well as people.

9 Information about _____ different tours is available on _____ separate page on _____ website.

10 Around half of _____ human body is _____ water, which is _____ surprise to some people.

11 _____ quality of _____ accommodation is _____ great asset for any hotel.

Accuracy in IELTS

1 In each text below, find an irrelevant piece of information, two extra articles and two words in the wrong form.

1 Soon everyone will have access to virtual tours of places such as the Stonehenge in the UK or the Grand Canyon in the USA just by wearing a headset. Such immersion is an exciting new development, which could help people 'see' places that they might not have the opportunity of visit normally. And it will also help the environment. However, it could also increase pressure on already overcrowded tourist sites and, at the same time, make the people more isolated socially as they retreat into a virtual world of artificial memory.

2 Holidays to the distant places are more popular than ever before. This has resulted from a combination of factors such as a decrease in the cost of travel, as people strive to find the next memory experience. It has also resulted in an expansion of the leisure industry, which is important. For example, in the past travelling by plane was restricted to a small number of wealth people, but now that costs have come down and more people have the larger disposable incomes, they can afford to spend more on new leisure experiences like travelling form China to Europe.

Introduction

The IELTS Speaking module lasts between 11 and 14 minutes and has three parts. The exam is recorded.

The examiner assesses your ability to communicate effectively in English.

Part 1

Part 1 takes between four to five minutes. You will be asked general questions about yourself, such as your family, your job/studies or your interests and a variety of similar and familiar topics. You will be assessed on your ability to give opinions and information on these topics.

1   Work in pairs. Look at the two sets of Part 1 questions about Friends and Crafts and decide how you would answer each question. Then choose a set each and ask each other the questions.

> **A**   **Friends**
>
> Do you prefer to go out with one friend or a group of friends? Why?
>
> What do you do when you go out?
>
> Do you think it's important to keep in contact with friends you make at work or on courses? Why/Why not?

> **B**   **Crafts**
>
> Do you like making things, e.g. cooking, pottery or painting? Why/Why not?
>
> Do you think learning crafts is important in our lives? Why/Why not?
>
> Tell me about a traditional craft in your country.
>
> Do you think these will be popular in the future? Why/Why not?

2   Look at the following beginnings to possible answers to the three questions in set A. Decide which one is not suitable and why.

1   I like friends.

2   We tend to go to the cinema or the theatre, because ...

3   Yes, sometimes, because ...

4   There are many reasons, but perhaps the most important is ...

3 Using the correct sentence rhythm and stress helps your intelligibility, and good pronunciation leads to a higher score. You can help yourself relax as you speak by developing a rhythm and breathing properly. Look at sentence 2 above. You can create a rhythm by stressing the important words like verbs and nouns:

*We **tend** to **go** to the **cinema** or **theatre**, **because** …*

Say these words and then read the sentence beginning. Take a shallow breath at the comma before the word because. Decide which words you should stress in sentence 4.

4 Work in pairs. To help you understand the examiner better, decide which nouns and verbs the examiner will stress in the questions in set A. Then do the same with the questions in set B.

5 Think of your own sentence beginnings for set B. Then decide which words to stress and practise saying the nouns and verbs as in exercise 3.

6 Take turns asking and answering the questions again, using a different set from the one you chose in exercise 1.

Part 2

In Part 2 the examiner will give you a Task Card with a topic from a wide range of areas. You will be given one minute to think about the topic and make notes before you speak. You should speak for one to two minutes. When you have finished speaking, the examiner will ask one or two questions to round off the topic. You will be assessed on your ability to speak at length about a topic, organise your ideas and use appropriate language.

1 Work in pairs. Decide which Task Cards **1–6** the candidate notes **a–f** relate to.

1 Describe a place where you enjoy studying.
You should say:
where this place is
when you first visited this place
what this place is like
and explain why you enjoy studying there.

2 Describe a skill that you would like to learn.
You should say:
what the skill is
when you would like to learn this skill
where you would like to learn this skill
and explain why you would like to learn this skill.

3 Describe something expensive you bought but you didn't use/haven't used.
You should say:
what the item is
when you bought the item
where you bought the item
and explain why you didn't use/haven't used it.

4 Describe a meeting with someone that changed your life.
You should say:
who this meeting was with
when this meeting happened
where this meeting happened
and explain why this meeting changed your life.

5 Describe something you have made that you are proud of.
You should say:
what you have made
where you made it
how you made it
and explain why you felt proud about making the item.

6 Describe a website that you like.
You should say:
what this website is
how often you visit this website
what special features this website has
and explain why you like this website.

a
maps
weekly
detailed maps
see world
learn
have fun

b
table
carpentry class
wood saw nails hammer
polish
challenging

c
friend
3 years ago
course
funny/laugh
reliable
helpful

d
café
near river
month ago
cheerful
relaxing
friendly
great view

e
guitar
last August
on holiday
little time
annoying
not relaxing

f
musical instrument
soon
class – irritating
privately
relaxing
helps concentration
healthy

2 Work in pairs. Decide how the words in the notes for the first two topics relate to each part of the topic.

3 Look at the possible answer for the topic in Task Card 3. Underline the paraphrase the speaker uses for the notes that they prepared.

The item that I'd like to talk about is a musical instrument, a guitar that I had planned to learn how to play. I actually acquired it at the end of the summer when I had a few days off and was visiting my friend in another town. I saw it in a new music shop in the town centre. At first, I was going to buy the guitar online, but decided to buy it there and then. But I haven't actually played the instrument much at all, mainly because I haven't really had any spare time as I've been very busy at work and also socially with friends and family. So what happens is I keep putting off practising the guitar and it just sits there in the living room unused. And another reason is that I've never learnt to play a musical instrument before, so I've found it quite irritating and challenging when I've tried to do basic things on it. So, all in all playing the guitar's not good at helping me unwind and I should've thought about it before buying it. But friends've told me I should persevere and take classes as they say playing an instrument helps them to improve their ability to focus before studying or working, which I think would help me too.

4 🔊 **18** Listen to a candidate talking about Task Card 2 in exercise 1. Identify the differences between the notes about the candidate's answer.

5 Decide whether you think the changes make the answer better or not. Give reasons.

6 Work in pairs. Each choose a card for your partner. Make your own notes or use the notes above. Then take turns talking about the topic on your cards. When you have finished speaking, give each other feedback using the checklist on page 181.

Part 3

In Part 3, you will have a discussion with the examiner, which will last between four and five minutes. The discussion will be linked to the topic in Part 2, but it is more abstract so you are not encouraged to talk about personal experiences. You will be assessed on your ability to communicate and justify views and discuss and analyse issues.

1 Work in groups. Look at the following Part 3 questions and discuss what you might include in your answers.

Information on the web

How useful do you think websites are for bringing information to people? What about training or advertising?

In what ways can websites benefit small businesses?

In business terms, are people more influenced by what they see nowadays on the web than on television? In what ways?

Distance learning

How can the web be used for distance learning?

Should the training that is available on the web be regulated more? Why? How?

How do people in your country feel about awarding degrees and diplomas based solely on learning over the internet? Give reasons and examples.

---

2 🎧 **19** Listen to Part 3. Number the examiner's questions **1–6** below in the order that they are asked.

1 How essential do you think it'll be for workforces in the future to be proficient technologically?

2 Do you think it's important to keep acquiring new skills throughout one's life?

3 Should preparation of children and young people for work focus on computing skills at the expense of practical skills?

4 Do you think people will have to work longer in the future?

5 How can people ensure that work does not control their lives?

6 In what way do you think learning only computing skills can be a disadvantage in life?

3 Work in groups of three. Take turns asking and answering the questions in exercise 1. The third student should use the checklist on page 181 and give feedback on criteria agreed by the student being examined.

IELTS Speaking checklists

IELTS Speaking Part 1

See the checklist for Part 3.

1 Did you paraphrase the question?
2 Did you develop your answer by giving simple reasons?
3 Were your ideas relevant to the question?
4 Did you avoid repetition of words and structures?
5 Did you use a range of grammar, vocabulary and complex structures?
6 Did you concentrate too much on accuracy rather than fluency?
7 Did you speak clearly?
8 Did you speak too quickly or slowly?
9 Did you speak using the correct rhythm or sentence stress?
10 Did you use the correct word/phrase stress?

Remember this section is personal not abstract.

IELTS Speaking Part 2

See checklist for Part 3 and 1–5 below.

1 Did you make notes?
2 Were your notes short—no more than about ten words?
3 Did you answer all the parts of the question in order?
4 Did you refer to your notes as you spoke?
5 Were your notes easy to glance at as you spoke?

IELTS Speaking Part 3

1 Did you paraphrase the question?
2 Was your answer organised?
3 Did you develop your answer by giving reasons and examples?
4 Did you also develop your ideas by expressing contrasts, causes, effects, purposes and conclusions?
5 Was your answer abstract as required or was it too personal?
6 Were your ideas relevant to the question?
7 Did you avoid repetition of words and structures?
8 Did you use a range of grammar, vocabulary and complex structures?
9 Did you concentrate too much on accuracy rather than fluency?
10 Did you speak clearly?
11 Did you speak too quickly or slowly?
12 Did you speak using the correct rhythm or sentence stress?
13 Did you use the correct word/phrase stress?

The importance of infrastructure

Vocabulary: Nouns related to systems

1 👥 Work in groups. Describe the photographs and decide what aspects of urban infrastructure you can see in each. Then discuss the questions below.

- What other types of infrastructure systems are there? Why are they important?
- Which is the most important and why?
- In what ways do the various systems help people? Are they ever a hindrance? How?

2 Complete the questionnaire for yourself and two other students.

Questionnaire

Have you used each of the following systems today?

	You	Student 1	Student 2
1 transport system	☐	☐	☐
2 road network	☐	☐	☐
3 water service	☐	☐	☐
4 electricity grid	☐	☐	☐
5 telephone network	☐	☐	☐
6 satellite system	☐	☐	☐
7 internet	☐	☐	☐
8 GPS system	☐	☐	☐

3   Work in groups. Compare your findings by answering the following questions:

- Were any systems used by everyone? Which one(s)?
- Were any systems not used by anyone? Which one(s)?
- Which system was used most/least often?

4   Work in pairs. Decide how the nouns on the left below are related to the words in *italics,* for example *infrastructure* and *lines,* etc. are related to railways because ... Try to do this on your own before looking at the words in the box below to help you.

1 infrastructure	*lines*	*bridges*	*tunnels*	*viaducts*
2 network	*mobile*	*fibre-optic*	*browse*	*satellite*
3 system	*dish*	*communications*	*channel*	*weather*
4 web	*host*	*access*	*server*	*connection*
5 supply	*tap*	*treatment*	*filter*	*purification*
6 grid	*national*	*generators*	*cables*	*pylons*
7 supply	*pipelines*	*industry*	*fields*	*appliance*
8 industry	*field*	*wells*	*refineries*	*exploration*

> electricity   gas   telephone   oil   satellite   water   internet   railway

5   Work in pairs. For sentences **1–7**, complete each gap with a word from exercise 4.

1 _____ is produced on wind farms, which then feed into the national _____ .

2 _____ is sent via _____ from _____ in remote areas and to people's homes.

3 The safety of the _____ _____ is taken for granted in many countries, but without the process of _____ the water many people are drinking is putting their lives at risk.

4 The transport of _____ from the _____ to the _____ can cause pollution, as we have seen with spillages at sea.

5 A _____ can be used to connect people in remote areas of the world that don't have landlines, and it can also be used to collect data on the _____ .

6 The revival of interest in the train as an efficient means of transport has led to investment in _____ like new _____ connecting various towns.

7 If you have wireless _____ to the _____ , you can browse and download information anywhere, but you have to make sure the _____ is secure.

6   Work in pairs. Think of an incident where a system or part of a system worked well or did not work. Describe to your partner what happened and how you reacted, if it did not work.

Listening
Section 3

1   For **1–7** below, tick (✓) the items that are related to the research process. For each, decide what they mean and how they relate to the process.

1   aims and objectives   2   lectures   3   research question

4   research findings   5   data analysis   6   teaching

7   literature review

2   Work in pairs. Decide which item in exercise 1 you think is likely to be the most difficult. Give reasons.

---

20   **SECTION 3**   *Questions 21–30*

Questions 21–23

*Choose the correct letter, **A**, **B** or **C**.*

21   Andrei's research is on

     A the impact of road networks on urban areas.
     B the link between people and urban transport infrastructure.
     C the main reasons behind system breakdowns in cities.

22   Tracey is finding that the examination of her data

     A is demanding a lot of effort.
     B is a straightforward and interesting task.
     C is a very rewarding experience.

23   What did Tracey think as she commenced her research project?

     A She assumed that it was going to be much more difficult.
     B She imagined she would never be able to begin.
     C She felt relaxed about the whole process.

Questions 24–28

What comments does Tracey make about the various aspects of her research?

*Choose **FIVE** answers from the box and write the correct letter, **A–G**, next to Questions 24–28.*

Evaluation	Aspects of research	
A fairly easy	24 research question	....
B very easy	25 literature review	....
C fairly difficult	26 research proposal	....
D very difficult	27 methods design	....
E especially challenging	28 aims and objectives	....
F very tiring		
G time-consuming		

Questions 29 and 30

*Choose **TWO** letters, **A–F**.*

Which **TWO** of the following does Tracey recommend Andrei should contact for help with writing?

     A main library   **D** research supervisor

     B private teacher   **E** language centre

     C student union   **F** course tutor

Word building: Modal verbs to adjectives

Look at the comment by Andrei from the end of the Listening on page 236.

A: OK, but there's likely to be a fee involved.

The meaning of the adjective *likely* can be expressed in the following ways:

… will probably be …

it is probable that … will be …

1   Work in pairs. For **1–9** below, <u>underline</u> the most suitable word in *italics*.

   1 Can the communications systems be improved? Yes, it's *probable/possible/certain*.

   2 They wouldn't build an extension of the railway line. They were very *unwilling/willing/likely* to do so.

   3 They didn't need to build more refineries. It was *unnecessary/necessary/possible*.

   4 The satellite should improve communications dramatically. At least that's the *unlikely/certain/expected* result, but nobody is sure.

   5 The government should hit its target. But that's only a *obligatory/probable/possible* outcome, not a certainty.

   6 The oil company could do what it wanted without any interference from the government. They were *able/willing/possible* to do anything they wanted.

   7 Do safety measures have to be imposed on every construction project? Yes, I think it's *compulsory/optional/certain*.

   8 Oil will run out some time. It can't last forever; that's *essential/certain/obligatory*.

   9 They don't have to build a motorway through the nature reserve; it's not *possible/essential/probable*.

2   Work in groups. In the following extract from IELTS Speaking Part 3, <u>underline</u> the modal verbs that show possibility, probability and obligation. Choose a suitable adjective from exercise 1 to replace each one. Make any other necessary changes.

Examiner: Can faster communication systems like broadband have an impact on people's lives?

Candidate: I think the development of faster communication systems than we have now can have an impact on local as well as national economies, as they should enable people to do business faster. Obviously, they can't solve every problem, but they can at least help. For a while, governments wouldn't invest in fibre optics, but now the cables are being installed everywhere. For example, in my home country they provide jobs for local people …

3   What developments in infrastructure do you think there will be in your country in the near future?

   Which developments do you think are necessary?

1   Work in groups. Look at the title and discuss what you think the Reading Passage is about.

2   Scan the Reading Passage to find words and phrases relating to infrastructure. Compare your list with another group and then with the rest of the class.

READING PASSAGE

You should spend about 20 minutes on **Questions 1–13**, *which are based on the Reading Passage below.*

Cycling for Transportation and Health: The Role of Infrastructure

A   To help address health and other policy concerns, policy makers and professionals are looking at ways to increase the use of walking and cycling for everyday travel. While most of the focus on "active living" has been on walking, cycling may have a greater potential to substitute for motorized vehicle trips because of its faster speed and ability to cover greater distances. Bicycle commuting has been shown to be an activity that meets recommended intensity levels and to be related to lower rates of unhealthy weight and obesity.

B   The potential for cycling as a transportation mode has been recognized nationally through objectives to raise cycling rates and significant increases in funding for building new infrastructure. Several states and cities have also adopted aggressive policies and programs to increase cycling. However, the United States lags far behind many other developed countries, particularly several European countries, with respect to the share of people traveling by bicycle. Moreover, most bicycle travel in the United States, particularly among adults, is for recreation, not daily travel. This is in contrast to cycling in countries such as the Netherlands, Denmark, and Germany.

C   This research aims to provide insight on whether cycling for everyday travel can help US adults meet recommended levels of physical activity and what role public infrastructure, particularly bicycle lanes, paths, and bicycle boulevards, may play in encouraging this activity. Using global positioning system (GPS) technology, the study collected information on cycling behavior from a convenience sample of 166 bicyclists from March to November 2007 in the Portland,

Oregon metropolitan area. The results can lead to policy recommendations for infrastructure investments and planning and zoning policies to encourage more cycling for everyday travel.

D   Each participant in this study was provided with a specially programmed personal digital assistant with GPS to carry on all bicycle trips for 7 days. These units were chosen because they could be programmed for the participant to enter some data. Several actions were taken to try to improve the accuracy of the GPS data. Prior to use, the units and software were tested in different weather conditions, in various parts of the city, including downtown and under tree cover, and on different places on the bicycle. With location points collected every 3 seconds, the remaining points usually provided enough data to recreate the route. Participants were also asked to turn the unit on and wait for satellites to be detected before starting their trip. At the start of each bike trip, the participant tapped on the screen to enter his or her trip destination (e.g., work, shopping, exercise) and the weather details.

E   The study does have several limitations. First is the under-representation of people who cycle only occasionally or even less than 5 days a week. Most of the participants were everyday bicyclists. Therefore, they are likely to be more confident than less frequent bicyclists. This is likely to affect route choices. Second, the data collection method may have influenced behavior. Six of the 164 participants noted that they bicycled more or on different routes than intended because of the GPS device. Third, at least 8% of the bicycle travel was not recorded by the GPS units. It is unknown whether or how the missed travel might have differed from the recorded travel in terms of route choice. Malfunction of the GPS units, including dead batteries, accounted for about half of the missed travel.

F   The study demonstrated that cycling for transportation can be used by adults to meet the recommendations for daily physical activity. A supportive environment, like that found in the Portland region, appears necessary to encourage cycling for everyday travel, allowing more adults to achieve active living goals. The first part of that environment is bicycle infrastructure that addresses people's concern about safety from motor vehicles. In Portland, this includes a network of bike lanes, paths, and boulevards. Building such a network requires a comprehensive plan, funding, and political leadership. In Oregon, state law requires that both bicycle and pedestrian infrastructure be built whenever roads are built or rebuilt (with few exceptions), and that cities, counties, and the State spend a reasonable share of their state highway funds, usually defined as 1%, on pedestrian and bicycle features.

A network of different types of infrastructure appears necessary to attract new people to cycling. Simply adding bike lanes to all new major roads is unlikely to achieve high rates of cycling. For people concerned with safety and avoiding traffic, a well-connected network of low-traffic streets, including some bicycle boulevards, may be more effective than adding bike lanes on major streets with high volumes of motor vehicle traffic. Opportunities to build separate paths are often limited in existing neighborhoods due to space constraints and costs. Public agencies can, however, look for such opportunities when building other infrastructure, such as new rail transit lines, along existing transportation corridors, and when expanding to new undeveloped areas.

G The findings and limitations of this study point to additional analysis and research. The detail of the data allows for more extensive analysis than presented here. Comparing different types of cyclists (e.g., men and women) may provide insights into how to increase cycling among groups that traditionally do not bicycle for transportation in the United States. Comparing the actual bicycle routes to shortest path or other possible routes can provide estimates of how much cyclists value different types of infrastructure, based on how far they went out of their way to use it. Collecting similar data from other locations and from a larger number of different types of cyclists would be a valuable addition to this work.

Questions 1–6

The Reading Passage has seven sections, **A–G**.

Choose the correct heading for each section from the list of headings below.

List of Headings
i How the scope of the research is limited
ii The impact of constructing more bike lanes
iii Possible advantages of cycling for daily travel
iv What the research showed
v Potential for increasing cycling for transport purposes
vi The need for more research
vii An improvement in the accuracy of GPS
viii The research methodology
ix What the aim of the study is

1 Section **A**

Example	Answer
Section **B**	v

2 Section **C**

3 Section **D**

4 Section **E**

5 Section **F**

6 Section **G**

Questions 7–10

Do the following statements agree with the claims of the writer in the Reading Passage?

Write:

YES   *if the statement agrees with the claims of the writer*

NO   *if the statement contradicts the claims of the writer*

NOT GIVEN *if it is impossible to say what the writer thinks of this*

7 In the Netherlands, people cycle more for recreational than commuting purposes compared to the United States.

8 It is possible that the research on cycling in Portland will influence policies relating to the encouragement of daily cycling.

9 The GPS units employed in the study required considerable training for participants before use.

10 All of the participants in the study cycled on a daily basis.

> ### Questions 11–13
>
> *Choose the correct letter* **A**, **B**, **C** *or* **D**.
>
> **11** According to the information in section F, it seems that safety for cyclists
>
>   **A** necessitates the introduction of wider lanes and paths for cyclists.
>
>   **B** depends on having an infrastructure for cycling for daily travel to develop.
>
>   **C** means that cycling for daily travel should be restricted to adults only.
>
>   **D** accounts for a disproportionate share of the Oregon state budget for highway funds.
>
> **12** A common restriction to the construction of separate cycling lanes and paths is
>
>   **A** objections from local neighbourhood lobbies.
>
>   **B** the confusing network of different types of infrastructure.
>
>   **C** the further congestion of already busy streets.
>
>   **D** the lack of space.
>
> **13** A comparison of the different bicycle groups will possibly show how to
>
>   **A** improve the different routes that cyclists use on a daily basis.
>
>   **B** promote cycling among USA citizens for whom it is not a normal means of transport.
>
>   **C** encourage the general public to cycle at least once a week.
>
>   **D** develop other research projects into infrastructure for cycling.

3 Do you think cycling should be encouraged among all age groups? How? Give reasons and examples.

Language focus: Concession and developing ideas

1 You can make your argument more persuasive by conceding or acknowledging a point of view and then adding your own. Look at the following sentence from the Reading Passage on page 186:

While most of the focus on "active living" has been on walking, cycling may have a greater potential to substitute for motorized vehicle trips …

The sentence uses the structure *while … , may …*. Which of the structures below can also be used?

1 *Although … , may …*

2 *may … , but …*

G Read more about concession in the Grammar reference on page 226.

2 Work in pairs. Rewrite **1–8** below so that they contain the words in brackets. Make any necessary changes and be careful with punctuation.

Example:

I can't deny this is an admirable idea. We will have to wait and see what the future holds. (though)

Though I can't deny this is an admirable idea, we will have to wait and see what the future holds.

1 Increasing the capacity of the phone network is a good solution to the problem. It is not the only one. (although … may)

2 This is a sound argument. I think I'd want to see more funds made available for new carriages as well. (may … but)

3 The facilities available are endless. Inner city conditions are cramped. (while … may)

4 I don't like the idea of computers controlling systems like transport. They perform a vital function. (nevertheless)

5 I agree with the creation of high-speed communication systems. I can't help thinking that they will lead to more demands on workers and hence more stress. (much as)

6 They are expensive to maintain and upgrade. Extensive metro systems exist in many major cities. (may … but)

7 I partly agree with the opinion expressed here. I think it is naive to suggest that increasing the fares will in the end lead to a better transport service. (but)

8 It's clear the quality of public services is improving. More needs to be done. (nonetheless)

3 Sentences **a–e** below develop the idea of five of the sentences in exercise 2. Match **a–e** below with a suitable idea in exercise 2.

a It'll just put more cars on the road, and then revenue will decrease and there will be another problem.

b The trains themselves could also be refurbished.

c We need to ensure they are working for us and not us for them.

d The line rental, for example, could be reduced.

e This, in turn, will increase costs for companies.

4 Use your own ideas to develop the other three sentences.

5 👥 Work in pairs. Think of at least three issues in the news at the moment that you partly or largely agree with. Prepare reasons and examples to support your opinion and then add an outcome. Use the words and phrases for conceding and adding your opinion in exercises 1 and 2.

6 Explain your opinions on the issues you have chosen to another pair of students.

Speaking
Part 2

1 Work in groups and discuss the differences and similarities between the Part 2 Task Cards below.

A

> Describe your favourite street or square.
>
> You should say:
>> where the street or square is
>> what the street or square is like
>> how often you go there
> and explain why it is your favourite street or square.

B

> Describe a street or square you'd like to live in.
>
> You should say:
>> where the street or square is
>> when you first came to know about the street or square
>> what the street or square is like
> and explain why you would like to live in the street or square.

2 Paraphrase the underlined phrases. Compare your answers with another group

1 <u>The street that I'd like to</u> describe is in the area where I now live just south of the River Thames in Central London. **2** <u>The street's got a wide variety of</u> small shops with flats above them. It's also got a small park with sports facilities on the west side of the street, and so it gets lots of sun. **3** <u>The street may be full of cafés and different places to eat … and has several art galleries, but it's</u> fairly quiet and peaceful. **4** <u>I like the street very much so</u> I walk along it three or four times a week. **5** <u>I find it attractive because</u> it's relatively traffic-free even though it is right in the centre of London, **6** <u>and yet it has the feel of</u> a small village. **7** <u>The street is also pleasant to walk along because</u> without much traffic it's peaceful. And there're no large shops like supermarkets and department stores and it's unlikely that there'll be any in the future, making it a relaxing place to be. **8** <u>At any time of the day, you'll find</u> people having a stroll, … looking in the windows of the shops, or sitting in one of the cafés watching the world go by.

3 Decide which of the topics in exercise 1 is being described.

4 Spend one minute making notes for the topic in exercise 1 that wasn't discussed in exercise 2.

5 👥 In pairs, take turns talking about the topic. When you have finished, look at each other's notes and decide whether you think your partner followed their notes or adapted them as they spoke. Give feedback.

Speaking
Part 3

Don't forget!
- Try to paraphrase the examiner's question and develop your answer with reasons and examples.

1   Work in groups. Look at the questions below. Decide how to begin your answers without repeating the adjectives *necessary*, *possible* or *likely* in each case.

> **Transport systems**
>
> Do you think it is necessary to invest more in private or public forms of transport? Give reasons and examples.
>
> How do you think it is possible to improve people's experience of using transport infrastructure such as roads and railways?
>
> Some people think that flying cars are as likely as driverless cars in the future. Do you agree or disagree with this?

2   Work in pairs and take turns asking and answering the questions. Give feedback using the checklist on page 181.

Writing
Task 1

1   Work in groups and describe the table below in your own words.

> **WRITING TASK 1**
>
> You should spend about 20 minutes on this task.
>
> *The table shows the number of overseas visits to the UK by country of residence and mode of travel in two years.*
>
> *Summarise the information by selecting and reporting the main features, and make comparisons where relevant.*
>
> Write at least 150 words.
>
> **Number of overseas visits to the UK by country of residence and mode of travel (thousands)**
>
> | | Air | | Tunnel | |
> |---|---|---|---|---|
> | | **2011** | **2013** | **2011** | **2013** |
> | **Belgium** | 167 | 183 | 569 | 746 |
> | **Bulgaria** | 57 | 71 | 6 | 12 |
> | **France** | 1,339 | 1,441 | 1,514 | 1,761 |
> | **Germany** | 2,070 | 2,129 | 141 | 218 |
> | **Italy** | 1,445 | 1,562 | 24 | 23 |
> | **Portugal** | 260 | 251 | 4 | 7 |
> | **Sweden** | 756 | 766 | 19 | 3 |
> | **Total World** | 22,631 | 23,754 | 3,670 | 4,479 |

2   Work in groups. Answer questions **1–6**. Compare your answers with another group.

   1 How do you 'read the table'?

   2 What do the numbers relate to?

   3 What is the trend in each case?

   4 How does *Total World* relate to the other data?

   5 Will this line of information help you write the overview?

   6 What is the clear trend of the overview?

3 Decide which two of the following introductions are suitable for the question in exercise 1.

1 *The table provides a breakdown of the number of overseas visitors to the UK according to country of residence and mode of travel in 2011 and 2013.*

2 *The table compares the number of UK visits from various countries by different means of transport in two years, 2011 and 2013.*

3 *The data provides information about visits in thousands to the UK from a selection of countries according to two means of transport in 2011 and 2013.*

4 Work in pairs. You can add data in your answer in different ways as shown below. Explain at least two of the different ways in your own words.

- *... and ... , respectively: The number of visits made to the UK from Sweden was slightly higher in 2013 compared to 2011, 766,000 **and** 756,000 **respectively**.*

- *from ... to: Trips to the UK by air from Sweden rose between 2011 and 2013, **from** 756,000 **to** 766,000, respectively.*

- *with + noun + verb + ing: Trips to the UK by air from Sweden rose in 2013 compared to 2011 **with numbers rising** to 766,000 from 756,000, respectively.*

- *verb + ing: Trips to the UK by air from Sweden rose between 2011 and 2013, **increasing** from 756,000 to 766,000, respectively.*

- *with + noun: Trips to the UK by air from Sweden rose in 2013 compared to 2011 **with a rise** to 766,000 from 756,000, respectively.*

5 For **1–7** below, combine the two sentences using the structure in brackets.

Example:

Trips to the UK by air from Sweden rose in 2013 compared to 2011. The rise was from 756,000 to 766,000, respectively. (with + noun)

Trips to the UK by air from Sweden rose in 2013 compared to 2011 with a rise to 766,000 from 756,000, respectively.

1 There was a gradual increase in visits by air from Belgium between 2011 and 2013. Visits rose from 167,000 to 183,000. (*from ... to*)

2 The general trend for the number of overseas visits by air and by tunnel from Bulgaria was clearly upward. It climbed from 57,000 for the former in 2011 to 71,000 in 2013, and by tunnel from 6,000 to 12,000, respectively. (verb + *ing*)

3 Visits from France by air and tunnel also went up. They rose from 1.339 million to 1.441 million, and 1.514 million to 1.761 million, in 2011 and 2013 respectively. (*with* + noun)

4 Trips from Germany by air and by tunnel saw an increase. They were 2.070 million and 2.129 million for the former and 141,000 and 218,000 for the latter. (... and ... , respectively)

5 As regards Italy, there were 1.445 million trips to the UK by air and 24,000 trips by tunnel in 2011. There were 1.562 million trips by air and 23,000 trips by tunnel in 2013. (*with* + noun)

6 Trips from Portugal by air fell and by tunnel they rose. The number of trips by air fell from 260,000 to 251,000 and trips by tunnel rose from 4,000 to 7,000, respectively. (*with* + verb + *ing*)

7 The overall visit numbers by air and tunnel went up between 2011 and 2013. They were 22.631 million to 23.754 million and 3.67 million to 4.479 million, respectively. (*from ... to ...*)

6 Write your own answer for the Task 1 question on page 208. When you have finished, check your answer using the checklist on page 139.

Vocabulary: Nouns related to systems

1   Add the words in brackets to the appropriate space in the texts **1–5** below.

 1 The railway infrastructure consists not just of _____ and viaducts that carry the railway _____ across rivers and valleys, but also of _____ that take the network through mountains and sometimes under the sea. (bridges/lines/tunnels)

 2 The _____ supply goes through a process where the water undergoes _____ that involves purification and filtering before we turn on the _____ . (tap/treatment/water)

 3 Electricity comes to us via cables and _____ from huge _____ that supply the national _____ . (generators/grid/pylons)

 4 The oil industry is an essential part of the energy infrastructure in many countries of the world. The oil is extracted from _____ in _____ both on land and under the sea with _____ being conducted in some of the most inhospitable places on the planet. (exploration/fields/wells)

 5 Nowadays _____ to the internet for many people is made using different _____ , but increasingly the device of choice for people of all ages is the smartphone rather than PCs, laptops or tablets, as _____ speeds rise around the world. (access/connection/hosts)

2   Write a sentence about one of the following:

 1 Satellite systems: receiver, dish, communications, channel, weather

 2 The gas supply: pipelines, industry, fields, appliance

 3 Telephone network: mobile, fibre optic, browse, satellite

Word building: Modal verbs to adjectives

1   Use the hint in brackets to choose the correct word in each sentence.

 Example:

 It's (not probable and not certain) that high-speed train networks will replace the aviation network in the future.

 It's possible that high speed train networks will replace the aviation network in the future.

 1 Infrastructure like roads and light transport systems are (more than possible) to expand as urban populations increase.

 2 The new rail extension line (probable) be finished ahead of schedule.

 3 An ability to use a wide range of systems like the internet is (essential) in the modern world.

 4 The train is (should) to arrive on time.

 5 It is (more than possible, not unlikely and not certain) that we will be talking about flying lanes in cities soon rather than cycle lanes.

6 It's (no option) for all drivers to pay on toll roads.

7 It is (can't do without it) for the government to increase investment in the improvement of the waterways such as canals.

8 The authorities were (wouldn't do it) to plant more trees between parks to create a natural pathway for urban areas.

9 Rural infrastructure such as roads (think of the word necessary) as much attention as urban does.

Language focus: Concession and developing ideas

1 Link the two sentences using the words in brackets. Check if the order of the sentences needs to change. Make any necessary changes to the punctuation.

1 The running and maintenance costs are high. Metro systems are efficient at carrying millions of passengers around major cities worldwide. (may/but)

2 Increasing people's access to the transport system by reducing fares is a good approach to reducing unemployment. It is not the only one. (although/may)

3 I think the infrastructure is still not extensive enough yet for them to have an impact. Electric cars help the environment. (nevertheless)

4 I think it is foolish to suggest that increasing the fares at peak hours will improve the train service. I partly agree with this opinion. (but)

5 Personally, I am wary of automation in transport systems such as aviation. Computers make them much safer. (though)

6 More improvement is necessary. It's clear the integration of transport systems such as trains, trams and ferries has been transformed in recent years. (nonetheless)

7 It is definitely worthwhile having more cycle lanes. The volume of traffic won't be reduced. (may/but)

8 I agree that communication systems such as broadband should be more advanced. It will lead to a more stressful working and home life. (much as)

Accuracy in IELTS

1 Find five grammar mistakes and two mistakes relating to data.

1 Passengers numbers on the ferry soared between 2012 and 2016, from 135,000 to 567,000.

2 Passenger journeys on the metro system rose in 2016 compared to 2015 with numbers increase to over 4 million a day compared to 3.5 million respectively.

3 The proportion of visitors to the UK by air overall fell from 2011 to 2013, decreasing from 7.5%, to 8.9% respectively.

4 The number of people using the station went substantially between January and June 2016 with a jump from 410,000 to 349,000.

5 The number of visits made to the UK from Sweden was noticeably lower in 2015 compare to 2012 (155,000 and 210,000 respectively).

Vocabulary: Money matters

1 👥 Work in groups. Describe each of the photographs. Then discuss the questions below.

- What is your reaction to the following quote?

  'Real riches are the riches possessed inside.'
  B. C. Forbes

- Will cash, paper money and coins, disappear in the near future? Give reasons and examples from your own experience.

- Some people think it is important for children and young people to be taught 'financial literacy' and money management in the modern world. To what extent do you agree or disagree?

2 Make a list of words and phrases associated with the word *money*. Then compare your list with another group.

3 Work in pairs. Noun phrases can be formed with a noun + noun, for example *money* collocates with *government* and *problems* to form the noun phrases *government money* and *money problems*. Decide whether the following words go before or after the word *money*.

1 management	**3** pocket	**5** paper	**7** counterfeit
2 market	**4** laundering	**6** sponsorship	**8** box

4 Work in pairs. For **1–9** below, circle the noun that is in the correct position.

Example:

finance	government/state/capital	finance
1 cash	reserves/flow/payment/settlement/limit/crisis/crop	cash
2 currency	conversion/markets/speculation/fluctuation/reserves/crisis	currency
3 credit	agreement/arrangement/facilities/terms/limit/transfer	credit
4 debt	collection/repayment/burden/mountain	debt
5 savings	account/plan/bank	savings
6 spending	consumer/government/public	spending
7 expenditure	consumer/government/public/welfare/education	expenditure
8 income	capital/investment/household/family	income
9 finances	company/government/state/family/household	finances

5 For **1–8** below, cross out the incorrect words in *italics*.

Example:

More *government money* ~~government~~ was allocated to improve local bus services.

1 A *cash crop cash* is a valuable source of income for many families in agricultural communities, but *cash flow cash* can be a problem because produce is usually seasonal. This can lead to a *cash crisis cash* for local farmers.

2 *Money paper money* was invented by the Chinese.

3 *Education expenditure education* has declined at a time when few working in the field think it should. The current *expenditure level expenditure* should at least be maintained.

4 *Family finances family* are often the concern of the *finance minister finance*, especially when making funding decisions.

5 *Management money management* needs to be taught as much to adults at work and students in university as to schoolchildren.

6 A fall in a country's foreign *currency reserves currency* can trigger a *currency crisis currency*.

7 Many prominent individuals have called for the *burden debt burden* of some nations to be reduced by cheap loans or complete cancellation.

8 My grandparents encouraged me to open a *savings account savings* when I was very young and I still have it.

6 Work in groups. Think of at least three ways that money has directly or indirectly affected your life in the past week, for example, paying for transport with cash or an electronic card, etc. Take turns describing your experiences. Ask questions about each other's experiences.

1 💬 Work in groups. Discuss the main ways you are familiar with for purchasing items. Are any methods becoming more common? Explain why.

2 Skim **Questions 31–40**. Discuss the topic of the talk and list as much detail about the topic as you can. Compare your list with another group.

🎧 21   **SECTION 4**   *Questions 31–40*

Questions 31–34

*Choose the correct letter, **A**, **B** or **C**.*

31 The speaker says that money is more than an economic tool and has a

    A psychological and historical dimension.

    B social and psychological dimension.

    C social and historical dimension.

32 According to the speaker, money is an invention resulting from the human capacity to

    A allocate symbols a value.

    B label the world.

    C create special symbols.

33 What does the speaker say about accepting any object as money?

    A The community needs to establish procedures for its use.

    B Its use needs to be accepted by the user and the community.

    C Laws need to be introduced to make it legal tender.

34 When bartering goods, the seller had to

    A agree a standard of exchange as part of the purchasing process.

    B accept whatever the local common medium of exchange was.

    C find someone who was willing to purchase the goods for sale.

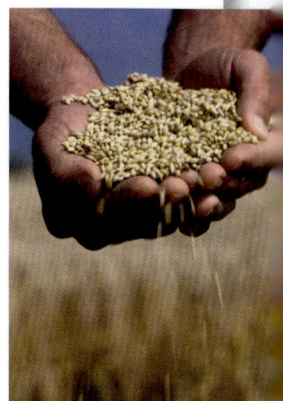

Questions 35–40

Complete the notes below.

*Write **NO MORE THAN TWO WORDS** for each answer.*

Commodity money

Commodity money depended on the acceptance of certain objects as money that was inherently **35** ……………………...………. for every person.

All metals were accepted as commodity money – being convertible into precious tools, e.g. **36** ……………………...………. and ……………………...……… .

Metals, e.g. gold and silver, had secondary advantages – identifiable and **37** ……………………...………. .

Metal coins

They acted as a **38** ……………………...………. for exchanging goods and services.

Representative money

When adopted, representative money was a **39** ……………………...………. in human consciousness.

Psychologically, there needed to be a transfer in the sense of value from a usable material object to an **40** ……………………...………. symbol.

Socially, there had to be a group agreement on the common usage of the symbol.

Word building: Values and beliefs

1   Look at the following quote from the speaker in the Listening on page 237.

... the values and principles of all societies in the world.

What do you think the terms *values* and *principles* mean here?

2   Match the words below to their meaning **a–g**.

1 principles		**a**	feelings that something is true or real
2 ethics		**b**	major ideas or theories that a system of beliefs is based on, for example in politics or education
3 values		**c**	things that people do that are traditional or usual
4 customs		**d**	principles of right or wrong behaviour
5 beliefs		**e**	a set of principles people use to decide what is right and wrong
6 standards		**f**	things that are generally accepted
7 morals		**g**	ideas about what is good and right that you try to follow in your life and behaviour
8 ideals		**h**	principles and beliefs that influence the behaviour and way of life of a group or community

3   Work in pairs. Make a list of as many words as you can from the word *standard*.

4   Complete the gaps in the text below with words relating to the word *value*. Use the prompts given to help you.

> **1** _____ (plural noun) are standards that individual people attach great importance to. If you **2** _____ (verb) something in your life, then you treasure it enormously.
> **3** _____ (plural noun) like precious objects made of gold and diamonds may be
> **4** _____ (adjective) to some people as status symbols, but they are **5** _____ (adjective) when compared to attributes like honesty, integrity, loyalty and trust.

5   Complete the gaps with words relating to *principle*. Use the prompts given.

> Philosophy can teach people the **1** _____ (plural noun) of right and wrong, but it
> is becoming increasingly difficult for people to be **2** _____ (adjective) in life and
> maintain a high moral standard. Unfortunately, **3** _____ (adjective) people are found
> in all walks of life, whether it be business or politics, so one must be on one's guard to make
> sure one doesn't do anything that compromises one's **4** _____ (plural noun).

6   Complete the gaps with words relating to *ideal, moral* and *ethics*. Use the prompts.

> People are often accused of being **1** _____ (adjective) rather than realistic when
> pursuing their **2** _____ (plural noun). It is easy to attack someone whose personal
> **3** _____ (plural noun) or **4** _____ (adjective) stance you don't agree with.

7   Work in groups. Discuss the question below.

'People today get their values from national figures like politicians and celebrities. What are the advantages and disadvantages of this? Give reasons and examples.'

Reading
Questions 1–13

1 Work in pairs. Scan paragraphs **A–D** in the Reading Passage below for words that are synonyms of **1–8**.

1 markers	**3** weight	**5** elements	**7** benefit
2 assess	**4** happenings or facts	**6** vital	**8** mainly

2 Work in pairs. Each choose one paragraph to skim. Then briefly explain what it is about to your partner. Find another pair of students that have chosen the same paragraph and check that you agree.

READING PASSAGE

*You should spend about 20 minutes on **Questions 1–13**, which are based on the Reading Passage below.*

Measuring subjective wellbeing

A   Subjective wellbeing concerns people's self-reported wellbeing (e.g. life satisfaction, happiness, psychological wellbeing). Survey questions of this nature aim to measure how people think and feel about their wellbeing rather than relying on more traditional objective indicators such as the level of educational achievement, employment, crime or material wellbeing. Indeed, human perception is fundamental to the definition of wellbeing and it can be argued that the only person who really knows whether a person is feeling well is the experiencing self (Layard, 2005). Survey questions that ask people to evaluate their own wellbeing allow for individual differences in terms of values and identity to be expressed. Although one person may answer a life satisfaction question by placing significant emphasis on their salary and job security, another may answer the same question by placing significant emphasis on their family relationships and health. This means that such measures capture what people think and feel rather than focussing on observable phenomena that sometimes have little bearing on peoples' wellbeing.

B   Objective measures of wellbeing often fail to tap into what people think or feel, so have to assume certain observable factors influence wellbeing in certain ways. Generally speaking, objective measures focus on either objective-list or preference-satisfaction accounts, with a view to either improving objective circumstances such as health and education (Sen, 1999) or increasing the choices people have by raising average incomes (Harsanyi, 1982). Although objective measures of wellbeing are crucial, they cannot tell the whole story and the array of indicators currently available (e.g. numeracy, literacy and crime rates) sometimes complicates the picture, with many observable factors acting as proxies for what really matters.

C   The main advantage of asking people to assess their own wellbeing is that paternalism (prescriptive questions that assume certain things are good or bad for wellbeing) can be avoided and people's thoughts and feelings are placed at the centre of policy. Although objective measures tend to correlate well with subjective wellbeing (Di Tella & MacCulloch, 2007; Oswald, 1997), they generally only account for a small proportion of one's life satisfaction or happiness (Galloway et al, 2005) Scottish Executive, 2005). Measures of subjective wellbeing, however, are seen by many as getting to the heart of the issue (Layard, 2005).

D   Although Victorian social policy emphasised the importance of promoting mental health, the rise of behaviourism in the 1950s heavily influenced disciplines such as Psychology and Economics and encouraged the measurement of what is observable (behaviour) to the exclusion of what is unobservable (the mind). By and large, UK social and economic policy since the Great War has focussed predominantly on improving the economy and meeting the material needs of the population. Mental health and psychological needs have been conceived as harder to measure, unreliable and within an individual's own responsibility. Objective measures of wellbeing have been favoured for some time because they're easier to measure and observable through behaviour.

E Nonetheless, an encouraging literature is now emerging suggesting that subjective wellbeing is a valid construct that can be reliably measured. Much recent research indicates that measures of subjective wellbeing tend to correlate well with other people's views, behavioural data, brain activity and objective characteristics such as unemployment (see Layard 2005 for a useful review). Crucially, the last 10 years have seen a number of government and non-government reports begin to unpick how the UK could generate meaningful data of this nature. Political momentum has also gathered pace alongside the abundance of research now regularly published in fields as diverse as behavioural economics, psychology, neuroscience and philosophy.

F Strong arguments are developing suggesting that now is a good time to generate national data on subjective wellbeing. The idea is that these data can then be used by policy makers alongside other measures that go beyond GDP (Dolan & White, 2007; Michaelson, Abdallah, Steuer, Thompson & Marks, 2008). The well-cited 'Easterlin Paradox' demonstrates that UK levels of life satisfaction and happiness have not risen since the 1950s despite unprecedented economic growth, and although this research has been criticised for not taking into account the use of bounded measures to measure subjective wellbeing, it does suggest that much more than economic growth is required to elevate wellbeing.

G Whether measured as an end to itself or as a means to an end, such subjective wellbeing data could be used to: a) monitor 'the state of play'; b) inform new policy; c) promote public wellbeing; and d) evaluate the impact of new or existing policies on wellbeing. The evidence suggests that various social and economic factors affect self-reported wellbeing, so it should be possible to influence subjective wellbeing via policy. A growing body of research also suggests that high levels of subjective wellbeing are a partial cause of various positive life events and outcomes (Lyubomirsky, King, & Diener, 2005).

H Interest in measuring subjective wellbeing has grown considerably over recent years in the UK. Indeed, a number of major social surveys in the UK already include subjective wellbeing questions, and it seems that various policy areas could make use of these data. The question therefore is not *whether* to measure subjective wellbeing, but *how* to do this from now on. The balance between exploiting data that already exist and generating new data needs to be explored further, based on whether unmet user requirements exist.

Questions 1–5

The Reading Passage has eight paragraphs, **A–H**.

Which paragraph contains the following information?

1 the fact that objective measures of wellbeing do not give a full picture of wellbeing

2 research stating that data on subjective wellbeing can be used with measures other than GDP

3 suggestions for use of data on subjective wellbeing

4 a reference to the focus of government policy of satisfying the population's material needs

5 an explanation of the term subjective wellbeing

Questions 6–9

Look at the following statements and the list of people below.
*Match each statement with the correct person/persons, **A–F**.*

6 Objective measures of subjective wellbeing usually compare well with wellbeing itself.

7 The only one who can gauge wellbeing is the individual.

8 According to research, positive life events and outcomes can to some extent result in raised subjective wellbeing.

9 Measuring wellbeing objectively may be carried out to enhance people's lives.

	List of people	
A Layard		**D** Di Tella & MacCulloch
B Sen		**E** Galloway et al
C Harsanyi		**F** Lyubomirsky, King, & Diener

> ### Questions 10–12
> *Complete the sentences below.*
> *Choose **NO MORE THAN TWO WORDS** from the passage for each answer.*
>
> **10** Recent literature shows that subjective wellbeing is a measurable ………. .
>
> **11** There is proof to suggest that ………. wellbeing is impacted on by different social and economic influences.
>
> **12** Data on subjective wellbeing could be utilised by a number of ……………
>
> ### Question 13
> *Choose the correct letter **A**, **B**, **C** or **D**.*
> Which of the following is the most suitable title for the Reading Passage?
>
> **A** How to measure subjective well-being
>
> **B** How to balance existing and new data
>
> **C** An emphasis on promoting mental health
>
> **D** Measuring subjective wellbeing

3 Is it really possible to measure people's subjective well-being? Why/Why not? Is it useful to do so? Give reasons for your answer.

Language focus: Substitution and ellipsis

1 Look at the following quote from the speaker in the Reading Passage on page 198. Then answer the questions below.

Although one person may answer a life satisfaction question by placing significant emphasis on their salary and job security, another may answer the same question …

1 What does the word *another* replace?

2 What happens if the words are repeated?

3 Which common expression in speech do you know where the word *so* is used like another to substitute?

G Read more about substitution and ellipsis in the Grammar reference on page 226.

2 Work in pairs. Match texts **1–8** below with a suitable continuation **a–h**.

1 Companies can help local communities to develop by putting back some of the profits they have made from the local people.

2 My grandmother told us how to behave when we were young

3 People follow the traditions and ways of the society they belong to.

4 The government should introduce philosophy into the school curriculum.

5 I left home when I was 18 to go to university.

6 Detailed analysis has been done on what makes people happy,

7 My family have always adhered to the traditions of the community we came from and

8 According to some people, moral standards on television are declining and should therefore be raised.

a and continued to do so when we were adults.

b but ways need to be found to apply such research for the benefit of the public.

c I suppose I will continue to do so in spite of the pressures to the contrary.

d In doing so they believe that the general behaviour in society will be improved.

e I did so with some trepidation, but it turned out to be exciting in the end.

f Doing so would have a beneficial effect on student behaviour.

g Handing down such customs from generation to generation is important if a community is to survive.

h Such philanthropic behaviour would set a good example for other organisations.

3 For **1–8** in exercise 2, underline the words and phrases of substitution and the words they replace.

4 For sentences **1–7** below, cross out any unnecessary words.

1 Although the government wanted to stop funding the railway venture, they weren't able to stop funding it.

2 The banks didn't want the policy on extending loans to small businesses to change, but the government did want the policy to change.

3 Some people don't believe that there is a clear link between happiness and money, while others do think there is.

4 The college was praised for student behaviour and success as it hoped it would be praised.

5 The university didn't invest as much in delivering subjects like philosophy as it could have invested.

6 My father laid down the law with us when we were children, but my mother didn't lay down the law.

5 What happens if people use substitution a lot in writing or speaking?

Speaking
Part 3

1 Work in pairs. Read the following Part 3 questions and decide what the focus is of each question, e.g. *examples of different factors, an evaluation of a factor with reasons*.

Well-being

What factors contribute to people's general sense of well-being?

Do you think having free time is the key factor in people's well-being? Why/Why not?

Some people think modern life is too stressful for people to be generally happy. To what extent do you agree or disagree?

Money and its effects

How does money impact on people's well-being in activities such as work and leisure?

In terms of social development, do you think the pursuit of money has a negative or positive effect? Why/Why not?

In the future, do you think money will have a greater or lesser role to play in our lives? Give reasons.

2 Work in groups. Match the ideas in the list below to a suitable question and suggest your own ideas.

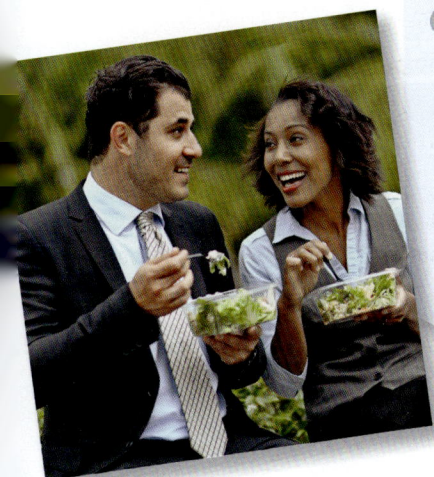

a factors such as technological gadgets/money/time
b exciting, not stressful
c allows people to do things they want
d brings greater freedom
e free time not everything, other factors
f lesser – money may even disappear
g health/work/friends/leisure time
h beneficial, as it allows improvement in …
i reduces/increases anxiety
j pleasant neighbourhood

3 Work in pairs. Look at the beginnings of the six answers to the questions in exercise 1. Decide whether they involve the use of ellipsis or substitution.

1 I think there are many, such as …

2 I don't think so, because …

3 I actually think it's not as much as it was in the past, because …

4 Enormously. For example, it …

5 It's mostly beneficial, I think, as it …

6 In the short-term, money …

4 Work in pairs. Take turns asking each other the questions. When you have finished, give each other feedback using the checklist on page 181.

Writing
Task 1

1 Work in groups. Describe the bar charts and pie charts in the Task 1 question below. Use the words and phrases in the box below.

proportion	constitute	reflect	vast majority	only	pattern
similarity	difference	quarter	age group	year-olds	

WRITING TASK 1

You should spend about 20 minutes on this task.

The charts show the frequency of happiness of different age groups and two groups of workers in Europe in the previous four weeks.

Summarise the information by selecting and reporting the main features, and make comparisons where relevant.

Write at least 150 words.

Frequency of being happy in the last four weeks by selected age groups in Europe

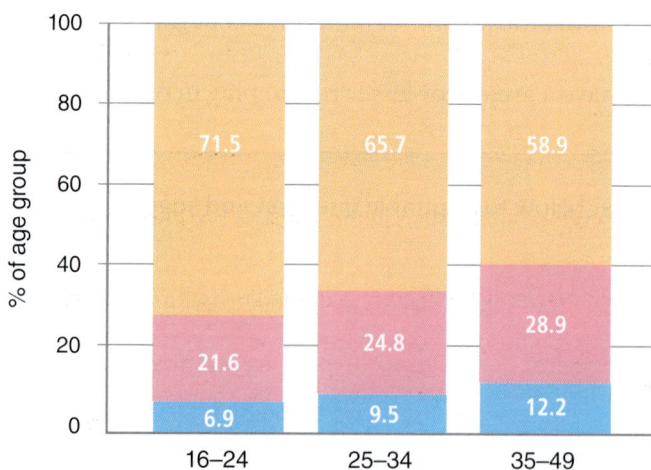

Frequency of being happy in the last four weeks by full-time and part-time workers in Europe

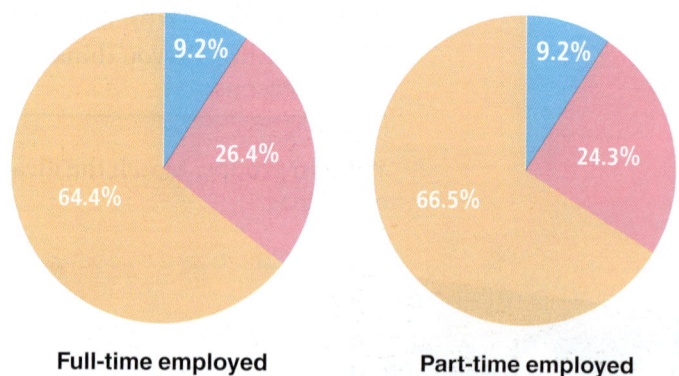

Full-time employed — 9.2%, 26.4%, 64.4%

Part-time employed — 9.2%, 24.3%, 66.5%

Bar chart (% of age group):
- 16–24: 6.9, 21.6, 71.5
- 25–34: 9.5, 24.8, 65.7
- 35–49: 12.2, 28.9, 58.9

A little/none of the time　Some of the time　All/most of the time

2 Work in groups. Decide what other words and phrases or what other structures you can use to express the same ideas as those listed in exercise 1.

3   Work in groups. Compare your answers to exercises 1 and 2 with another group.

4   Decide which words and phrases in the model answer for the writing task in exercise 1 can be replaced by items **a–g**. Compare your answers with a partner and say which you prefer and why.

   a the latter workers

   b the proportions for those in the next age group were noticeably different

   c as opposed to

   d mirror

   e most 16–24 year olds stated that

   f provide information about

   g a link

   > The charts illustrate the degree of happiness reported among selected European groups in the last four weeks.
   >
   > Overall, there seems to be a correlation between age and the frequency of being happy. In the 16–24 age group, the vast majority cited they were happy some of the time and all/most of the time, 21.6% and 71.5% respectively, with only 6.9% being happy a little or none of the time. There was a marked difference in the proportions of those aged 25–34, with just under two thirds (65.7%) being at least mainly happy and just under a quarter (24.8%) being so some of the time compared to 9.5% for those who were happy little or none of the time. Whereas most 35–49-year-olds were happy some or all/most of the time (87.8%), a greater proportion of this age group stated that they were less so (12.2%).
   >
   > The full-time and part-time workers' responses reflect those of the three age groups with identical proportions (90.8%) among both groups being happy at least some of the time, but a greater proportion of part-time workers being slightly happier all or most of the time (66.5%).

5   Work in groups. Read the model answer in exercise 4 again and identify an example of **1–8** below.

   1 a synonym for the verb 'said'

   2 an overview

   3 the verb that is used to show a connection between the data in the stacked bar charts and the pie charts

   4 a paraphrase that combines two items in the legend 'happy some of the time' and 'all/most of the time'

   5 at least one example of the use of ellipsis

   6 two complex sentences

   7 an adjective that means *exactly the same*

   8 nouns that are used to summarise the data

6   Work in groups. Paraphrase the first and last paragraphs and compare your answers with another group.

7   Write your own answer for the Task 1 question on page 209. When you have finished, check your answer using the checklist on page 139.

Vocabulary: Money matters

1 Decide whether the words in the noun + noun phases are in the correct order. Correct the mistakes.

1 money paper

2 education expenditure

3 debt mountain

4 payment cash

5 savings account

6 household income

7 crisis currency

2 Fill only one blank space in each sentence below with a suitable word.

1 Countries try to build up _____ reserves _____ to buy foreign products.

2 _____ sponsorship _____ helps many artists and young people achieve their ambitions in life.

3 When I was a child, I kept my savings in a _____ money _____ shaped like a red telephone box.

4 Many countries are not restricted to just one _____ crop _____ such as rice or wheat.

5 To develop the financial literacy of the general public, children at school should be given lessons on _____ management _____ .

6 Do you have much _____ money _____ left after paying for all your outgoings?

7 _____ family _____ are as much a concern for finance ministers as health, housing and welfare.

8 The cancellation of a _____ burden _____ can be an enormous relief.

Word building: Values and beliefs

1 Put the words in brackets in the correct form.

1 Would you say that you are realistic or (ideal) when dealing with different situations?

2 Where do you think people today get their (value) from? Is it from TV personalities or other famous people?

3 In any job nowadays, it's not easy to make sure you do not compromise your (principle). Do you agree?

4 Who or what would you say you (value) most in life? Do you agree having physical and mental well-being is (value)? Are material possessions such as cars and jewellery more (value) than people?

5 Many people around the world are concerned that their local (custom) are disappearing in the face of globalisation. Do you think they should be concerned?

Language focus: Substitution and ellipsis

1   Substitution: Complete the second sentence in your own words.

   1 It is essential for people to aim for physical as well as mental well-being.
If they do _____ .

   2 Thinking classes should be introduced in secondary schools.
Doing _____ .

   3 Education on money management is crucial to help people control their finances.
Such _____ .

   4 Children can attend extracurricular classes relating to their hobbies.
By doing _____ .

   5 I will start university next term. *I know I'll do* _____ .

2   Ellipsis: <u>Underline</u> the two correct phrases in *italics* in each sentence below.

   1 At first, students had little interest in learning about different currencies, but they *did/didn't/had* in the end.

   2 I wanted to change courses, but I *wasn't able to/couldn't/mightn't*.

   3 There are many who don't think that education and happiness are connected, while others *do/think they are/think*.

   4 Fortunately, I finished my essay by the deadline, just as I thought I *would/will do/would have*.

   5 We didn't pay as much attention to speed of delivery as perhaps we *could have/did/should have*.

   6 He will attend the class tomorrow, but I *will/won't/might not*.

   7 Did you put as much effort into completing the assignment as you *could have/might have/would have*?

   8 It is argued that a happy family life is more important than a satisfying career, yet it's obvious that it *is/must be/will be*.

Accuracy in IELTS

1   Use the hints in brackets to find the two mistakes in each sentence below.

   1 There was greater proportion of household income in 2016 allocated to accomodation expenses than in 2010, 27% and 33% respectively. (spelling mistake, missing word)

   2 The majority of the increase in expenditure education was in building project in the last four years. (word order, missing letter)

   3 Young people accounted the second largest aged group participating in volunteering. (missing word, extra letter)

   4 A similar pattern was seen in 25-35 age group with a smaller proportion open a savings account in 2016 compared to 2015. (wrong word form, missing word)

   5 It seem that there was little difference between the proportion of cash payments and credit card payments in first five years of the period. (missing letter, missing word)

   6 The charts provide informations about the proportion of people involved in volunteers work by age group. (extra letter, extra letter)

   7 The number of volunteers in the 15-19 age group felt from 11% to 10% between the two years. (wrong word, wrong word)

   8 Nearly twice many people stated that they found paying by contactless cards more convenent than using cash. (missing word, spelling mistake)

   9 There were slight fluctuation in the numbers of sponorship grants allocated each year. (missing letter, spelling mistake)

Additional material

Unit 1 (page 15)

You should spend about 20 minutes on this task.

> The graph below shows Twitter use by age group in the USA between November 2010 and May 2013.
> Summarise the information by selecting and reporting the main features, and make comparisons where relevant.

Write at least 150 words.

Twitter use by age group, over time

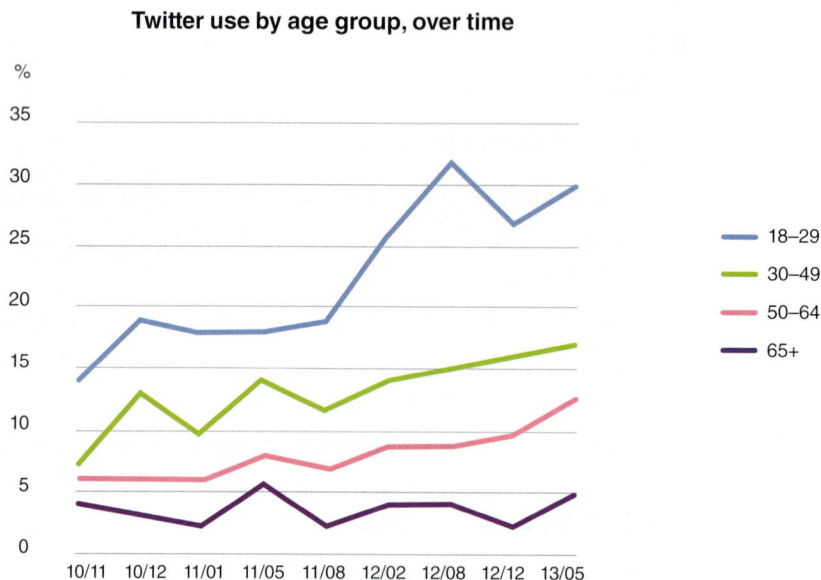

Unit 3 (page 39)

You should spend about 20 minutes on this task.

> The table below illustrates UK participation in selected sports by gender between 2005/06 and 2008/09.
> Summarise the information by selecting and reporting the main features, and make comparisons where relevant.

Write at least 150 words.

Sports participation, by sex, 2005/06 to 2008/09

	% Men	% Women
Swimming or diving (indoors)		
2005/06	13.3	18.0
2006/07	12.2	16.6
2007/08	12.2	16.8
2008/09	13.0	16.5
Cycling (health, recreation, training, competition)		
2005/06	12.7	7.0
2006/07	13.3	6.8
2007/08	13.8	6.5
2008/09	14.4	6.4
Jogging, cross-country, road-running		
2005/06	6.9	3.5
2006/07	7.8	4.8
2007/08	7.5	4.3
2008/09	7.6	4.8

Unit 5 (page 69)

You should spend about 20 minutes on this task.

> *The charts show projections for global production by sector in 2030 and 2050.*
> *Summarise the information by selecting and reporting the main features, and make comparisons where relevant.*

Write at least 150 words.

World, projected production by sector

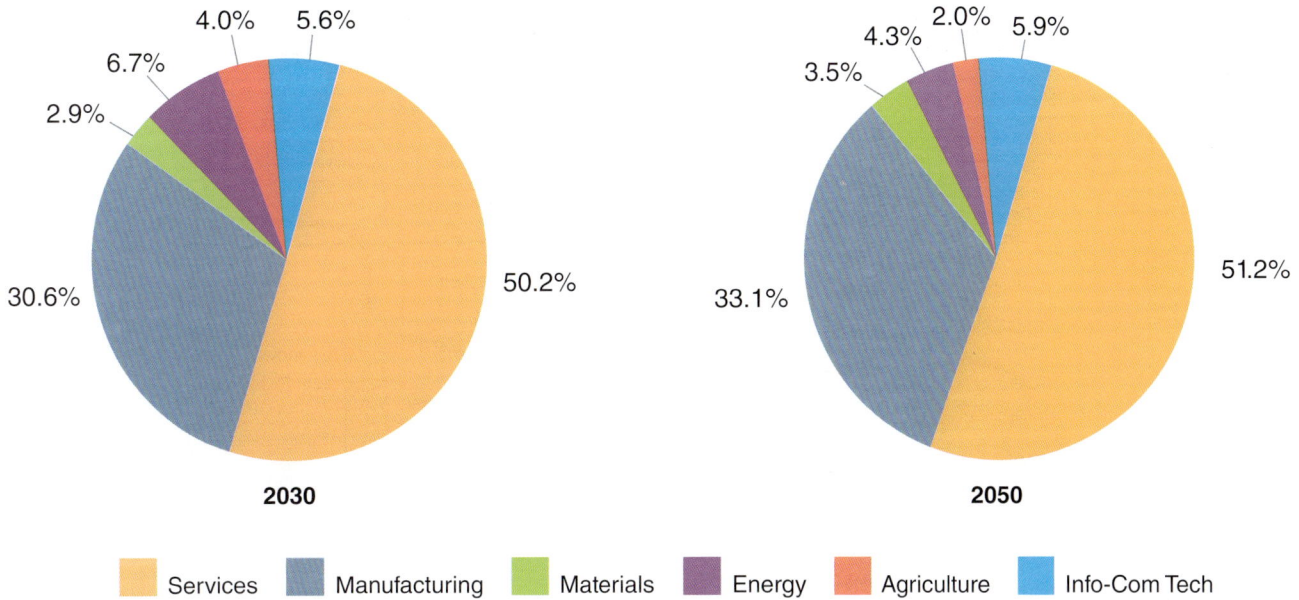

4.0%   5.6%
6.7%
2.9%
30.6%   50.2%

2030

4.3% 2.0% 5.9%
3.5%
33.1%   51.2%

2050

■ Services ■ Manufacturing ■ Materials ■ Energy ■ Agriculture ■ Info-Com Tech

Unit 6 (page 81)

You should spend about 20 minutes on this task.

> *The diagram below show the production of a lead pencil.*
> *Summarise the information by selecting and reporting the main features, and make comparisons where relevant.*

Write at least 150 words.

The production of a pencil

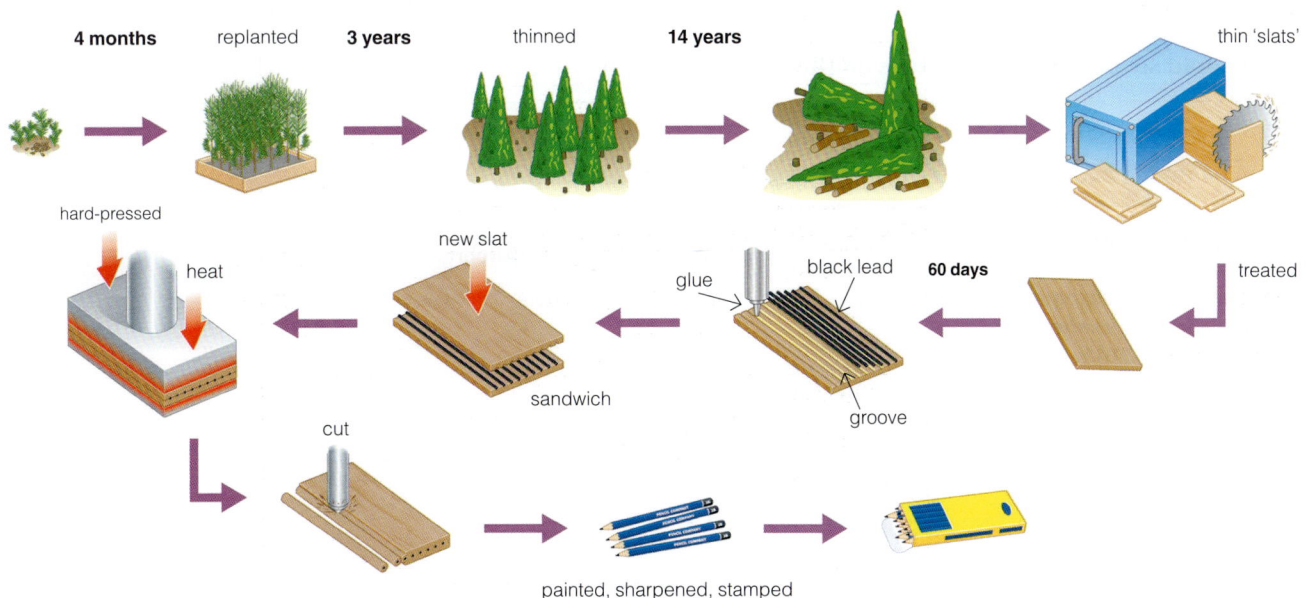

4 months   replanted   **3 years**   thinned   **14 years**   thin 'slats'

hard-pressed
heat   new slat   glue   black lead   **60 days**   treated

sandwich   groove

cut

painted, sharpened, stamped

Additional material

Unit 8 (page 113)

You should spend about 20 minutes on this task.

> The maps below show the changes experienced by the town of Harton at the beginning of the 21st Century.
> Summarise the information by selecting and reporting the main features, and make comparisons where necessary.

Write at least 150 words.

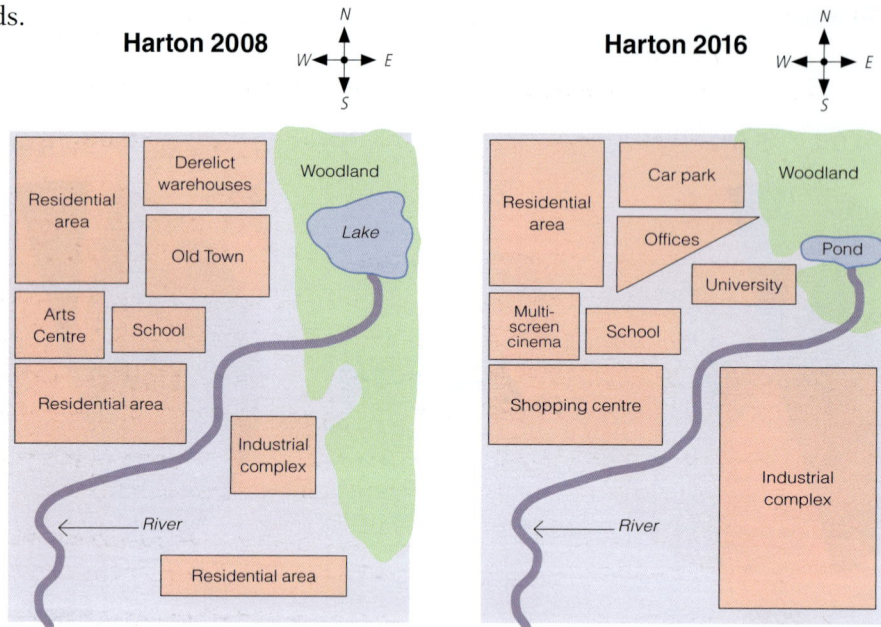

Harton 2008

Harton 2016

Unit 8 (page 113) Student A

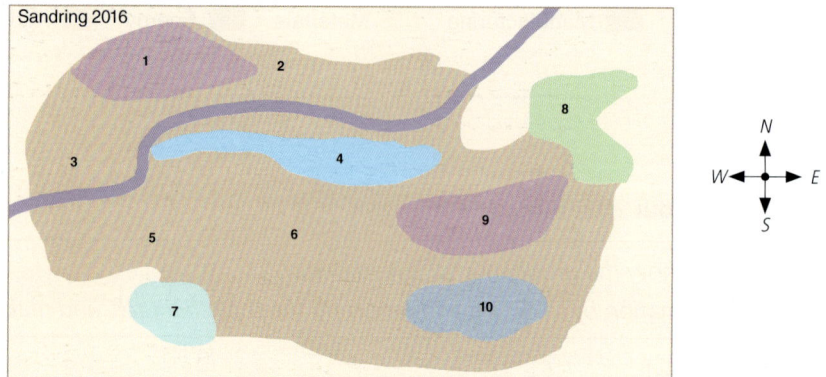

Sandring 2016

Unit 13 (page 191)

You should spend about 20 minutes on this task.

> The table below shows the number of visits to selected countries from four UK airports in 2013.
> Summarise the information by selecting and reporting the main features, and make comparisons where relevant.

Write at least 150 words.

**Number of visits abroad (000s):
by UK airport used and main
country visited 2013**

	Airports			
	Heathrow	Gatwick	Manchester	Stansted
Canada	187	91	50	.
Austria	86	148	66	44
Finland	58	25	53	8
Irish Republic	278	158	111	187
Lithuania	1	15	.	33
Spain	273	1,896	1,715	814
Total	**884**	**2,334**	**1,995**	**1,087**

Unit 14 (page 203)

You should spend about 20 minutes on this task.

> The charts below show the frequency of being happy in the last four weeks by labour status and by age group.
> Summarise the information by selecting and reporting the main features, and make comparisons where relevant.

Write at least 150 words.

Happiness in the last four weeks by age group

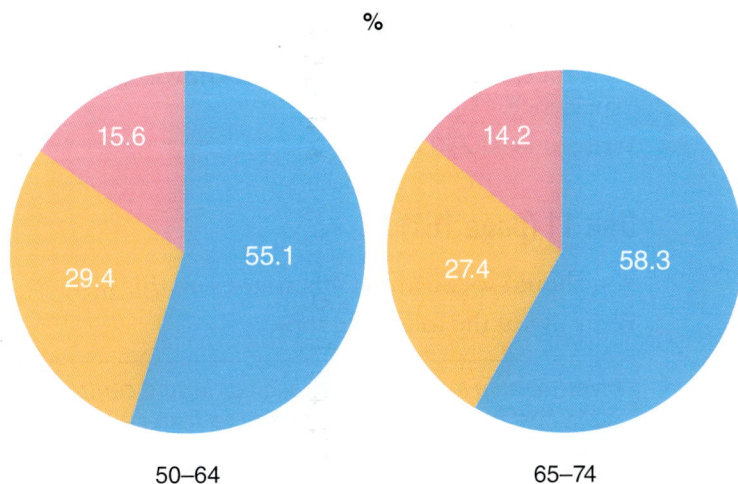

Happiness in the last four weeks by labour status

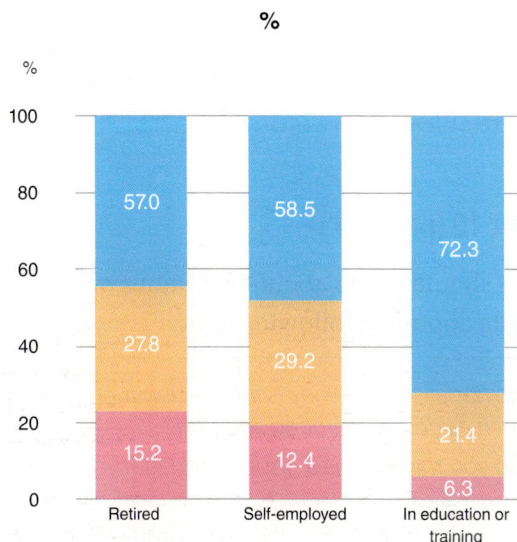

%

- A little/none of the time
- Some of the time
- All/most of the time

WRITING TASK 2

Unit 2 (page 27)

WRITING TASK 2

You should spend about 40 minutes on this task.
Write about the following topic:

> Some people think that technology is now an invaluable study tool for young people. Others, however, believe that it is harmful for the studying process.
> Discuss both these views and give your own opinion.

Give reasons for your answer and include any relevant knowledge or experience.
Write at least 250 words.

Unit 4 (page 57)

WRITING TASK 2

You should spend about 40 minutes on this task.
Write about the following topic:

> Many people feel that urban environments are more unhealthy than they have ever been.
> What do you think are the main causes of this problem? What measures can be effective in tackling this problem?

Give reasons for your answer and include any relevant examples from your own knowledge or experience.
Write at least 250 words.

Additional material

Unit 7 (page 101)

You should spend about 40 minutes on this task.
Write about the following topic:

> *Nowadays, experience is more valued in the workplace than knowledge in many countries.*
>
> *Do you think the advantages of this outweigh the disadvantages?*

Give reasons for your answer and include any relevant examples from your own knowledge or experience.

Write at least 250 words.

Unit 10 (page 149)

You should spend about 40 minutes on this task.
Write about the following topic:

> *Nowadays technology is influencing modern art in areas such as design, painting and film.*
>
> *Do you think this is a positive or negative development?*

Give reasons for your answer and include any relevant examples from your own knowledge or experience.

Write at least 250 words.

Unit 12 (page 173)

You should spend about 40 minutes on this task.
Write about the following topic:

> *Some people think that the increase in international travel has a negative impact on the environment and should be restricted.*
>
> *To what extent do you agree or disagree?*

Give reasons for your answer and include any relevant examples from your own knowledge or experience.

Write at least 250 words.

Unit 9 (page 125)

You should spend about 40 minutes on this task.
Write about the following topic:

> *Some people think it is important to construct new buildings rather than wasting money on maintaining old ones.*
>
> *To what extent do you agree or disagree with this opinion?*

Give reasons for your answer and include any relevant examples from your own knowledge or experience.

Write at least 250 words.

Unit 11 (page 161)

You should spend about 40 minutes on this task.
Write about the following topic:

> *Investment in local amenities such as leisure centres is the best way for the government to foster a good community spirit.*
>
> *To what extent do you agree or disagree?*
>
> *What other measures do you think might be effective?*

Give reasons for your answer and include any relevant examples from your own knowledge or experience.

Write at least 250 words.

WRITING TASK 1

Unit 8 (page 113) Student B

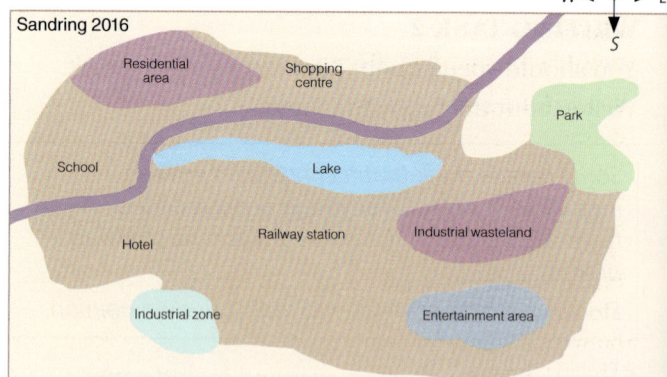

Sandring 2016

Wordlist

Unit 1

A Describing people

Adjectives
artistic
adventurous
ambitious
artistic
considerate
conscientious
creative
helpful
patient
reliable
sporty
supportive
talkative

Nouns and adjectives
talent/talented
humor/humorous
care/caring/careful
generosity/generous
confidence/confident
society/sociable/social
knowledge/knowledgeable
punctuality/punctual

B IELTS Reading

Choosing headings for paragraphs or sections

Nouns and their synonyms
comparison
ranking
methods
reasons
popularity
importance
impact
means
how (various media) affect

C Useful words and phrases from the Reading Passage
communication methods
the impact of/have little impact on
alternative means of
spend time with/interact (with)
communication devices
While this does not necessarily mean that
Mobile devices help facilitate frequent connections
between
This compares with
have access to

D Verbs of movement

Verbs
dip/fall slightly and quickly recover
fall slightly and then level off
fall gradually/decrease steadily
fluctuate/be erratic
hit a low/reach their lowest point
hit a peak/reach a high
plummet/plunge

remain stable/stabilise
rise gradually/increase slowly but surely
soar/rocket

Nouns
a climb
a decline
a dip
a drop
a fall
an increase
a peak
a plunge
a rise
fluctuations

Unit 2

A Verbs of cause and effect

Verbs	Nouns
achieve	achievement
advance	advancement
affect	effect
damage	damage
destroy	destruction
deteriorate	deterioration
enhance	enhancement
harm	harm
improve	improvement
influence	influence
produce	production
promote	promotion
result	result
ruin	ruin
shape	shape

Phrases to describe cause and effect
bring about an increase in …
bring about the destruction of …
cause (enormous) damage to …
change the shape of …
do harm to …
have a/an   (dramatic) effect (on …)
                    (huge) impact (on …)
                    (positive/negative) influence (on …)
lead to   (significant) improvement (in …)
lead to the ruin of …
make better links between …
result in a (sharp) deterioration in …

B Evaluating adjectives

Positive and negative adjectives

appealing	→	unappealing
convenient	→	inconvenient
effective	→	ineffective
harmful	→	harmless
important	→	unimportant
inspiring	→	uninspiring
necessary	→	unnecessary
practical	→	impractical
worthwhile	→	worthless

Synonyms

Unimportant	→	insignificant/trivial
useless	→	impractical
valueless	→	worthless
harmless	→	safe
important	→	critical/crucial/essential/key/vital
useful	→	helpful valuable convenient
valuable	→	helpful precious invaluable
harmful	→	dangerous

C Linking devices

although/but/however
as/because/since
also/furthermore/moreover/similarly/what is more
accordingly/as a result/and so/so/for instance/
consequently/therefore
in order to
for example/for instance

D Useful words and phrases from the Reading Passage

in the early stages of this development …
the process of urbanization goes hand in hand with …
there is reason to believe that
played an important role in
emerge as the center of …
become the seat of …
exercised a certain degree of …
there is reason to believe that …
can be regarded as the culmination of …

Unit 3

A Sports

Sport	Place	Equipment
bodybuilding	gym	weights
boxing	ring	glove/shorts
diving	sea	oxygen tank
football	pitch	ball/goal
golf	course	clubs/irons
running	track	shoes/spikes
swimming	pool	costumes/trunks
tennis	court	racquet/ball

Types of sport

combat	outdoor
equestrian	racket/racquet
indoor	table
motor	water

B Adjectives ending in -ed/ing

Verbs and adjectives

annoy	annoying/annoyed
challenge	challenging/challenged
excite	exciting/excited
exhilarate	exhilarating/exhilarated
fascinate	fascinating/fascinated
inspire	inspiring/ inspired
interest	interesting/interested
invigorate	invigorating/invigorated
irritate	irritating/irritated
motivate	motivating/motivated
refresh	refreshing/refreshed
thrill	thrilling/thrilled

C Adjectives with prepositions

addicted to …
bored with …
capable of …
enthusiastic about …
fond of …
indifferent to …
interested in …
keen on …
mad about …
passionate about …

D Useful expressions to describe data

a greater smaller proportion of …
a third of (the number of) …
a quarter of …
a third of …
some noticeable differences
half of …
three-quarters of …
twice as many …
three times as many …
five times the number of …
half as many …
forty/40% of …
over fifty/50% of …
proportionately
the bulk of …
three/four out of every ten …

E Useful words and phrases from the Reading Passage

build the foundation of …
become a guinea pig
create the illusion of …
discover what goes on
ensure the experience is memorable
experience a few seconds of thrills
exhilarating (ride)
figure out how to …
push the boundaries of …
relive their (terrifying) experiences
spend hours (living out)
This can lead to
trigger the release of a …
understand the broad effects of …

Unit 4

A General nouns

Nouns and collocations

adverse/unfavourable/trying	circumstances
main/likely/probable	cause
significant/political/current	event
favourable/false/good	impression
burning/controversial/major	issue
memorable/festive/state	occasion
golden/excellent/perfect	opportunity
acute/serious/insurmountable	problem
ideal/happy/dangerous	situation
imaginative/effective/perfect	solution
(company) crisis	
amusing incident	
unexpected outcome	
faint possibility	

B Useful expressions
It was too good an opportunity to miss.
It is a rather awkward situation.
It is a divisive issue that arouses passion.
It was an annoying incident.
It was the happiest event of her life.

C Uncountable nouns with countable nouns as examples
accommodation like flats
cash like coins
clothing like shirts
crime like burglaries
equipment like computers
fruit like oranges
furniture like chairs
information like bank details
litter like bottles/cans
luggage like suitcases
media like magazines
merchandise like goods
rubbish like bottles
(bad) weather like storms

D Linking devices
although
but
despite the fact that
even if
even so
however
much as
nevertheless
nonetheless
still
though
while
yet

E Developing ideas by expanding the meaning of adjectives

Adjectives and verbs
alarming	frighten
appealing	attract
interesting	fascinate
motivating	encourage
satisfying	please
shocking	stun
worrying	trouble

F Useful words and phrases from the Reading Passage
a skills shortage
be at a disadvantage
due to lack of suitably qualified candidates,
half of the respondents said …
it's no surprise when companies have problems with
recruiting a new generation of engineers and technicians
more needs to be done to encourage young people to take up …
there are areas that are harder to recruit
they would focus more on …
this implies that …
which is good news for graduates …

Unit 5

A Adjectives/noun collocations
agricultural society
dominant culture
general public
governing elite
indigenous people
modern civilisation
thriving community
urban population

B Forming adjectives from nouns

Adjectives ending -al
agriculture	agricultural
industry	industrial
nation	national
technology	technological
tradition	traditional

Adjectives ending -ous
danger	dangerous
luxury	luxurious
population	populous
space	spacious

Adjectives ending –ful
beauty	beautiful
success	successful
use	useful

Verbs of prediction
Verb	Noun	
anticipate	it is anticipated that …	anticipation
estimate	it is estimated that …	estimation
expect	it is expected that …	expectation
forecast	it is forecast(ed) that …	forecast
predict	it is predicted that …	prediction
project	it is projected that …	projection

C Useful words and phrases from the Reading Passage
adapt accordingly
have made it possible to …
key characters
post a photo on Instagram
predictions … came true
Several experts have made their predictions about what
the world of 2045 will look like.
the latest fad in …
make long-term forecasts
this can be done by …
(we won't be able) to tell the difference between … .
this means …
(to the point where) there is no longer a perceptible
difference between …
wearable technology

Unit 6

A Conservation

Collocations
admire the scenery
breathtaking view
derelict factory
dominate the landscape

Wordlist

planting season
tree conservation
panoramic view
spoilt/unspoilt countryside
spectacular scenery
tranquil countryside
visit open spaces

B Transitive and intransitive verbs

Transitive	Intransitive	Both
bear	appear	break
collect	become	break up
create	blossom	decrease
crush	bloom	disperse
cultivate	come out (of)	grow
	disappear	increase
gather	emerge	ripen
harvest	exist	smell
lay	fall	eat
make	flow	weave
plant	go down	
pollinate	happen	
produce	look	
reap	occur	
transplant	open up	
utilise	rise	
sow	sprout	
pick		
roast		

C Describing sequences

Linking words and phrases
initially/first
then/next/following that/after that
as soon as/once/after/before
finally
when/where

Nouns to summarise stages in sequences
assembly
collection
delivery
harvesting
packaging
pasteurisation
recycling
separation
storage
transportation

D Useful words and phrases from the Reading Passage
evidence suggests that …
which are widely distributed across …
it has been noted that …
its ability to thrive in tough conditions
investigations are being carried out on how …
likewise, …
olive oil is classified according to …
requires further processing to yield
the oil is obtained from the fruit shortly after harvesting.
the olive has shaped the landscape
the beneficial qualities of olive oil have been attributed to
the fruit is then cured

Unit 7

A Work
(a teacher) by profession
career ladder
earn a livelihood
have a good job/occupation
hold down a job
improve their job prospects
job opportunities
good/academic qualifications
work ethic
work-life balance

B Collocations

Adjective/noun/verb collocations

considerable/enjoy/derive/accrue	benefit
huge/gain/outweigh/take	advantage
once-in-a-lifetime/career/seize/waste	opportunity
enormous/achieve/guarantee/depends on	success
excellent/offer/boost/career	prospects
distinct/obvious/suffer/have	disadvantage
total/result in/ensue	failure
outstanding/impressive/represent/a lack of	achievement
huge/show/make/room	improvement
good/deserve/throw away/arise	chance
Verb/noun collocations with additional verbs	
enjoy	advantage
gain	benefit
come up/give somebody/grab/take	a chance
end in/expect	failure
offset	disadvantage
constitute/scope for	improvement
provide/squander	opportunity
damage/have	prospects
enjoy	success

C Useful words and phrases from the Reading Passage
(work in a communal space,) as opposed to working from home
counterparts
creating the right kind of work environment
first, unlike (a traditional office)
… is also witnessing growth in the number of …
… may also be derived from …
(experience that) meets the needs of their respective members
remote workers
… see their work as meaningful
So what are the implications for traditional companies?
the lessons of coworking spaces can be applied to …
when it comes to (cultivating our community), …

Unit 8

A Nouns relating to places

Adjectives and nouns
(residential) area
(business) district
(magnificent) location
(safe) neighbourhood
(beautiful) place
(northern) region
(beautiful/spectacular) setting
(derelict) site
(open) space
(tourist hot) spot
(pedestrian) zone

B Useful expressions for describing places
covered with …
fed by …
full of …
located near …
overlooking …
surrounded by …
stretching into the distance
with …

C Verbs relating to changes in maps
chop trees down/down trees
convert … into …
create a …
demolish
give way to …
knock … down/down …
make way for …
pull … down/down …
replace … with …
… take (their) place
(tear … down/down …)
(completely) transform
turn … into …

Verbs and nouns

build	building
change	change
construct	construction
develop (into)	development
expand	expansion
extend	extension
transform	transformation

D Location

Location phrases

North	in the north of … , north of … , to the north of …
South	in the south of … , south of … , to the south of …
East	in the east of … , east of … , to the east of …
West	in the west of … , west of … , to the west of …

Verbs of location
there is …
lies …
is situated …
is sited …
is located …
stands …
runs/flows …

E Useful words and phrases from the Reading Passage
… have little need of complex maps
to suit the needs of people
digital tools at their disposal
examples of images date to
… is still having a huge impact on human progress
have also been variously associated with
further, …
have very sophisticated
their contribution to cartography is not insignificant
What exactly constitutes a map has made …

Unit 9

A Beauty

Adjectives relating to reactions
beautiful
breathtaking
dazzling
ecstatic
emotional
evocative
humbling
impressive
magnificent
majestic
melancholic
nostalgic thoughtful

Useful expressions for describing reactions
be taken aback by …
evoke memories of …
fill (someone) with …
humble (someone)
impress (someone)
make an enormous impression on (someone)
make (someone) feel …
make (someone) thoughtful about …

B Prefixes *over-* and *under-*
overawed
overcome
over/underestimated
over/underpriced
over/understated
overtaken over/underrated
overrun over/undervalued
underfunded

C Useful words and phrases from the Reading Passage
embracing technological progress and
inspired by …
transformed the … from what was then seen as … into …
become a popular (London) landmark
attempts to popularise industrial buildings by …
it necessarily involves not only, … but also …
possess a complex spatial knowledge of …
can broadly be identified with
share characteristics
record for posterity
show a profound knowledge of …
throughout his career

Wordlist

Unit 10

A Art

People in the arts
play actor, actress, lead (role), playwright, director, producer, costume designer, set designer
exhibition: visitor, exhibitor, designer, artist sculptor painter
musical: singer, actor/actress, writer, song-writer, producer, conductor, musician, pianist, violinist, percussionist
book: novelist, writer, illustrator, author, reader, editor
sculpture: sculptor, artist,
video game: designer, writer, illustrator artist, software programmer, producer, engineer
film: actor/actress, director, star, starlet, producer, distributor, scriptwriter, fan

B Useful words and phrases from the Reading Passage
an art installation
a work to be placed in
a curator
made possible by (funding)
imbues the garden with
indistinguishable,
the artist proposed instead that she would create …
the garden, based on the gradual disappearance of …
the logistical challenges were many
to coincide with
to expedite planning

Unit 11

A The family

Words relating to family members
ancestor
family
family tree
young/old generation
grandparents
household
niece/nephew
offspring
parents
relatives
siblings
widow/widower

B Suffixes –hood and –ship

Nouns and relevant verbs
(reach) adulthood
apprenticeship
boyhood
brotherhood
(spend) childhood
craftsmanship/musicianship
fatherhood/motherhood
(face) hardship
(show) leadership
membership
(reach) nationhood
neighbourhood
parenthood
partnership
professorship
(cultivate/maintain) relationship
(withdraw) sponsorship

Collocations with the word *relationship*
broken
build
close
family
long-lasting   relationship(s)
network of
parent-child
professional
special

C Useful words and phrases from the Reading Passage
it takes a village to bring up …
kinship
a wide network of relatives
responsible for his or her upbringing
the interests of the entire community
take precedence over …
that role transcends age and gender
socialization contributes to cohesion

Unit 12

A Adjectives with multiple meaning

alien	strange/extraterrestrial
curious	inquisitive/unusual
different	dissimilar/service/diverse/unusual
foreign	from or in another country/unfamiliar
fresh	new/cold and windy/recently made or prepared
novel	book/original
new	recently arrived/inexperienced
odd	unusual/irregular
pristine	new and untouched/morally good
strange	unexpected/unfamiliar/odd
unique	treasured/happening only in one place/ not the same as something else

B Words related to memory
memento (n.)
memo (n.)
memorabilia (n.)
memoirs (n.)
memorable (adj.)
memorial (n.)
memory (n.)
memorise (v.)
remember (v.)

C Useful words and phrases from the Reading Passage
… diversity reflects the maturity of the ecosystem
… also supports a variety of …
… which are all listed as vulnerable
… is also of cultural importance
… are of cultural and historical significance
… have a cooperative and integrated approach to managing …

Unit 13

A Words related to systems

electricity grid	cables/generator/national/pylons
gas supply	appliances/fields/industry/pipelines/works
oil industry	exploration/field/refineries/slick/wells
railway/train infrastructure	bridges/lines/tunnels/viaducts
satellite system	channel/communications/dish/receiver/weather
water supply	filter/pressure/purification/tap/treatment

B Modal verbs to adjectives

can/may	possible
could/can	able
didn't need	unnecessary
don't/didn't have to	not essential
have to be	compulsory
may	permissible
should	expected/probable/likely
will	certain
wouldn't/won't	unwilling

C Useful words and phrases from the Reading Passage

addresses people's concern about …
appears necessary to attract new people to cycling.
are looking at ways to …
… have also adopted aggressive policies
… like that found in the Portland region,
may have a greater potential
might have limitations
opportunities to build separate paths are often limited
the results can lead to …
this is in contrast to …
the study demonstrated that …
to help address health and other policy concerns
to substitute for …
to try to improve the accuracy of the …

Unit 14

A Money matters

Collocations with *money*

counterfeit government paper public sponsorship taxpayers'	money

money	laundering management market box

credit	agreement arrangement facilities limit terms transfer

currency	conversion crisis fluctuation markets reserves speculation

Collocations with words relating to money

consumer education government public welfare	expenditure/spending

capital state government	finance

company family government household state	finances

capital family household investment	income

cash	crisis crop flow limit payment reserves settlement

debt	burden collection collector mountain

expenditure	cut level pattern

finance	department director minister

income	bracket group statement tax

savings	account bank plan

B Values and beliefs

Nouns
(a high) moral standard
individual morals
invaluable objects
moral stand
personal morals
set of principles
standards of behaviour
system of ethics
traditional values
valueless objects
Adjectives
principled
unprincipled
Collocations
accuse someone of being moralistic
adhere to a strict ethical code
attach importance to one's beliefs/values
compromise one's principles
follow customs
take a moral stand
treasure valuables
value something

C Useful words and phrases from the Reading Passage
although objective measures of (wellbeing) are crucial,
they cannot tell the whole story …
ask people
by placing significant emphasis on …
despite unprecedented economic growth
… has focussed predominantly on improving
it can be argued that …
fields as diverse as …
much recent research indicates that phenomena
interest in measuring subjective wellbeing has grown
considerably over recent years
tend to correlate well with …
the main advantage of asking people to assess their own
wellbeing is that …
to evaluate their own wellbeing
various social and economic factors affect

Grammar reference

Unit 1

Likes and dislikes

1 The verbs *like, love, enjoy, can't stand/bear, detest, dislike, hate* and *loathe* can be followed by a noun.
   I like football.
   I hate spiders.

2 The verbs *enjoy, fancy, dislike, detest* and *loathe* can be followed by a verb + *-ing* only.
   I enjoy swimming. (NOT I enjoy to swim.)

3 The verbs *can't stand/bear, like, hate, love* and *prefer* can be followed by a verb + *-ing* or *to*.
   I like **playing/to play** *baseball.*
   I can't bear **watching/to watch** *sport on TV.*

4 You can use *like* with a verb + *-ing* or *to* to express a particular meaning.
   I **like to go** *for a swim every morning.* (I think that this is a good idea but don't necessarily enjoy it.)
   I **like going** *for a swim every morning.* (I enjoy it.)

5 *prefer*
   You can use the following to express a preference for one thing compared to another:
   • *prefer* + noun + *to* + noun. Use the *-ing* form if the things are activities.
   I **prefer books to** *computer games.*
   I **prefer surfing** *to sailing.*
   • *prefer* + *to* + infinitive + *than* + infinitive without *to*
   I **prefer to read** *novels* **than play** *computer games.*

6 *I'd rather*
   You can use the following to express that you *would rather* do one thing compared to another:
   • *would/'d rather(not)* + verb
   I'd **rather go** *to the concert.*
   I'd **rather not watch** *the horror film.*
   • *would/'d rather* + verb + *than* + verb
   I'd **rather** *play the piano than go out.*

7 *would like/love/prefer/hate*
   Would like/love/prefer/hate must be followed by *to* + infinitive.
   I'd **love to go** *to a live concert.*
   I'd **prefer to eat** *in than go to the restaurant.*

Present simple, present continuous and past simple

A Present simple
You use the present simple:
• for an habitual action
   I **get up** *before 8 am every day.*
   Lectures **start** *at 9 am every day.*
• to show how frequently people do things
   I sometimes **arrive** *late, because the buses are not reliable.*
• to describe states and situations
   I **know** *the area very well.*
   My work **requires** *a lot of contact with people.*
• with common state verbs which are not normally used in the present continuous (see present continuous)
   I **like** *sport.*
   I **love** *swimming and skiing.*

• for possession and senses (such as taste, thoughts, feelings, smell)
   I **have** *a bicycle.*
• *Ah, yes, I think I know the place well.* to describe stages in a process or lifecycle, and thus in a narrative
   The sun **rises** *and* **heats** *the water, which then* **evaporates** *and* **forms** *clouds.*
   My grandmother **helps** *us a lot and* **makes** *us* **feel** *happy.*
• to give directions
   You **come** *out of the main station entrance, and you* **turn** *left and just* **walk** *about 100 metres and you are here.*
• for facts, general statements and truths
   Water **boils** *at 100°C.*
   It's clear that car sales **fall** *steadily over the period.*
   Cities generally **attract** *a lot of people from the countryside.*

B Present continuous
You use the present continuous:
• to describe actions and events which are happening 'around now' (the actions and events may not be apparent at the time of writing or speaking)
   The earth **is becoming** *warmer year by year.*
   More and more students **are applying** *for the course.*
   I'm **doing** *a course on pottery at the moment.*
• to describe an action that is in the process of happening as you speak or write
   You **are preparing** *for IELTS if you are using this book.*
   The baby's **sleeping.** *Try not to wake her.*
• to talk about the future (see Unit 5)

C Present simple or present continuous?
1 You use 'state' verbs like *know, promise* and *understand* only in the present simple.
   I **promise** *I'll come to the party.*
   I **understand** *what you are saying.*

2 For verbs that have a 'state' and 'action' meaning, you use the present simple to describe 'states' and the present continuous to describe 'actions'.
   State: *I* **think** *studying languages is important.*
   Action: *I'm* **thinking** *about this problem. Give me a few minutes.*
   State: *I* **have** *a pen.*
   Action: *The government* **is having** *difficulties.*
   State: *This perfume* **smells** *nice.*
   Action: *The cat* **is smelling** *the food. Maybe he'll eat it.*

3 With *always*
   Present simple: *He* **always gets up** *at 7 am.* (He does it as a matter of routine.)
   Present continuous: *He's* **always talking** *about his health.* (He does it more than I think he should.)

4 With the verb *to be*
   Present simple: *She* **is** *very persistent.* (This is part of her personality.)
   Present continuous: *She* **is being** *very persistent at the moment.* (This is unusual for her. This is not her normal behaviour.)

219

D Past simple

You use the past simple:

- to describe a completed action, event or state in the past which is not connected with now. The time in the past may be clear from the information around the sentence

  *At one time, people **believed** that the world was flat. (But they don't now.)*
  *He **lived** in China for a long time.*
  *Dickens **wrote** many brilliant novels. (He wrote them a long time ago.)*

- to describe an action or event at a particular time, or during a particular period of time
  *I **stayed** in London for two months in 2008.*
  *Sales **rose** between 2005 and 2009.*

- to describe habitual actions in the past
  *I **attended** classes in pottery for three months.*

Unit 2

Past simple and present perfect

1 Past simple
For use, see Unit 1.

2 Present perfect
You use the present perfect:

- to describe actions or events that have a connection with the present
  *I **have just passed** my exam. Look at my certificate.*
  *I've **just fixed** the TV! Look, it's working!*

- to talk about an action or event that has happened at any time up to now, but you don't know or mention when. The emphasis is on the fact the action or event has happened, not the time that it happened
  *I **have lived** in West Africa.*
  *He **has visited** France.*

- to talk about periods that continue to the present
  *My parents **have lived** in their house **since 2001**.*
  *I **have studied** hard **for the past month**.*
  Note the contrast between the past simple and the present perfect.
  *I **did** a lot of work yesterday (no connection with the present), but I **haven't done** much today (connection with the present).*
  *I **visited** Spain ten years ago, but I **haven't been** to Italy.*
  *When **did** you **finish** the book?*
  Or
  ***Haven't** you **finished** it yet?*

2 Present perfect continuous
You use the present perfect continuous to describe periods up to and including the present.
*She's **been watching** that film all afternoon.*
*I **have been learning** English since I was ten.*

Habit in the past – used to and would

You use *used to* and *would* to describe habitual actions and events in the past.

1 You use *used to* to describe habits or states in the past which no longer happen or exist.
*I **used to** live in the countryside.*

*I **used to** play chess quite a lot when I was a child.*
Note that *used to* becomes *use to* with questions and negatives.
*I **didn't use to** play outdoor games much.*
***Did** your parents **use to** travel much when they were younger?*

2 You use *would* to describe past habits, but not states.
*I **would** work for my uncle every Tuesday evening when I was 16.*
*I **used to** own a collection of antique clocks.*
(NOT *I would own a collection of antique clocks.*)
Would is often used to reminisce about the past and in descriptive writing.
*On spring afternoons, I **would** go for long walks with my friends and look at the wildlife.*
Note that you usually don't use *would* in negative or yes/no questions.

Adverbs of frequency

1 You use adverbs of frequency to indicate how often something happens. Common adverbs of frequency are *always, usually, normally, regularly, often, frequently, sometimes, occasionally, rarely, hardly ever, seldom, never*.

2 You use adverbs of frequency after *be* and auxiliaries, but before all other verbs.
*I **am always** on time for lectures.*
*He **has never eaten** noodles before.*
*Politicians **rarely pay attention** to the opinions of the people.*

3 You can invert the subject and the verb when you use *never, rarely* and *seldom* at the beginning of a sentence.
***Never have I seen** such an impressive PowerPoint presentation from a student.*

Unit 3

Adjectives with prepositions

Some adjectives are followed by a particular preposition (when used with the verb *be*). Sometimes a different preposition is used depending on whether you are referring to 'people' or 'things'. You can check this in a dictionary, but they include:
*angry/annoyed/happy/upset **about** (things)*
*good/bad **at***
*late/famous/ready **for***
*different **from***
*interested **in***
*afraid/fond/frightened **of***
*keen **on***
*kind/married/used **to***
*angry/annoyed/bored **with** (people)*
When you use a verb after the proposition, you use the verb + *-ing* form.
*He's **keen on playing** football.*
*I'm **interested in learning** about other cultures.*
When you learn new adjectives which are followed by prepositions, try to learn the adjective and the preposition together.

Comparison

A Comparative adjectives

1 One syllable adjectives

You form the comparative from adjectives with one syllable by adding -er.

high → high**er**

For one syllable adjectives ending in -e, you add -r.

large → larg**er**

For one syllable adjectives ending in a consonant, you double the final consonant.

big → bi**gger**

2 Two or more syllable adjectives

You normally form the comparative from adjectives with two or more syllables with *more/less*.

exciting → **more/less** exciting

3 Adjectives ending in consonant + -y

You form the comparative from adjectives ending in consonant + y, by changing -y to -i.

dr**y** → dr**ier**

eas**y** → eas**ier**

Note some adjectives can be formed with -er or *more/less*.

The river **is shallower/more shallow** here than over there.

Theme parks with thrilling rides are **becoming commoner/more common** than in the past.

B Superlative adjectives

1 One syllable adjectives

You form the superlative from adjectives with one syllable by using *the* before the adjective and adding *-(e)st* to the adjective.

long → **the** long**est**

2 Two or more syllable adjectives

You form the superlative from adjectives with two or more syllables by adding *the most/least* before the adjective.

interesting → **the most/least** interesting

3 Adjectives ending in consonant + -y

You form the superlative from adjectives ending in consonant + y, by changing -y to -i.

dr**y** → **the** dr**iest**

eas**y** → **the** eas**iest**

C Irregular comparatives and superlatives

Some common adjectives have an irregular comparative and superlative form.

good → better → the best

bad → worse → the worst

far → farther/further → the farthest/the furthest

She is a **better** player than he is.

The performance of the team was **worse** than last time.

D Comparative adverbs

Like comparative adjectives, you form comparative adverbs by adding *-(e)r* to one syllable adverbs and using *more/less* with two or more syllable adverbs.

Computer sales rose **faster** over the last decade compared to the previous one.

Attendances at the cinema fell **more dramatically** in the first quarter than the second.

E Comparative structures

1 *than*

You can make comparisons by using *than*.

Sales were greater in 1980 **than** in 1990.

2 *as + adjective + as* to compare two equal things

You can compare two equal things by using *as* + adjective + *as*.

I'm **as tall as** my sister.

3 *not as + adjective + as* to compare two things that are not equal

You can compare two things that are not equal by using *not as* + adjective + *as*.

Computer sales were**n't as high** in June **as** they were in January.

F Words to strengthen or weaken comparisons

You can add words and expressions to strengthen or weaken comparisons.

1 Comparatives

Words and expressions that can be added to comparatives include: *a bit, a little, slightly, much, (quite) a lot, far, significantly, considerably, a great deal, twice, three times*.

Book sales rose **much/a lot/far more slowly** in the last quarter.

The number of shoppers was **a little lower** last month compared to this month.

2 Superlatives

Words and expressions that can be added to superlatives include: *by far, easily, a long way*.

The Indian architect's building was **by far the most popular** in the competition.

Sweden is the company's **smallest** market, **by a long way**.

3 With *as ... as ...*

Words and expressions that can be added to modify the structure *as ... as ...* include: *(not) nearly, not quite, almost, just, half, twice, three times*.

The population of the town **is three times as** big **as** it was in 1960.

The rest of the team were **not nearly as** good **as** the captain.

Unit 4

Countable and uncountable nouns

1 Countable nouns

Countable nouns have a singular and a plural form. They are used with the singular or plural form of a verb.

I have **a car**. The **car works** well.

I have **two cars**. The **cars work** well.

Note some common countable nouns only have a plural form. These include *goods, means, trousers, stairs*.

The **goods are** already with the customer.

2 Uncountable nouns

Uncountable nouns only have one form and are used with the singular form of the verb.

The **information is** in the leaflet.

(NOT *The informations are in the leaflet.*)

In order to quantify uncountable nouns you use phrases like *a piece of/a bit of/a slice of/a sheet of*, etc.

The leaflet contains **several pieces of information**.

Can I borrow **two sheets of paper**?

Note that *news* is followed by a singular verb.
*The news **is** on in a few minutes.*

3 Some nouns can be countable or uncountable depending on the meaning. The countable meaning is specific and the uncountable meaning is general. Examples include:

a business (a company) *business* ('business' in general)
a painting (a work of art) *painting* (the activity)
a noise (a specific noise) *noise* ('noise' in general)
a fruit (a specific type of fruit) *fruit* ('fruit' in general)
***Fruit is** good for you.*
***Two fruits**, apples and pears, **are** grown in this region.*

4 Many common nouns are uncountable in English, but countable in other languages.
***Accommodation is** expensive in London.*
***Information is** available on the website.*
***The furniture is** very modern.*
***The weather is** very good today.*

5 Some nouns can be used with the singular or plural form of a verb. These include *army, class, company, crowd, data, family, government, group, public, team*.
*The government **is/are** preparing for the next election.*
*The family **is/are** very happy with the new house.*
Note that in Australian and American English the singular verb is used with *government*, etc.

Making suggestions

You can use the following to make suggestions:
- modal verbs like *should/ought* to to make strong suggestions
  *Shopkeepers **should/ought to** be made responsible for cleaning the area around their shops.*
  Note that you can use **must** to express a very strong suggestion.
  *Shopkeepers **must** be made responsible for cleaning the area around their shops.*
- modal verbs like *could/might* to make weak suggestions
  *A new body with strong powers **could/might** be set up to tackle the problem of international pollution.*
- fixed phrases that introduce suggestions. These are followed by *would be … /is to …*
  *The **best way to/A good way to/One way to** improve the environment **would be/is to** …*
  *A **good idea would be/is to** …*

Unit 5

Ways of looking at the future

1 **Simple future**
You use the simple future to make predictions.
*The train **will** arrive late.*
***I'll be** better this evening, don't worry.*
*Attendances at the cinema **will continue** to rise.*
You can use with the following verbs to describe graphs:
predict
forecast
project
estimate
anticipate
*It **is predicted** that sales **will rise**.*

2 **going to**
You use *going to* + infinitive for plans and intentions in the near and distant future.
***I'm going to** train to be an accountant after I finish my university course.*
Going to is also used to make predictions when there is evidence in the current situation.
*There's **going to be** a storm – look at those clouds.*
Note *going to* should not be used to make predictions in graphs in IELTS Writing Task 1 answers.

3 **Present continuous**
You use the present continuous for arrangements or plans that have already been made. There is usually a time expression.
*We're all **flying** to Bangkok next Sunday.* (We have planned the trip and bought the tickets.)

4 **Future perfect**
You use the future perfect to make predictions about actions that will be completed before a certain point in the future.
*Everyone **will have left** by 9 pm.*
*Sales **will have reached** 2000 a month by the middle of next year.*

5 **Future continuous**
You use the future continuous to talk about actions or events that will be happening at a particular point in time in the future.
*Sales **will be rising** at the rate of ten million units per year at the end of the decade.*
***I'll be writing** my dissertation by then.*

6 **Future perfect continuous**
You use the future perfect continuous to emphasise the duration of actions or events that will be happening at a particular point of time in the future.
*People **will have been living** on other plants for a long time by then.*

7 **Present simple**
You use the present simple to talk about future events that are based on a fixed schedule or timetable.
*The train **leaves** at 8.00 am.*
*The film **starts** in 15 minutes.*
You also use the present simple to talk about the future after the following words: *when, after, before, unless, in case, as soon as, until, by the time, the next time*.
*When I **visit** Dubai again, I'll take more photographs.*

8 **Common phrases to talk about the future**
You can use the following common phrases to talk about the future:
*… **be about to** …* for the immediate future
*The world of technology **is about to** undergo another major change.*
*… **be bound to** …* for certainty
*She **is bound to** succeed as she is very intelligent.*
*… **be to be** + verb …* for fixed arrangements
*He **is to be made** into chairman of the company.*
*… **be set to** … / … **be (un)likely to** …* for probability.
These are useful for IELTS Writing Task 1.
*Shopper numbers **are set to** rise dramatically.*
*Sales **are likely to** fall in the coming months.*

Unit 6

Transitive and intransitive verbs

1 A transitive verb has an object.
*The tree **produces fruit** every year.*
An intransitive does not have an object.
*I usually **walk** to class.*

2 You can use transitive verbs in the active and the passive.
*Farmers **produce** much of the food we eat.* (active)
*Much of the food we eat **is produced** by farmers.* (passive)

3 You cannot use intransitive verbs in the passive.
Car sales fell over the period.
(NOT *Car sales are fallen over the period.*)
The sun rises in the east.
(NOT *The sun is risen in the east.*)

4 Some verbs can be either transitive or intransitive.
*The farmers **grow fruit** on the hillside.* (transitive active)
*Fruit **is grown** on the hillside.* (transitive passive)
*Fruit **grows** on the hillside.* (intransitive)

5 Certain verbs like *become* can be followed by a noun or an adjective. It is a linking verb like the verb *to be*
The flowers become seeds. ('become' + noun)
The fruit becomes ripe. ('become' + adjective)
Note the old-fashioned use of the verb *become* as a transitive verb.
The hat becomes you. ('The hat suits you.')

Unit 7

Conditionals 1

1 **First conditional: *if* + present simple + *will* + infinitive**
You use the first conditional to talk about situations in the present or future and their possible results.
*If young people **focus** on skills for the modern age, they **will never be** out of work.*
You can also use *may/might/going to/can* instead of *will* in the main clause.
*If it is difficult, I **can** help you.*
*If the train is late, we **may** miss the beginning of the concert.*

2 **Second conditional: *if* + past simple + *would* + infinitive**
You use the second conditional to talk about imaginary or unlikely situations in the present or future.
*If he **learnt** to drive, it **would open up** new job opportunities.*
*If I were you, I'd **learn** to drive.*
Note that *If I was you* is often used in spoken English.
You can also use *could/might* instead of *would* in the main clause.
*If he learnt to drive it **could/might** open up new job opportunities.*

3 **Third conditional: *if* + past perfect + *would have* + past participle**
You use the third conditional to hypothesise or speculate about the past.
*If I **had spent** more time studying, I'd **have been** less nervous about the exam now.*
You can also use *could/might* instead of *would* in the main clause.

*If I had spent less time studying, I **could/might** have been less nervous about the exam now.*

4 You can begin with *were* in the second conditional and *had* in the third conditional and change the word order as follows:
Were he to learn to drive, it would open up new job opportunities.
Had I spent less time studying, I'd have been less tired before the exam.
This form is more formal.

5 You can use *unless* instead of *if not* in conditional clauses.
Unless I get some money, I won't be able to travel abroad to study.
*If I **don't** get some money, I won't be able to travel abroad to study.*
Unless he had saved a lot of money, he could have never managed to travel abroad.
*If he **hadn't** saved a lot of money, he could have never managed to travel abroad.*

Unit 8

Referring in a text

1 You use the following pronouns to refer back to a noun:
- *it* for singular nouns
*The neighbourhood where I was brought up used to be very busy, but now **it** is very quiet and peaceful.*
*The place I like to visit when I go home is near my parents' house. **It** is a very secluded spot on a hill by the river.*
In the example above, it is clear that *it* refers back to the noun place. The word *spot* helps you to understand this.
- *they* for plural nouns
*A number of sites are still lying idle, yet **they** could be used for houses.*

2 You can use the following to refer to a noun, event or idea, or the latter part of the previous sentence.
- *this*
*The government brought about **a massive transformation of the area**, but **this** (change) needs to be further supported.*
In the example above, *this* refers to the massive transformation of the area. The word *change* can be added. *It* cannot be used because it might not be clear whether it refers to the government, the transformation or the area.
The district has become more prosperous in recent years. This has led to an increase in house prices in the area.
In the example above, *this* refers to the idea that the district has become more prosperous in recent years. *It* cannot be used.
- *these*
*Many new buildings were constructed in the district in the last few years. **These** have brought many new people into the area.*
In the example above, *these* refers to the many new buildings. *They* is not correct as it might refer to 'the last few years'.

- **that**

  You can use *that* to refer back to a noun, event or idea, but *it* is not as common as *this*.

  The region has many wild animals roaming around the plains. **That** *is what makes* **it** *very exciting to visit*.

  In the example above, *that* refers to the many wild animals roaming around the plains. The pronoun *it* refers to the region.

- **those**

  The speakers' **recommendations** *were endless, but only* **those** *that were cost-effective were adopted*.

  In the example above, *those* refers to some of the speakers' recommendations not all of them.

3 You can use the pronoun *it* to refer back to *this* or *that* in a text.

   The setting for the film was decided upon at the last minute, but **this** *did not cause any serious problems*. **It** *did, however, mean it cost a lot more*.

   In the example above, *this* refers to *decided upon at the last minute* and *it* refers to back to *this*.

4 You can often use *this, that, these, those* followed by a noun to refer back to nouns, events or ideas.

   The committee suggested that **the financial district should be expanded**. **This recommendation** *was accepted*.

   Wildlife like tigers and lions *are often held in captivity, but* **these creatures** *need to be allowed to roam freely*.

   In the past, people used to believe **strange things** *about the natural world. However,* **those ideas** *went out of fashion years ago*.

Unit 9

Modal verbs for evaluating

1 **Expectations and suggestions**

   You can use *should/ought to* to express suggestions.

   The government **should** *increase taxes to fund education*.

   You can also use *should/ought to* to express expectations.

   The increased investment in education **should** *help improve standards*.

2 **Drawing conclusions**

   You can use *must* to draw conclusions about the present.

   The house **must** *be very expensive. Look at the size of the garden!*

   You can use *must/mustn't have* + past participle to draw conclusions about the past.

   The paintings **must have cost** *a lot of money*. (They are by a famous artist and look very expensive.)

   They **mustn't have spent** *a lot of time preparing for this production*. (It wasn't very good.)

3 **Making criticisms**

   You can use *should/shouldn't have* + past participle to make criticisms about the past.

   The council **should have protected** *the building as it was very important historically*. (They were wrong not to protect it.)

   They **shouldn't have knocked** *the building down as it was very important historically*. (They knocked it down which was not the right thing to do.)

   You can also use *could have/might have* + past participle to make criticisms or show annoyance.

   They **could have protected** *the building!* (It was worth protecting, but they didn't.)

   Private companies **might** *at least* **have contributed** *to the cost of the new building!* (They didn't contribute and I think they should have!)

4 **Weak possibilities and weak suggestions**

   You can use *could/might* to express weak possibilities and suggestions.

   The coins we found **could** *be worth a lot of money*. (It is possible, but I'm not sure.)

   They **might** *put works of art like sculptures to make the city more attractive*. (I'm not saying they should do it, but it is a possibility.)

   They **could/might** *like to build a new art gallery to help improve the area*. (I'm suggesting this would be a good idea.)

Unit 10

Defining and non-defining relative clauses

Relative clauses contain a relative pronoun: *which, that, where, who, whose, whom*. You can use them in sentences to provide additional information about nouns.

There are two types of relative clauses: defining and non-defining.

A Defining clauses

Defining clauses provide essential information which identifies 'who' or 'what' is being referred to. You do not use commas at the beginning or end of the clause.

The artist **who** *painted the pictures in this gallery has used very vibrant colours*.

The film **that/which** *we saw last week was very exciting*.

You can leave out the relative pronoun only if it is the object of the clause and only in defining clauses.

The water-colour (**that/which**) *she painted in her teens has just sold for a record sum*.

The artist (**who/whom**) *I saw this morning was very famous*.

In speech, you can use *that* instead of *who/whom*.

The artist (**that**) *I saw this morning was very famous*.

A Non-defining clauses

Non-defining clauses provide additional information, which can be left out. You need to use commas at the beginning and the end of the clause. In speech, you indicate a non-defining clause by pausing briefly at the commas.

The square, **which** *is very small with many old buildings, is my favourite place in Paris*.

You cannot leave out the relative pronoun in non-defining clauses when it is the object of the clause.

The square, **which** *I visit very frequently, is my favourite place in Paris*. (NOT *The square, I visit very frequently, is my favourite place in Paris.*)

You cannot use *that* to introduce a non-defining clause.

~~The square, that is very small with many old buildings, is my favourite place in Paris.~~

1 **that/which**

   You use *that* or *which* when referring to things. You use *which* rather than *that* with prepositions.

   My mobile phone, **for which** *I paid a lot of money, has been stolen*. (NOT *My mobile phone, for that I paid a lot of money.*)

2 who/whom

You use *who* or *whom* when referring to people. You can use *whom* as the object of the word *who*. *Whom* is more formal and it is not often used in speech.

*The artist **who/whom** I saw this morning was very famous.*

You use *whom* with prepositions. This is quite formal and is only used in formal writing.

*The manager **to whom** I sent the cheque has disappeared.*
*The manager **who** I sent the cheque to has disappeared.*

3 whose

You use *whose* to show that something belongs to someone.

*That's the film director **whose** film just won the award.*

4 when/why/where

You use *when* when referring to a time and *why* when referring to a reason. You can leave out *when* and *why* in defining clauses.

*The reason (**why**) the bridge looks so elegant is the materials used.*

5 where

You use *where* when referring to a place.
You cannot leave out *where* in defining clauses.
*The town **where** I was brought up has expanded.*
(NOT *The town I was brought up has expanded.*)

Unit 11

Conditionals 2

1 Even if ...

You can use *even if* for emphasis.
***Even if** it doesn't solve the problem, it's surely worth a try.*
***Even if** they spent a lot of the money on the programme, it would be worth it.*

2 Supposing/what if/imagine/let's say ...

You can use *supposing/what if/imagine/let's say ...* for speculation.
***Supposing** you inherited a lot of money, what would you do?*
***Imagine** you could do any job for a day, what would you choose?*

3 Otherwise

You can use *otherwise* as an alternative to *unless/if not*.
*More money needs to be put into upgrading the broadband system; **otherwise**, it will slow down.* ('Unless more money is put into upgrading the broadband system, it will slow down.')

4 If only

You can use *if only* to express regret.
***If only** I had spent more time learning to play the violin when I was younger, I'd be much better now.*

5 If ... should ...

You can use *if ... should ...* as a variation of the second conditional.
***If** the government **should** introduce a law to promote electric cars, there will be a lot of support for it.*

6 On condition that/provided/provided that/as long as

You can use *on condition that/provided/provided that/as long as* as a variation of *if*.
***Provided that** the roads are clear, traffic will move freely.*

Unit 12

Articles

There are two types of articles that are used with nouns: definite and indefinite. The indefinite article – *a/an/zero* article with *s* – is used with countable nouns and the zero article without *s* with uncountable nouns. The definite article – *the* – is used with countable nouns in the singular and plural and with uncountable nouns.

1 Indefinite article: a/an

You use *a/an*:
- when you introduce a countable noun for the first time
  *He bought **a book** this morning.*
  ***A new car** was launched today.*
- with a countable noun which is one of a group
  *I played **a song** from the CD.*
- for someone's occupation
  *He's **an artist**.*
- with certain numbers/quantities
  *I bought half **a kilo of** tomatoes.*
  *I invited about **a dozen** people.*
- with hours, days, weeks, years and decades
  *I visit him once **a week**. She earns nearly $50 **an hour**.*

2 Definite article: the

You use the definite article:
- with uncountable and countable nouns that have been mentioned before
  *He bought **a book** this morning. **The book** was very expensive.*
- when it is clear what the context is for the noun
  *I had lunch in a restaurant near home today. **The food** was fabulous.* ('The food' in the restaurant)
- when there is only one in a system
  ***The sun** was hidden by clouds this morning.*
- with plural countries and abbreviations of countries names
  the Netherlands   the UAE
- with mountain ranges, rivers and oceans/seas
  the Alps   the Amazon   the Pacific
- with nationalities
  ***The Irish** have migrated to many different countries.*
- with groups of people
  ***the** young*
- with instruments
  *I have played **the piano** since I was ten.*
- with superlatives
  the best/worst
- with time
  *in **the past/future***
  Note *at present*.

3 Zero article (no article)

You use the zero article:
- with countable and uncountable nouns when you are talking generally
  *I buy **apples** every week.*
  ***Happiness** is easy to find.*
  - with names of cities, countries, states and roads
  Sao Paulo   Germany   Oxford Street
- with geographical areas, lakes, mountains and islands
  Northern Europe   Lake Victoria

Mt. Kilimanjaro   Corfu
- with days, months and years
  Tuesday   February   1979
- with meals when you talk about them generally
  *Let's go out for **dinner**.*
  Compare:
  The dinner we just had was very cheap.
- with company names
  Starbucks   YouTube   Google

Unit 13

Concession

1 Conjunctions

You can use linking words like *although/though/while* to highlight your ideas. You concede or agree with someone else's idea and then add your own.
***Although/though** I agree with the proposal, I think it is better to increase pensions for those over 75 years of age.*
You can use *while* and *whereas* to compare two things and emphasise the difference between them.
***While** the home team was slow and clumsy, the away team was fast and precise.*

2 *may/might* with *although/though*

You can use the modal verbs *may* and *might* with *although/though* to make concessions. ***Although/Though** this idea **may** be sound, there are better ways to tackle the problem.*

3 *may/might* with *but*

You can use *may/might* with *but*.
*This **may** be a very good way to improve the cohesion of society, **but** it must be done in conjunction with other measures.*

4 *much as*

You can use *much as* with verbs of feeling, approval and agreement to express concessions.
***Much as** I approve of the solution to the problem, I don't **believe** it is the best way to deal with the situation.*

5 Adverbs

You can use adverbs like *nevertheless/nonetheless*.
The policy is not popular with the general public.
***Nevertheless/Nonetheless**, it needs to be continued.*

Unit 14

Substitution and ellipsis

A Substitution

You can use the following for substitution in speech and writing to avoid repetition:
- so
  *Are you coming to the party this evening? I think **so**.*
  Here *so* is replacing that *I am coming to the party*.
  Note that you do not use it instead of *so*.
  You can also use so at the beginning of a clause.
  *Many people think the situation is getting better and **so** do I.*
- ***do/don't/did/didn't***
  *The public didn't support the idea of privatizing health care in any way, but the government at the time **did**.*

Here *did* is replacing *did support the idea of privatizing health care.*
*The government's advisors wanted to reduce investment in health provision, but ministers **didn't**.*
Here *didn't* is replacing *didn't want to reduce investment in health provision.*

- ***to do so/doing so***
  The social care provided needs a complete overhaul.
  ***Doing so/to do so** would require considerable sums of money.*
  Here *doing so/to do so* is replacing *to overhaul the social care provided.*

- ***neither/nor***
  *I haven't visited any cities outside London, **neither/nor** has my family.*
  Here *neither/nor* replaces *not visited any cities outside London.*

- ***not***
  *Do you think that people need money to be happy? I hope **not**!*
  Here *not* replaces *people do not need money to be happy.*

B Ellipsis

1 You can use the following to avoid repetition:
- Leave out words to avoid repetition after *and/but*
  I live in the countryside and commute to work in the city.
  *(INSTEAD OF **I** live in the countryside and **I** commute to work in the city.)*
  I go to museums in Lisbon a lot and to the street markets.
  *(INSTEAD OF **I** go to museums in Lisbon a lot and **I** go to the street markets.)*
- *used to* to avoid repetition of verbs
  I think people don't read books a lot now, but they used to.
  Here *used to* is replacing *read a lot of books in the past.*
- modal verbs to replace the main verb
  *The government don't put much effort into finding ways to increase the happiness index of the population but I think they **should**.*
  Here *should* replaces *the government should put much effort into finding ways to increase the happiness index of the population.*

2 You cannot leave out:
- main verbs after the verb *be*
  Many people are involved in volunteer work, but more could be done.
  (NOT Many people are involved in volunteer work, but more could be.)
- *been* after a modal verb in the perfect passive
  People of my generation were not given enough information about focusing on quality of life as opposed to money, when they should have been.
  (NOT People of my generation were not given enough information about focusing on quality of life as opposed to money, when they should have.)

Listening scripts

Unit 1

🎧 01

(M = Maggie; D = Director)

M: Hi. My name's Maggie. I think I spoke to you yesterday about coming in to see you about the drama classes.

D: Oh yes. Hi. How can I help you?

M: We're new to the area and I'd like my children, Terry, Andrea and Jasmine, to join the drama classes. They love acting, singing and dancing and they're very energetic and I also thought it would be a good way for them to make friends.

D: Oh yes, we offer dancing and singing as well as acting classes and the club's a good place for everyone to meet new people. We have different social and family groups and everyone here's very friendly.

M: Great. Can I just ask you some questions about the drama classes?

D: Yes sure. What would you like to know?

M: Mmm, what classes are there and when are they held?

D: Well … during the week, we have classes for different age groups. … By the way, what ages are your children?

M: Terry's 8. Andrea's 12 and Jasmine's 16.

D: Well, for the youngest age group, those aged 7–11, the times are 5.30 pm –6.30 pm on Tuesday evening and for those aged 12–15 between 4 and 6 pm on Wednesday evening … and for those 16 and above it's 6–8 pm on Friday evening.

M: Is there anything at the weekends?

D: Yes. We also have workshops on Saturdays from 10 am–1 pm, but they're usually for older members, 18 and above. We also have social outings to theatres, at discount rates. So it's possible for whole families to come. We even get free theatre tickets at times, which we announce on our website.

M: Oh that's good to know. And what about school holidays?

D: Well, during the holidays, we run summer camps for young people up to the age of 16. These usually run from 10 am–1 pm and 2 pm –5 pm Monday to Friday. They are combined with the youth club activities and run during August.

M: And what about performances?

D: For each level, we aim to have at least one show a year in the summer. There is no pressure for anyone to perform, but we do encourage everyone to get involved one way or another, either acting or behind the scenes. Usually everyone is really enthusiastic to take part.

M: Is it possible to have a look around?

D: Yes, sure. The building's used by other groups. … We have no changing facilities, just a large room with lockers where people can put their things, if necessary. But we advise people to come dressed for the workshops … in loose clothing and trainers.

....

M: Can my kids join immediately?

D: Yes they can. We always ask people to come and have a go first of all. Children usually come to meet new people and then want to come back, even the shy ones.

M: That's a good sign. Is there a fee?

D: There's a joining fee of £14 a year per person and then there's a separate fee for the Saturday workshops, but they're usually very cheap. It's just to pay the workshop trainer, as we survive on small grants and gifts.

M: OK. I think I'd like to bring the children along.

D: Great! What's your full name and address?

M: My name's Maggie Campbell.

D: Is that C–A–M–P–B–E–L–L?

M: Yes.

D: And the address?

M: It's 133 Arbuthnot Drive. I'll spell it. It's A–R–B–U–T–H–N–O–T.

D: And the postcode?

M: It's RV27 8PB

D: And the children's names again?

M: Terry, he'll come for the Tuesday class, so that's 17 March. And Andrea, she'll come for the class on 18 March. And Jasmine on the 20th.

D: Can I take a mobile number?

M: It's 07700336601.

D: And your email address?

M: It's M-A- …

Unit 2

🎧 02

Welcome. My name's Darren Timpson, and I'm the Director of the Penwood Museum and I'm here to announce the winners of our annual competition, which as usual runs in conjunction with our summer exhibition. Each year the competition has a specific theme. And the theme we chose for this year's competition is 'the use of technology to improve links between the local community and the museum'. Entrants could choose from a selection of the museum's artefacts to create exhibits on this topic. We've had loads of entries from secondary schools, which is important as more local teenagers are getting involved.

I just want to give you some background information about this year's competition. The competition was open to groups of young people from institutions like schools and youth clubs, who were aged between 15 and 19 on the final entry date for the competition, which was 13 May. While preparing their competition entry, the competitors were allowed to use the educational facilities at the museum and to look for help from local sponsors, but were not allowed to buy any equipment. We then had seven shortlisted exhibits, which visitors to the museum of all ages were allowed to vote on for the first three places.

The prize-winning exhibits are having a big impact on Penwood Museum attendances, which have risen by up to 45 per cent since the summer show opened. The first prize in this year's competition has been won by a group of seven young people, who chose various exhibits from the museum's collection of equipment from the 1950s to the 1970s. They arranged them with modern versions and then recorded their own reactions and comments to the exhibits. They then did the same with the comments made by visitors aged 65 and over. And so can we have a round of applause for the winners from Tigers Community Centre, who called their entry *Technology – now and then*?

And the second prize winners are Tabard High …

....

Before we have some refreshments, I'd like to draw your attention to some of the video commentaries on the winning exhibit which have been left by members of the public, and which are very moving … and some very funny. I particularly liked seeing the recording of the reaction of several people when they talked about an early wooden-framed TV from their childhood. They remembered their first TV, which they thought still fitted in with today's trends. They remembered how they would sometimes all go round to someone's house to watch TV as a special treat. But they thought the modern TV screen with the remote was much easier to watch.

As for the collection of old radios, it has to be seen. They are really huge old wooden-framed radios in perfect working order and in perfect condition. Some teenagers' reactions to the radios were very funny; they couldn't believe how big they were. And the older visitors, all of whom used to have one, said they liked them. But they also thought they were too big to fit into living rooms these days. A few more items worth looking at from the display are old kitchen items. Young people thought the cooker from the 1950s looked funny alongside the latest microwaves.

Nearly all interviewees who were aged 65 and over used microwave ovens, which they thought were much handier. Seeing old typewriters on display next to slim laptops made them look weird and cumbersome. All those who were 65 and over preferred the laptops, which they thought were thrilling. The other electronic items on display were a collection of old and fairly recent cameras. They also thought the older cameras were 'well made', and better than the newer ones'.

I'd like to thank you all for coming and please give a round of applause for all the entrants to the competition.

Unit 3

🎧 03

(T = tutor; M = Marco; K = Kelly)

T: OK Kelly and Marco. We arranged this tutorial so you could give me an update of your joint project, the, mmm … case study on the work you've been doing at the Janson … Adventure Sports Centre. Is that right?

M: Yes. That's it. Mmm … it's won quite a few awards lately … it's not that far from the university campus.

T: Right … . Yes, I have it here. Fire away.

M: Well, at first we were going to look only at the management structure of the Centre, but, mmm … we decided to examine the reasons that have made it more successful than other centres. The Centre's success has not just come from its many achievements; it's also attracting people of all ages from a wide range of backgrounds. Mm … we talked to staff and members and …

T: How many people did you talk to?

K: There're just over 600 members overall and 43 staff, including freelance trainers. So far we've talked to mm … oh, about 39 members.

T: Didn't you think of giving a questionnaire to everyone?

K: We decided against it.

T: Why was that?

K: Well, we thought that face-to-face interviews, however brief, would be better as we'd be able to probe people gently to give us more details, if need be.

T: And your findings so far?

M: The members we've spoken to all think that the centre's very well-run. The site and event managers're very focused and work well together. And the management team includes representatives from the Centre users.

K: This means that when decisions are made, they're not taken in isolation of the members, as so often happens in other organisations. The management team's then in touch with the members and vice versa.

T: You seem to have learnt a lot so far.

M: I agree. It's been a really challenging, but exhilarating experience being there. I can't wait to go in every day.

···

T: OK. Would you like to tell me a bit about the reasons behind the success of the Centre? Kelly, would you like to go first?

K: OK. Mmm … well … when we questioned the people we asked what they thought … the most important reasons for the Centre's success were. There were three factors that stood out from all the others …

T: Can you say something more about each of these specific points, Marco? Would you like to go on?

M: Well, as Kelly said, we isolated three main factors that were clearly more important than others. We found that, for most people and organisations like businesses, having award-winning courses that encouraged team-building and leadership development were absolutely crucial to the success of the Centre. They felt that the quality of the courses, which had been validated by external assessors, were important to … having confidence in the Centre.

T: Yes. That doesn't sound surprising considering how many centres and clubs are not as professional as this centre appears to be. We can't expect them all to be perfect, but … . And the next factor?

M: Mmm … I personally thought the quality of facilities would come next, but a close second was the quality of the coaching, which is more professional than most places the respondents have come across.

K: Like Marco, I expected facilities to come next, and …

M: … most people said the Centre managed to attract some really top quality people working as coaches. They see their job as pushing participants to realise their full potential. They are really good … the most experienced coaches are those running courses in team-building in management. They are also very motivating leaders, who are passionate about what they do.

T: And the third factor? … Kelly?

K: Mmm … the next factor is the range of courses and adventure opportunities. There are outdoor endurance courses covering trekking, mountain climbing, obstacle courses and the Centre also offers to design specific courses for companies. It was really thrilling to see all this in action as the staff worked to become the best in their field.

T: It sounds as if you've got a lot out of this experience.

M: It's the sort of place I'd like to work after I've graduated.

K: Me too.

Ready for Listening

Section 1

🎧 04

(R = receptionist; C = Clara)

R: Good morning. How can I help you?

C: Hi. Mmm … I'm not registered as a patient here at the moment as I moved to the north of the city, and I was wondering if it was possible to register again now and make an appointment as well.

R: Yes, I can register you today, but all the appointments for today are taken, unless it's an emergency.

C: No, I can't say it's an emergency.

R: OK, so I can register you. Is it just for yourself?

C: No it's for the whole family, myself, my husband and my daughter as well.

R: I can check on the system to see if your details are still on here.

C: I moved to another doctor about four and a half years ago, so …

R: Well I can have a look.

C: OK.

R: Can you tell me your name and date of birth? And I can check using both.

C: My name's Clara Wight.

R: Is that W–H–I–T–E?

C: No. It's W–I–G–H–T.

R: Right. Mmm and your date of birth?

C: 23rd October 1990.

R: OK … let's see. … Was your address before 72 Crocket Street?

C: Yes. That's it! That was my old address.
R: We have basic details, but no records. They were all transferred to the other health centre you registered at when you moved. Mmm … and your present address?
C: It's 88 Palace Avenue.
R: And the postcode?
C: It's ZE24 2TP.
R: If you fill in this form for yourself and your family, then we can input the details.
C: OK. But do I need to bring any proof of identity?
R: I need proof of your address from a utility bill, etc.
C: I've not got any bills, but I've got letters saying we're connected for the gas and electricity and of course I've got a letter showing the tenancy agreement with our name and the address on it.
R: That should be OK.

....

R: The first available appointment I have is on Thursday at three o'clock with Dr Jackson.
C: Mmm that's a bit awkward as I've got to pick up my daughter from school. Have you got anything later?
R: I've got an appointment with Dr Barker at 4 pm on Friday …
C: Yeah that's OK.
R: But it's at our other health centre.
C: Where's that?
R: It's not that far. It's less than 10 minutes' walk from here on North Street. Do you know where the cinema is on North Street?
C Yes.
R: Well it's on the same side of the road between the cinema and the pharmacy on the opposite side of the road from the bank.
C: Yes …. I know it. There's a small park just further along on the same side of the road on the other side of New Street, where the bus stops.
R: Yes. That's it. We will send you a text to confirm – can I just confirm your mobile number's 07700 900807?
C: Yes, that's correct. Thanks for your help.
R: Bye.

Section 2
🎧 05

Good evening, everyone, and welcome to the official opening of the Glitz Theatre, an exciting new development on this side of the city. The renovation of the theatre has taken nearly three years of painstaking restoration work and the results of the effort that has gone into it all are clearly visible.

Before we proceed to the opening ceremony, I'd like to say a few words about the transformation of the theatre.

The venue has changed from being a rundown building to what can only be described as a modern theatrical experience, and for me it's wonderful to see so many of the original features of the building still intact, especially on the façade, where all the dirt has been removed. There is now multi-coloured glass panelling on the façade, so the entrance looks really welcoming.

The auditorium, which was not particularly welcoming in the past, has had a complete makeover to create something modern and up-to-date. And we now have a concert venue for a wide range of uses, where we can hold not just plays, but concerts for pop and classical music and for conferences. For the latter, we also have a new extension with rooms for meetings and educational purposes all fitted out with the latest technology along with an area for mingling and entertaining.

The foyer of the theatre here, as you can see, has been made bigger with a much larger ticket office and machines for collecting tickets that have been booked in advance. And where there was only a machine serving coffee and cold drinks and a few stools and high tables there's now a proper coffee shop selling a wide range of light refreshments, which looks rather inviting. The roof terrace, which used to be closed, is now accessible, with a landscaped garden and a restaurant open to the public all year round.

The basement, which leads out into a garden at the back, has been converted into a members' room with a café for light refreshments and an area for art displays or stalls. The theatre shop is no longer beside the ticket office; it is now next to the entrance to the basement café. It doesn't just sell sweets, as it did before, but also theatre-related memorabilia, including programmes and books, DVDs, CDs, posters …

....

And in the information pack you all have you may notice that there is a programme of events for the summer months, mmm … . As it's during the school holidays, there'll be a wide range of special events aimed at children. For the matinee performance each day, the theatre is offering free tickets to 200 children up to 16 years of age. And there'll be special rates for theatre-goers who book a meal in the roof-terrace restaurant as well. And we'll be having special evenings where there'll be concerts and plays by local

groups. And also every Wednesday tickets will be half-price for members of the theatre. The membership is only £70 a year and gives members and a guest access to member-only events and to previews and access to the members' restaurant in the basement.

And another innovation at the theatre is the monthly programme of lectures and master classes delivered by actors, producers and writers, on various aspects of the theatre. This is certainly a major development, which will definitely pull in many theatre enthusiasts, and hopefully revitalise the area.

I'd now like the Mayor to say a few words before opening …

Section 3
🎧 06

(Z = Zahra; T = Thomas)

Z: Hi Thomas.
T: Zahra, hi. So, have you decided yet what you're going to do your seminar paper on?
Z: Yes, I have. Mmm … it's all at an early stage so far, but it's on the impact of smartphone technology on our lives, but I'll probably restrict it to just the field of studying at university.
T: Well, that sounds very topical. If you think of it, smartphones only started to become popular around 2008 and look how quickly they've changed everything.
Z: Yes, of course. Things're happening so fast, … I love new technology, but it's all too much at times. It'll be interesting to research. At least, I think it will.
T: Yes, I do too. And how're you going to do the research for your seminar paper?
Z: Well, mmm, I thought of interviewing people in the student body and members of the public – I want a wide range of ages and backgrounds, but I haven't narrowed it down yet.
T: Any minimum age?
Z 16/17 minimum perhaps, but as for an upper age limit, not really.
T: Mmm … and what're you setting out to show?
Z: I'm not sure at this stage either, but something along the lines of … mmm … the idea that we are allowing smartphone technology to control the way we do things too much, but I haven't made up my mind yet. I'm just thinking on my feet here. I haven't really thought it right through to the end, to be honest.
T: What about your questionnaire?

Z: Mmm … , yes that's another thing. <u>What I'm not really decided about is the length the questionnaire should be</u>.

T: The best thing is to keep it short.

Z: Maybe. But I'll finalise the length when I sit down to type it up.

....

Z: I need to find someone to try out my questions on. I've got some already written.

T: I can be your guinea pig if you want.

Z: Great!

T: Fire away!

Z: Let's see, … . Let's start with this one … which electronic device do you use most frequently?

T: Mm, I love my tablet, but actually, I'd have to say it's probably my smartphone.

Z: What do you use it for generally?

T: Mmm … apart from communication like video-phoning my family and friends at home and social media, and listening to and downloading music, I use it for practically <u>everything</u>, but probably less and less for texting.

Z: On a scale of 1–10, where 1 is least useful and 10 most useful, how useful do you find your smartphone is for communication?

T: Very useful, so 8. Without it, I'd be totally lost.

Z: And what about studying? Do you use it in your studying?

T: All the time. I use it for mmm … for searching on the net, and I also use it for downloading documents and for writing or dictating notes or bits of assignments on my mobile …

Z: Mhmm …

T: … and recording <u>lectures</u> or parts of them when I can't be bothered taking notes on my mobile and then it transfers to my laptop automatically when I switch it on.

Z: And I thought I used my mobile a lot!

T: … but in the main I use it for studying more and more, rather than just browsing the internet.

Z: Using the same scale, what about using the mobile for studying then?

T: Well, let's see … . It's more essential than communicating for me, and so it's a score of … <u>9</u>.

Z: What about entertainment?

T: I can use it for music and music videos and films and TV <u>shows</u>.

Z: What score would you give it for usefulness?

T: Mmm … well, for that, I'd give a score of 7.

Z: What else do you use it for?

T: For many different things like the news, the weather, health checks, as my wallet, train tickets and as a TV remote control. I can't wait to get it connected up to more things at home. I think I'll end up using it for organising my entire home <u>life</u>.

Z: Do you think so? And the score for these other things?

T: A definite <u>8</u>.

Z: OK thanks, that's really helpful …

Section 4

🎧 **07**

Good morning everyone. The topic of my talk this week is a rather unusual method of bringing water to drought-ridden regions of the world. The methods people most think of, or read about in newspapers and/or see on TV, er … are preventing deforestation and encouraging reforestation to prevent water run-off from barren land, and hence to stop flooding. Another method is … er … <u>drilling bore holes to bring water from aquifers deep in the ground to irrigate the land</u>.

But the method I'd like to talk about today is the production of rain through seeding clouds. For those of you who are not familiar with this practice, it is basically a process where nature is coaxed, as it were, to produce rain. In many places in the world, <u>attempts have been made throughout history to produce rain in times of drought through magic</u>, but from the latter part of the last century scientists've been endeavouring to come to the rescue by chemical means.

And at times they've been trying not just to produce rain, but also to divert it so that it does not rain on special days, such as national or international ceremonies. Cloud seeding has been carried out since the middle of the last century, but no scientist can confirm that the practice is actually responsible for rain, and not nature itself. Because who can confirm that the clouds would not let loose a deluge anyway?

Having said that, I am aware there is some evidence that <u>seeding clouds to produce rain can lead to a 15% increase in rainfall</u>. But what would happen, for example, if the actions of cloud seeding in one place led to a disastrous deluge in another? It would also be tricky to prove that any damage was the responsibility of cloud seeders. <u>Some people are understandably against the practice of cloud seeding, as we don't really know the consequences of interfering with nature</u>.

Cloud seeding has apparently been used by Californian officials to replenish reservoirs. In other parts of the US, electricity utility companies are especially fond of seeding to bring more water to hydroelectric plants.

With national budgets devoted to agriculture running into the tens of millions, <u>if not billions of dollars in some cases, the interest in attempts to control the weather is not surprising and deserves attention</u>.

....

Last year the agricultural and meteorology departments at the university were given a 20 million dollar grant, funded in part by the government and various companies in the food and agricultural industry, to conduct research into cloud seeding to increase precipitation. While the research is aimed primarily at the US, it is hoped that the benefits accrued will have far-reaching consequences for other drought-ridden regions of the planet.

Now … let's see, mmm … if we look at this diagram here, we can see how cloud seeding works. There are two basic methods: from the air and from the ground. Looking first at seeding from the air, we can see that an aeroplane flies above the clouds from where it fires silver iodide into clouds by dropping <u>chemical</u> flares in order to increase precipitation. Silver iodide crystals then attach themselves to water droplets, which makes the water <u>freeze</u> and fall as rain or snow over high ground. If we now look at the diagram showing cloud seeding from the ground, we can see that there is a ground seeding <u>generator</u> here on the right, which has a tall chimney, and er … next to this on the left is, mmm … a <u>fuel tank</u> containing propane. Heat generated from the burning of the propane lifts the silver iodide crystals up to <u>cloud level</u> again leading to precipitation.

So let's now …

Unit 4

🎧 **08**

Good morning, I'm going to talk to you today about the importance of infrastructure developments such as railway systems in helping solve some of society's problems … and I'll also highlight some social and economic opportunities these have provided.

First of all, I'd like to give a brief overview of the history of the railway system and its effect on the world. The timeline given here shows the most significant <u>events</u> in the expansion of the railways in the UK in the early 19th century. Let's start with probably the most important year on the timeline, the year 1831, which saw the opening of the successful Liverpool to Manchester railway. This was powered by the locomotive, *The Rocket*, which was created by the engineer, Robert Stephenson. This is generally thought of as the first modern railway, because both goods and passenger traffic were carried on trains according to a scheduled <u>timetable</u>.

The success of the railway would not have been possible without previous <u>developments</u> to which Stephenson is indebted. As you see in 1803, the first horse-drawn railway was opened in south London by an engineer called William Jessop. The first railway steam locomotive was built in 1804 by an English engineer Richard Trevithick and in the year 1812, the first commercially successful steam locomotive, the *Salamanca* appeared on the scene at Middleton in Yorkshire in the north-east of England. After the success of the Stockton to Darlington railway in 1825 with the engine *Locomotion*, <u>money</u> flooded into the north-west of England as the region went through a period of rapid <u>industrialisation</u>, with the railway linking the rich town of Manchester and the thriving port of Liverpool.

And the social and economic effect of the opening of the Liverpool and Manchester railway on the commercial world? It was quite dramatic. By 1834, the number of passengers using the railway had risen to nearly half a million. Also more merchandise, including coal and <u>cotton</u>, was transported between the two cities using the railway. The age of the railway as a means of carrying people from one place to another had arrived. The increase in rail passenger numbers and in the movement of goods led to a drop in other <u>costs</u> such as those for road and canal use.

....

Just as the inventions of these earlier pioneers opened up travel between towns and cities in the UK, railways around the world are still creating trade links within countries and across borders, bringing communities and nations together.

Railway systems worldwide are responsible <u>for improving people's living standards by bringing jobs to people and people to jobs</u>. In India, for example, millions have access to work through the railways. The country comes top as regards the number of passenger-kilometres yearly, a staggering one billion passenger kilometres a year accounting for about one third of the total number of passenger-kilometres travelled globally in 2006. But the Swiss are the top rail travellers individually with about 2,500 kilometres each year according to the Switzerland Office for Statistics.

There are now many examples of modern high-speed links around the world, which provide business and tourist opportunities <u>generating jobs and trade links</u>. We have the Eurostar with passenger statistics showing the increasing popularity of the line, and the Sapsan, the high-speed link between Moscow and St Petersburg in Russia, and also the Bullet train in Japan and the high-speed rail link in China.

Now let's look at some of the business opportunities created in India in greater detail.

Unit 5

🎙 **09**

(M = Marcus; C = customer)

M: Good morning, Fair booking office. Marcus speaking. Can I help you?

C: Is that the booking office for the Fair on Futuristic Home Design?

M: Yes sir, that's correct. How can I help you?

C: Well, mmm … I'm attending the Fair and I'd just like to check a few things if that's OK?

M: Yes, sure.

C: OK. I understand the Fair opens the week after next on the Tuesday, and … the preview is on <u>Monday.</u>

M: Yes, that's right. There is a preview on Monday, but the Fair's not open to the general public on that day. But for the rest of the week it is.

C: OK, I see. That's fine. I've got two complimentary <u>day passes;</u> can you tell me if I can use them on any day?

M: Well, I'm not sure if there are any restrictions, … let's see … yes, here we are.

C: Yes?

M: You can use them on any day including the preview day, except Saturday. But you need to sign up for the workshops and seminars you want to attend in advance.

C: Oh, I see. I haven't decided which workshops or seminars to attend yet.

M: Mmm … well … Saturday you can't attend any with the passes you have, and Thursday they're already completely booked. I think the other days'll book up fairly quickly now, as there's a lot of interest from the general public and retailers.

C: You mean I won't be able to attend any workshops on Saturday even with my free pass?

M: I'm afraid not. It's better to register for the other days now.

C: OK. I suppose, mmm … I'll attend all the seminars on <u>Tuesday</u> and <u>Friday</u>. Do you need my name?

M: No, I just need to take your reference number from the day

passes. Your name will come up with the number; it'll be the same number on each one. I'll register one for Tuesday and one for Friday, and then when you use one it'll automatically cancel.

C: OK, the number is <u>S–F–6–7–99</u>.

M: … 99. Thank you, I've got that.

C: What about services like places to eat and so on?

M: Oh, there are 15 restaurants in all.

C: That's a lot.

M: There'll be lots of people … there are <u>three sandwich bars</u> and the others are different types of dining areas around the Fair. Some <u>restaurants from the area around the Fair venue</u> will be there doing special promotions at the Fair itself, so you won't go hungry.

....

C: Is there somewhere nice to stay nearby?

M: Oh yes. There're rooms at the nearby halls of residence, which are part of the university. They're just across the road from here.

C: How much are they?

M: A single room is £65 per night, which includes breakfast in the cafeteria. And there are some very pleasant family-run hotels in the area. They range from around £70 to about £90. It depends how much you want to spend really.

C: What about getting there? Are there good transport links?

M: Yes. We're very well located – about a 30-minute walk at most from the train and bus station, and about 45 minutes from the airport. There are lots of buses; the best one, which stops just by the main entrance, is bus 70. No, sorry, it's bus <u>17</u>. I keep getting them mixed up. You want the bus going in the direction of Brookfields. The buses run every 12 minutes and you catch it from Stop W close to the station.

C: OK. How much does it cost?

M: It only costs £3.20 from the station. But you can also buy a weekly ticket for £15.

C: How long does it take?

M: Ten minutes, but there may be lots of traffic.

C: OK.

M: And there's also a river bus.

C: A river bus?

M: Yes. You can take Route A to the <u>marina</u>. It runs every 20 minutes. You can catch it on the river front, which is <u>five</u> minutes' walk from the station.

C: Is it more expensive?

M: Not much. It's £<u>3.95</u> and there's no weekly pass. But the journey only takes 5 minutes and it's probably more pleasant and comfortable.

C: And taxis? Just in case.

M: Mmm, for a taxi … you'll pay a maximum of £20.

C: Mmm … well that all sounds OK.

Unit 6

🔊 10

I'd like to describe a place that is really very beautiful. It is a picnic area on a mountain top on the north coast of Ireland. It is close to where my father was born and I went there for the first time when I was about 14 years old with my family on holiday. And I've been back many times since. The place is special to me, because the surrounding landscape is breath-taking. I also like it because the views of the countryside below the mountain are really spectacular. The area is very scenic, but it's usually empty, as you need a car to get there and there are no facilities, so few people go there. That makes it very peaceful and somewhere to escape from the world. It isn't quiet because of the wind, but it is a place to relax.

🔊 11

Good morning and welcome to the Moorland Countryside and Woodland Programme. I'd like to give you some information about the programme and the short courses we run for people on woodland awareness.

We're actually a programme run by volunteers, and we were set up 15 years ago to educate people of all ages and backgrounds about the wonders of our woodlands and, hence, nature itself. And for the past five years we've been taking groups of youngsters in their teens on educational trips on Fridays, Saturdays and Sundays, mmm … from schools mainly from around the area, … but some've come from much further afield. At first, some youngsters're not very impressed by the setting, because we discourage them from using any electronic devices, especially smartphones, so they can engage more with the surroundings … this throws them quite a bit. But almost without exception, by the end of the three days they're here the young people don't want to leave and want to come back again. In fact, two of the workers here came with student groups five years ago, and when they left school they came straight to work for us.

The programme is completely self-sufficient, due in part to the sales from the plant nursery and also to donations, but the bulk of our income's now from running the educational and awareness courses.

This is a basic map of our centre. We're here at the entrance, and you can see the cabins running along the east side of the path as you go north. The first cabin, Beech Lodge, is for students. It's quite large and can accommodate 10 students in bunk beds. Then the next four cabins're for families, and the cabin after that, Chestnut Lodge, is for teachers, which can hold up to four adults. On the west side of the path, directly opposite the family cabins, are the educational facilities. They're quite up-to-date with all the latest wizardry. And next to that's the cafeteria, which is shared with visitors to the centre. Just beside the cafeteria is a family area with climbing frames for children. We don't allow open-air cooking here, because of the trees.

The plant nursery's that area you can see that runs all the way along the north part of the map.

……………………………………………………………

If you go over here, between the family area and the nursery, the path leads to the woodland itself. We're on a hill here and quite high up, … and as there's some spectacular scenery around here, we have breathtaking views of the countryside. You can see the river stretching for miles through rolling countryside. Fortunately, the whole woodland is protected by law, so nobody can chop down any trees.

The landscape here's not changed for hundreds of years. Some of the trees've been growing here rather a long time, and the aim of the scheme and the volunteers is to keep it that way. We advise people to stick to the paths, because it's very easy to get lost. As you walk through the woodland, you'll see workers removing dead wood and trees. I'd ask everyone not to remove anything like seeds or flowers from the woodland so we can try and conserve it for future generations.

Unit 7

🔊 12

(T = tutor; J = Jack; F = Francesca)

T: OK, if you want, we've got some time left for some feedback on your joint presentation today.

J: Yeah, we can do it now while it's fresh in our minds, if it's OK with Francesca.

F: It's OK with me.

T: So, Francesca, how do you think it went?

F: Well, mmm … I was really happy with it actually, but I'm glad it's over. I think the main advantage of doing the presentation was that we both learnt quite a lot about training and skills development for the workplace and how they improve people's opportunities in life, especially their job prospects.

J: And we learnt a lot from actually delivering the presentation as well, which is really useful for the future.

F: Yeah, that was important too. Mmm … as I said, I was pleased with it, but if I had to do it all over again, I'd change a few things.

T: Like what, for instance?

F: Well, mmm the first thing I'd do is work on the pace of the talk and make the delivery slower. And I'd keep a clock in front of me so that I was aware of the speed and … and the next thing is mmm … the length of the talk … I'd make the presentation time 15 minutes for each of us, because I think ten minutes each was much too short. If we'd given ourselves more time, it would have flowed better.

J: Yes, I agree. I thought the timing was a bit tight. I'd say maybe even 30 minutes each.

T: Mmm … 30 minutes might've been a bit long for both you and the audience.

J: Maybe you're right; 15 minutes each would probably have been better.

F: And the next thing is the order of the data. I thought the sequence was bad – it could've been a lot better.

T: Yes. If I had to give some particular advice, I'd say you needed to give yourselves a run through once or twice using the equipment, just to see what it's like. Doing it without preparation like that's not that easy.

F: No definitely not. And another thing for me is that we forgot to give out the handouts with the copies of our slides on them for people to take notes. I should've given them out before we started. And one final thing I'd do is … I'd check that everyone could see the screen properly, … mmm … I'd make sure the arrangement of the chairs in the room made it easy for everyone to see.

T: And Jack? What about you? How did you feel about it all?

J: Well, er … I agree with Francesca. Yeah … in everything she said. It's very difficult to make the delivery smooth. If … when I do it again, I'll definitely spend more time practising to make it run more smoothly.

……………………………………………………………

T: But would you add anything to what Francesca said?

J: Mmm … perhaps I'd try to pack less information into the time given. Er … I thought at first it would be the opposite. Er … I was afraid that we'd end up looking foolish. And also I think I'd spend less time on the information gathering phase because, unless time is devoted to practising, it'll not be possible to give a good performance.

T: Yeah, I think I'd agree. Anything else?

J: Yeah. I get very nervous when I speak in front of people. If I did it again, I'd make sure I practised speaking out loud and projecting my voice. I think the key for me is learning to steady my <u>nerves</u>.

F: But you were very calm!

J: Not inside I wasn't!

T: Well, it didn't show.

F: I think you need the nerves to keep you going, but maybe try to take your mind off it beforehand by exercising or something.

T: Is that everything?

J: Yeah.

T: OK. Well, you'll be pleased to know the feedback from the class questionnaires was that the presentation was <u>enjoyable</u>, so well done. I have to say that I agree with them.

J: Oh, thanks.

T: I'll make a copy for both of you of the <u>questionnaires</u>, if you want. And if and when you do give a talk again, you can keep them to refer to.

Unit 8

🎧 13

Well, in today's lecture we are going to explore early human migration out of Africa to colonise the world. Throughout history there've been waves of humans migrating as people have moved from one locality to another, sometimes quickly over very short distances … and sometimes slowly over very great stretches of land, mmm … in search of a new or different or better life. There now appears to be general agreement that the first movement of people of any real significance in any part of our planet originated in East Africa approximately <u>100,000</u> years ago. This first group of modern humans made their way across the Red Sea, which was then a dry bed. Then through Arabia and into what is now the Middle East. But these early pioneers soon died out.

Just like today, the Earth was subject to shifts in <u>temperature</u>. About 70,000 years ago the planet became warmer and another group of modern humans migrated out of their homeland of Africa, following basically the same route, and then moving on to South Asia. By about 50,000 years ago, modern humans had colonised China, and about <u>45,000</u> years ago they had reached Europe. These early humans

settled in the wide open spaces of Siberia about 40,000 years ago and about 20,000 years ago modern humans reached Japan, which was connected to the main <u>land mass</u> at that time.

Now, there was no land connection between Australia and South East Asia, so the first Australians who arrived around 50,000 years ago must have made the journey across the sea in <u>simple boats</u> to settle on the Australian continent.

Modern humans moved from Asia to North America, which was reached across what is now the Bering Strait through Alaska. This migration happened between 15 and 13,000 years ago. There is also some evidence to suggest that modern humans came across pack ice via the North Atlantic, but this theory has been discounted by some. Since that time, the American continent has been the destination of waves of human settlement.

....

Before we look at more modern examples of human movement, like the Anglo-Saxon migrations to Britain in the 5th century AD, the migration of Turks during the Middle Ages and the migration of the Irish to America in the mid-19th century, I'd like to look at a migration within the continent of Africa itself, that I'm personally very interested in.

If we look at the map of Africa, we can see some patterns that are common to other waves of human movement throughout history. The routes here show what is probably the most significant migration in Africa itself: that of the Bantu, who spread out from a small region in West Africa near the present day border of Nigeria and Cameroon, just around here on the map … to occupy roughly <u>30 per cent</u> of the continent by the year 1,000 AD. A trigger for this movement may have been the result of the cultivation of the <u>yam</u>, a starchy root vegetable, which Bantu farmers started to grow as part of their staple diet. This cultivation began around 2,750 BC, resulting in the expansion of the population. The Bantu people then spread out into the neighbouring territories, which were at that time sparsely populated. As the land of the rainforest could not sustain the farmers and their families for longer than a few years, they moved on, felling trees and creating new clearances in the forest to cultivate yams. With the numbers of the Bantu on the increase between 2,500 and 400 BC the people were constantly on the move, migrating south down through modern-day Congo … in central Africa, and reaching Zimbabwe and modern-day South

Africa by about 100 AD.

It was contact with <u>Sudan</u> in North Africa that introduced the Bantu to iron production, in which they excelled. Once they had exchanged knowledge of working in iron from Sudan, the quality of their work rivalled that produced by the Mediterranean people of the time. They now had better tools to cut down trees, clear forests and <u>work fields</u>. And there is one other benefit iron gave them, and that was a <u>military advantage</u> over their neighbours.

I'd say that migration has transformed the world from early times, and we all reap the benefits of different peoples coming into contact with each other.

Unit 9

🎧 14

(T = tutor; M = Malcolm)

T: Hi Malcolm. How are you?

M: Fine, thanks. And you?

T: Yes, I'm OK, thank you. You left a message when you booked this tutorial to say that you wanted to talk about your film project. Am I right?

M: Yeah.

T: So, how can I help you?

M: Well, I'm having difficulty getting my project started. I should've been about halfway through by now, but I haven't done anything at all really. I think I'm feeling a bit overwhelmed by it all.

T: Overwhelmed? In what way?

M: Mmm … I don't know. I may've chosen something that's <u>too abstract</u>.

T: Which is? Remind me what the focus of … ?

M: The title's 'Perceptions of Beauty in India'.

T: Yeah. That's a good subject; it's probably quite challenging, but very appealing.

M: I wanted to put together a moving digital photo collage of my travels around India last summer showing the beauty of the place. I was <u>completely overawed</u> by the whole experience.

T: How many did you take in all?

M: At least 600.

T: That is a lot. I'm sure it's a wonderful photographic record, but I think your problem lies there. Can you tell me? What did you take photographs of?

M: Buildings like palaces and official places like the government buildings in New Delhi by Lutyens – I think they're really underrated

People just think of the Taj Mahal, but India's not all like that. It's huge: it's got tradition, colour

233

and beauty at every corner. I've also got some <u>dazzling</u> images of places like the Ganges at Varanasi; the grandeur and splendour of the images simply take your breath away.

T: OK, I have a suggestion.

M: Yeah?

T: What about going through your digital stills on the computer and selecting the <u>ten images</u> which appeal to you the most? And …

M: I don't know if I could narrow it down to that.

T: Well, you'll be surprised. Select the top hundred, and then narrow that down to 25. And then you could …

M: I've just thought of an idea.

T: Yes?

M: I could mmm … Yes that's it! I could select the top ten as you suggest, and then find various people's views on these … and then do a video collage with the pictures swirling around like a <u>pop video</u>. Why didn't I think of that before! That's it!

T: Problem solved?

M: Yes, but now I have to do all the work!

....

T: Before you submit the project, there are a few things I'd like to say. The length …

M: Can the film be longer than 15 minutes?

T: I wouldn't advise it. There might have been a few people on the course last year who made 20-minute, or even 25-minute films, but I have to say they were the least successful. I think you'll find that it's good discipline to try to work within a short time limit <u>and overall concentrate on having an end product that is simple</u>.

M: Mmm …

T: And I'd say that ten minutes might be good …

M: Ten minutes! That's almost nothing.

T: You'll be very surprised. One minute per place fading out and in. It could be very effective. Remember the work we did on adverts and <u>the short attention span of people generally</u>, especially these days.

M: Yeah, I suppose you're right. I'm just thinking of all the materials – 600 plus stills down to ten, and then reduced to a ten-minute film. What about the format? How do I need to submit it?

T: Mmm … <u>all the information is on the department website. You can access it as per usual</u>.

M: What's it under?

T: Go to 'Digital Photography'. Then 'Year One', and then click on 'Film Project', and everything is there.

And don't forget <u>you have to fill in a submission form detailing the background of the project</u>.

M: Yeah, I … I know all that. But can't I just email it to you when it's done?

T: I'm afraid not, it has to go through the central process. We used to ask for copies burned on DVD, … four copies with the submission form, but we've been overtaken by technology, so you hand it in <u>on a memory stick</u>.

M: OK, I can do that.

Unit 10

🧑 **15**

(P = Presenter; D = Director)

P: Welcome on this lazy Saturday morning to Radio Hope. This is Charlie Carter, your host on your favourite show, *Your Chance* … and we have a lot for you this week.

I've got Jenny Driver the Director of the Horn Art Gallery in George Street and we'll be talking about developments on the art scene this week.

D: Thank you Charlie. Well, first, there's the new Public Art Project throughout the city, which opened last weekend in conjunction with the Horn Gallery and which has caused a sensation judging by the response on Twitter. And then we have a debate about charging for entrance to museums and art galleries. But first to the Public Art Project.

There has been some criticism that the public art on display is a waste of public money, but also <u>many people have suggested the sculptures on display could be made permanent</u>, which could encourage more people to visit the city and its museums and art galleries. Gallery attendance has definitely been on the increase since the public art sculptures were installed. The idea of a permanent public display is a very good one. But some people have also emailed in suggesting that instead of having only international artists, <u>the gallery could use the exhibition as an opportunity to support local sculptors</u> who get no help from the public funds, which is a valid suggestion.

P: Do you think the Project will achieve its objectives?

D: Well, I think so. The Public Art Project had two broad objectives, <u>which were to raise public awareness about art</u>, especially sculpture, which I think has been achieved with the increase in museum attendances. And,

<u>secondly, through tourism in the area, we wanted to make people more aware of the city nationally and internationally</u>. Both are difficult to gauge in the long term, but for the moment the number of people visiting the city seems to point to success.

P: What do you think about the idea of making all museums and art galleries free of charge?

D: There has been a fierce debate about this over the past year or so, because <u>people are deterred from visiting places of a cultural nature, like the Horn Gallery, because of the cost</u>. And while children are able to get in free, they rarely come with their parents, which is a bad thing. So, basically, I am for the change. From the survey we've had on our website, I think <u>about 75 per cent said they were for entrance being free</u>, only ten per cent were very definitely against and 20 per cent said they didn't know.

P: Have you any concerns about the removal of charges?

D: <u>There is one thing I and other people working in the gallery world are worried about, and that is the level of government funding</u>. We've always had subsidies from the government to run the galleries, but this has always been topped up by entrance fees. We're waiting to see if this will be reflected in the government's arts funding for next year.

....

P: Now, as you all know, we've been wanting to do some outside broadcasting on the show for a long time, and this week for the first time we will have two reporters on <u>the street</u> … because we think this is an important issue, … mmm and we want to gauge mmm … <u>public reaction</u> to the museum charge debate. We have one reporter, Angie Hunter, standing by outside the Horn Gallery. And we'll see what people really think about their art galleries being free or not. To make sure we get as wide a spectrum of people as possible we have another reporter, Alex Grey, who's standing in front of the <u>department store</u> in the pedestrian shopping precinct. So, if you're listening and want to make your views known, pop down to the precinct or the gallery. We'll be starting the outside broadcast in 15 minutes at 12.45, after we have got through the other items today, so …

Unit 11

🎧 16

(A= administrator; P = parent)

A: Accommodation Office, Tom speaking. How may I help you?

P: Yes, hi. My name's Margaret Williams.

A: Oh, hi.

P: Mmm … I understand that you're looking for host families for international students.

A: Yes, we're always looking for suitable families, as we have a lot of demand at the moment. How did you hear about us?

P: Mmm … from a friend, Mrs Dalton, who's already with your agency. We live in the same street as her in Maltby.

A: Ah yes … I know who you mean. You're quite close to several of our schools.

P: … and I just wanted to ask some questions about registering with you.

A: No problem.

P: OK. Can you tell me how we go about becoming a host family with you?

A: Well, once a family first approaches us, we like to make a preliminary visit to the home, have an <u>informal chat</u> and discuss all the registration details first.

P: That sounds great. Do we need to make an application at this stage?

A: No, we like to come and visit you first and provided we're then both happy after the <u>preliminary chat</u>, we usually begin the registration process there and then, and you can complete it and send it in by email.

P: What about references and things like that?

A: Mmm, if the application for registration is submitted and accepted, we need to do some background checks first of all, and we like to have at least <u>two references</u> from families or professional people. We'd only do these if you made a definite commitment to proceed.

P: OK.

A: We think it's better to check that a family's clear about what is involved in the whole process … then we can begin the application process.

P: How long does the process take?

A: It depends, but it's usually a few <u>weeks</u>, unless there are any delays. Once everything is agreed, we match students with suitable families at the beginning of a term and usually at the beginning of the academic year in <u>September</u>.

P: That all sounds reasonable.

A: Can I ask how many students you were thinking of hosting?

P: We thought that we would like to take <u>two</u> to start with. We have two daughters aged 14 and 15, so we'd like two students around a similar age … that would be ideal … it's easier then for them to strike up a friendship.

A: That shouldn't be a problem.

....

A: Obviously, we have to look at things like how far the host family home is from schools we cover, access to libraries, whether you have wi-fi, access to public transport and the <u>neighbourhood</u> in general.

P: OK. That sounds very reasonable. I think we'd like to proceed.

A: OK, that's good. We could actually do a preliminary visit at the end of this week, Thursday morning or Friday afternoon, or any time on Saturday, and have a more detailed chat and start the application process, if appropriate.

P: OK, we're both free on <u>Friday afternoon</u>.

A: That'd be fine. Can I have the number of your house?

P: It's <u>53</u>.

A: 53 and two more things … could I take a mobile number?

P: Yes, it's <u>08977 392251</u>.

A: … 392251.

P: Yes, that's right.

A: … and your email address?

P: It's <u>MAW973@maltby.co.uk</u>.

A: OK, I'll email you the confirmation of the meeting, and shall we say 2 pm?

P: Yes, that'd be …

Unit 12

🎧 17

Good evening. I'm really pleased to be asked to be part of your winter series on cities around the world and I can see from your programme that you have had speakers talking about a wide range of places from Asia to Africa and South America. This helped me narrow my choice down to three different places, and I finally decided on a city that made a huge impression on me, namely St Petersburg in Russia. Before we start, … <u>if you'd like more information about the places mentioned in the talk you can find it on my website and in my blog</u>, details of which I'll give you at the end.

All of the places I've visited over the years have made a profound impression on me. But my trip to St Petersburg will always stay in my memory. … <u>And I have to say that the city is definitely in the top ten places that I have ever visited for a holiday.</u>

The first time I went there was in winter … it was memorable, partly because I visited various cultural places like the Hermitage, the famous museum on the bank of the River Neva, a place that I had always wanted to visit. <u>But I remember my visit particularly well because it was very cold … the river was frozen solid and I saw moisture freezing in mid-air as the wind came off the frozen river</u>. The place was so magical. It's moments like this that make travelling so worthwhile. It was such a different experience from anything I'd ever had before.

The city is famous, like Venice, for its canals, but there is just so much to see, as it is a city full of beauty. The people are so welcoming, … <u>and what strikes you as a visitor is the richness of the heritage</u>. Near to the Hermitage Museum, that I have already mentioned, is a very striking statue, the Bronze Horseman, which is a memorial to Peter the Great. Other places that are worth seeing are the Mariinsky Theatre and the metro of St Petersburg, which although is not as famous perhaps as that of Moscow, is still worth seeing, especially the Avtovo metro station, which is without doubt one of the most beautifully decorated metro stations you're ever likely to see. <u>But for me, if I had visited nothing else in St Petersburg and had only gone around the Hermitage Museum, it would've been well worth the visit.</u>

....

For breaks to a city like St Petersburg, you have different ways of travelling and different types of holidays. You can fly direct to St Petersburg from London or you can visit the city as part of a <u>summer cruise</u> of the Baltic Sea that also takes in the Gulf of Finland. Visits don't have to be restricted to the city itself. In the city suburbs there're fabulous <u>palaces</u> and <u>gardens</u> to entice visitors. Apart from the famous Peterhof Palace, there's also the Catherine Palace with its famous Amber room and extensive park. So, if you are thinking of visiting the city, leave yourself some time to <u>explore</u> further than the centre of the city.

But of course, any holiday destination is a personal choice. For many people the word 'holiday' conjures up different things. For example, adventure holidays to places that are generally inaccessible are now increasingly <u>popular</u>, as are those to pristine beaches untouched by humans, but for me, even as a seasoned traveller, my trip to St Petersburg in the heart of winter among the ice and snow was a <u>novel experience</u> and a true adventure.

Now let's look at …

Ready for Speaking

Part 2

🎧 18

(E = examiner; C = candidate)

E: Now, I'm going to give you a card with a topic to look at. You have one minute to make notes and then I'm going to ask you to talk about the topic.

E: Can you talk about the topic?

C: The skill that I'd like to talk about is playing a musical instrument, mmm … like the piano, and I'd like to learn it in the near future. I know it's possible to go to a class to learn to play the piano, but mmm … I know I'd find that very annoying. I think learning to play the piano's one of those skills that'd be better to learn … to acquire by paying for individual tuition. I realise it might be expensive, but it'd be mmm … very rewarding in other ways.

Why I'd like to be able to take up the piano is because … it's mmm … very soothing to play and to listen to. It's a wonderful feeling to lose yourself in the music as you're playing. I've got several friends who are mad about music, and I've listened to them many times. They've played both classical and pop music to me, and they've found it thrilling to play for someone. And to me it is a very peaceful experience just sitting there and listening. As well as helping to calm people down, playing an instrument like the piano's mmm … very good for the brain as it keeps it active. One of my friends, who plays the guitar and the piano, says that he plays for about … half an hour before he does any homework, and it helps him to focus on his work and concentrate more. And it's healthy, because it helps take away part of the stress of modern life. Friends have also told me that it improves their ability to focus, and so they play before they study or do any work, which I think would mm … benefit me too.

E: OK. Thank you. Which type of music would you like to learn to play?

C: Mmm … I'd like to start with classical, but I'd like to learn jazz music later on and maybe some pop music.

Part 3

🎧 19

(E = examiner; C = candidate)

E: Let's talk about learning new skills generally. Do you think it's important to keep acquiring new skills throughout one's life?

C: Yes, I think it is.

E: Why do you think so?

C: Well, mmm, at the moment life is changing so fast with the advances that have been made in technology, and also through mmm … globalisation in the past few decades, so it's important for people of all ages to keep up-to-date with skills of all kinds.

E: How essential do you think it'll be for workforces in the future to be proficient technologically?

C: Mmm, I'd say it'll be vital, because more and more of the work that is done nowadays requires a lot of input using one form of technology or another, so that in the near future it will be almost impossible to find work, even basic work, without practical computing skills. Take car design, for example. It seems that technical drawing done by hand is less important now than knowing how to create new products on the screen. Soon designers'll be creating holograms of cars, not just three-dimensional computer images. And the same applies to architecture and teaching too.

E: In what way do you think learning only computing skills can be a disadvantage in life?

C: Mmm … first of all, people are already becoming over-reliant on computers for virtually everything. In the current knowledge-based society, where information is available literally at people's fingertips, there's a danger that people's knowledge'll decrease and accessing information'll become just like switching on the light without necessarily understanding what's happening. And people're in danger of losing their ability to do basic things.

E: Mmm, should the preparation of children and young people for work focus on computing skills at the expense of practical skills?

C: Mmm … I think it's a matter of balance, because we need the people to build computers and so on, and the people to learn to be able to use them for their work. Also, if any machines break down, we need people to be able to fix them. And so if education concentrates on training people to use machines to access knowledge at the expense of training

technicians, etc, then there'll be a major problem.

E: Do you think people will have to work longer in the future?

C: At one time, it was thought that people would have more leisure time in the future, but it seems that the opposite is true. As people are living longer worldwide, they're also being asked to work longer with the result that the age at which people will be drawing a pension, if they have one, will be later than it is now. And in fact it's already starting to happen in many countries like the UK and France.

E: How can people ensure that work does not control their lives?

C: It's not easy, but not impossible either. One way is to ensure that one has interests outside work, and that these interests are not connected with work in any way. For example, if people are involved in working in computers all day, they could find something that requires manual skills, like pottery.

Unit 13

🎧 20

(T = Tracey; A = Andrei)

T: Hi Andrei. How're you getting on with your research project?

A: I've just started, and it's giving me a headache. I really thought it'd be nothing like this, but then … I suppose it'll probably get easier, … I hope.

T: Getting started is always the worst part for me. I always hate getting down to it.

A: Well, yeah, it can be a real problem, but it doesn't have to be.

T: So … you're doing something … on the relationship between the public and systems such as roads and other transport in cities?

A: Yes, that's it. And you're looking at … ?

T: Cityscapes and their impact on people's moods.

A: Ah, yes.

T: It's given me lots of headaches too. What's your problem?

A: Oh, everything basically. I'm just trying to get my head around everything and don't know where to start.

T: Mmm … I'm in the middle of looking at data analysis, and I'm having a bit of a struggle myself at the moment.

A: You're at the data stage. Oh right. You're quite far on then.

T: Yeah. I am …

A: Could you tell me what your experiences have been as you're further along than me? It might make me feel a bit better.

T: Yeah sure. Looking back I don't know how I got to this stage, but mm … I found it fairly straightforward getting started. <u>I was expecting it to be much harder</u>, but it all came together rather quickly.

A: That's good to hear. So that's promising. But can you tell me about your experience say of mmm … coming up with the research question?

T: I thought I'd have difficulty turning my ideas into a research question, but it wasn't as bad as I thought. <u>In fact, I found it relatively painless</u>.

A: OK … I might ask for your help on that then. What about the literature review?

T: The literature review? <u>That I found really took up a lot of time</u>. But I have to admit, I actually like digging into things and getting to the bottom of problems, so part of that was me.

A: Yes, I agree it can be fun. I'm reading a lot to try and get myself to frame my research question, and I'm really getting into the literature.

T: Well, the thing I was very glad to get out of the way was writing the research proposal. <u>I was exhausted after that</u>, because it's important to make sure the research proposal's really clear on the focus of your research. It's not easy summarising everything and bringing it together.

A: And what about designing the methods?

T: <u>That was really easy to do – I enjoy analysing systems and putting them together, so I think I sorted the methods design out really quickly</u>. But what I found really agonising was writing the aims and objectives. <u>That was probably particularly hard to deal with</u>.

A: Yeah … they aren't easy.

....

T: Is all of this any help Andrei?

A: Oh yes. One of the problems is that it's OK to see things written on paper but it's the thinking behind it.

T: Yes, of course. It is.

A: Yeah. I appreciate it. My spoken English is not a problem, I think, but I've not done much writing and I'm going to find that bit difficult.

T: Well, you can get help you know.

A: Yeah? Mm, do you think I need a private tutor?

T: Oh no, that's not necessary, I'm sure. I know there's language support in the university if you are not a full-time student; you just need to contact <u>the Language Centre</u>.

A: OK, but there's likely to be a fee involved.

T: Mmm well you can get help through <u>the main library</u>. It's not just for lending books you know.

A: Really? I never thought of that.

T: It's so easy to get isolated and not know everything that's available.

Unit 14

🎧 **21**

As we continue our series on customs and traditions that influence the values and principles of all societies in the world, today we're going to talk about money. It is easy to think of money as just an economic tool in the world of finance, but it also has a <u>social and psychological dimension</u>. It is woven into the fabric of our society and thinking, and as such has, through history, despite people's criticism of its pursuit, helped lay down the standards and the ethics that govern modern society.

First of all, to look at the history of money we need to ask ourselves what money is. Money is, in fact, an invention of the human mind, … which is made possible <u>because we as human beings are able to give value to symbols</u>. And money is one of the most important symbols in all societies because it represents the value of goods and services. <u>If we accept any object as money – say a gold coin or a digital bank account balance – both the user and the wider community have to agree to this</u>. So, all the money that we use today has … mmm … not just an economic dimension, but a psychological and a social one as well.

Before we look at so-called 'commodity money' … with the introduction of coins and representative money, let's go back to the time of bartering. Before money was invented, bartering was the main way to exchange goods. An individual who had something of value, such as some grain, could directly exchange the grain for another item, which was seen to have an equivalent value, like a small animal, or a tool. <u>The seller of the grain, of course, had to find someone who wanted to buy it</u> and who could offer in return something the seller wanted to buy. There was no common medium of exchange such as money into which both seller and buyer could convert the commodities they wanted to trade.

So, the first stage in the evolution of money was commodity money. This involved accepting objects or commodities, such as grain or metals or animals, as being inherently <u>valuable</u> so they could be used as a common standard of measure and unit of exchange. People could accept any of these objects as money because they had inherent use value for every individual. … And, therefore, they would be widely accepted by other people.

All metals were accepted because they could be easily converted into precious tools, for instance, <u>axes and spades</u>. Metals such as gold and silver also had secondary advantages. They were also easy to identify and <u>visually attractive</u>. Gold, silver, copper as well as other usable objects such as salt and peppercorns are categorised as commodity money, since they combine the attributes both of a usable commodity and a symbol.

So people accepted foods and metals as money because they were sure of their value to themselves and to other people.

....

Then came metal coins, which were another step in the evolution from usable commodities such as grains to … symbolic forms of money. Metal had a use value of its own, but coins became accepted in trade for their symbolic value. They acted as a <u>standard measure</u> for exchanging other goods and services of value rather than for the use of the metal they contained.

The next stage in the evolution of money is that of representative money. Representative money is symbolic money that is based on useful commodities, such as the warehouse receipts issued by the ancient Egyptian grain banks, and more recent forms of paper currency that were backed by gold or silver. The adoption of representative money was a <u>significant evolution</u> in human consciousness. Psychologically, the individual had to transfer the sense of value from a usable material object to an <u>abstract</u> symbol. Socially, groups of people had to agree on the common usage of the same symbol.

The invention of representative money then had a profound effect on the evolution of both money and society and …

Sample answer sheets

BRITISH COUNCIL

idp IELTS AUSTRALIA

CAMBRIDGE ENGLISH Language Assessment
Part of the University of Cambridge

IELTS Listening and Reading Answer Sheet

Centre number:

Pencil must be used to complete this sheet.

0 1 2 3 4 5 6 7 8 9
0 1 2 3 4 5 6 7 8 9
0 1 2 3 4 5 6 7 8 9
0 1 2 3 4 5 6 7 8 9
0 1 2 3 4 5 6 7 8 9
0 1 2 3 4 5 6 7 8 9

Please write your **full name** in CAPITAL letters on the line below:

_____

Then write your six digit Candidate number in the boxes and shade the number in the grid on the right.

Test date (shade ONE box for the day, ONE box for the month and ONE box for the year):

Day: 01 02 03 04 05 06 07 08 09 10 11 12 13 14 15 16 17 18 19 20 21 22 23 24 25 26 27 28 29 30 31

Month: 01 02 03 04 05 06 07 08 09 10 11 12   **Year** (last 2 digits): 13 14 15 16 17 18 19 20 21

Listening	Marker use only	Listening	Marker use only
1	✓ 1 ✗	21	✓ 21 ✗
2	✓ 2 ✗	22	✓ 22 ✗
3	✓ 3 ✗	23	✓ 23 ✗
4	✓ 4 ✗	24	✓ 24 ✗
5	✓ 5 ✗	25	✓ 25 ✗
6	✓ 6 ✗	26	✓ 26 ✗
7	✓ 7 ✗	27	✓ 27 ✗
8	✓ 8 ✗	28	✓ 28 ✗
9	✓ 9 ✗	29	✓ 29 ✗
10	✓ 10 ✗	30	✓ 30 ✗
11	✓ 11 ✗	31	✓ 31 ✗
12	✓ 12 ✗	32	✓ 32 ✗
13	✓ 13 ✗	33	✓ 33 ✗
14	✓ 14 ✗	34	✓ 34 ✗
15	✓ 15 ✗	35	✓ 35 ✗
16	✓ 16 ✗	36	✓ 36 ✗
17	✓ 17 ✗	37	✓ 37 ✗
18	✓ 18 ✗	38	✓ 38 ✗
19	✓ 19 ✗	39	✓ 39 ✗
20	✓ 20 ✗	40	✓ 40 ✗

Marker 2 Signature

Marker 1 Signature

Listening Total

IELTS L-R v1.0

denote Print Limited 0121 520 5100

DP787/394

Please write your **full name** in CAPITAL letters on the line below:

_____

Please write your Candidate number on the line below:

_____

Please write your three digit language code
in the boxes and shade the numbers in the
grid on the right.

0 1 2 3 4 5 6 7 8 9
0 1 2 3 4 5 6 7 8 9
0 1 2 3 4 5 6 7 8 9

Are you: Female? ▭   Male? ▭

Reading   Reading   Reading   Reading   Reading   Reading

Module taken (shade one box):   Academic ▭   General Training ▭

	Marker use only			Marker use only
1	✓ 1 ✗	21		✓ 21 ✗
2	✓ 2 ✗	22		✓ 22 ✗
3	✓ 3 ✗	23		✓ 23 ✗
4	✓ 4 ✗	24		✓ 24 ✗
5	✓ 5 ✗	25		✓ 25 ✗
6	✓ 6 ✗	26		✓ 26 ✗
7	✓ 7 ✗	27		✓ 27 ✗
8	✓ 8 ✗	28		✓ 28 ✗
9	✓ 9 ✗	29		✓ 29 ✗
10	✓ 10 ✗	30		✓ 30 ✗
11	✓ 11 ✗	31		✓ 31 ✗
12	✓ 12 ✗	32		✓ 32 ✗
13	✓ 13 ✗	33		✓ 33 ✗
14	✓ 14 ✗	34		✓ 34 ✗
15	✓ 15 ✗	35		✓ 35 ✗
16	✓ 16 ✗	36		✓ 36 ✗
17	✓ 17 ✗	37		✓ 37 ✗
18	✓ 18 ✗	38		✓ 38 ✗
19	✓ 19 ✗	39		✓ 39 ✗
20	✓ 20 ✗	40		✓ 40 ✗

Marker 2 Signature		Marker 1 Signature		Reading Total	

Macmillan Education Limited
4 Crinan Street
London N1 9XW
Companies and representatives throughout the world

ISBN 978-0-230-49568-5 (with Answers)
ISBN 978-1-786-32864-9 (without Answers)

Text © Sam McCarter 2017
Design and illustration © Macmillan Education Limited 2017

This edition published 2017
First edition published 2010

Designed by xen
Illustrated by Oxford Designers & Illustrators pp47, 76, 80, 207; xen pp135, 145.
Cover design by Macmillan Education Ltd
Cover photograph by Getty Images/Ascent/PKS Media Inc
Picture research by Julie-anne Wilce

Author's acknowledgements
Sam McCarter would like to thank his students at Reache North West. He would also like to say thank you to the team at Macmillan for their expertise and patience, and to everyone who has contributed to this publication directly or indirectly.

The publishers would like to thank Adrian Cini, Ben Crawford, Sarah Emsden-Bonfanti, Karen Gundersen, Mark Harrison, Nareene Kaloyan, April Pugh, Suzannah Redmond, John Smith, Wayne Smith and Rhona Snelling.

The author and publishers would like to thank the following for permission to reproduce their photographs:
123rf dolgachov p10(bl); **Alamy** David Chapman p30(2), Peter Cripps p88(b), Eye Ubiquitous p182(3), Granger Historical Picture Archive p85(t), John Warburton-Lee Photography p116(2), ton koene p152(1), Gunta Podina p140(2), Stocktrek Images, Inc p60(1), nik wheeler p167(bl), World History Archive p106(c); **Ancient Art & Architecture Collection** C M Dixon p23(t); **Getty Images** John W Banagan p172(c), Matt Bird p60(2), Blend Images/KidStock p92(4), Blue Jean Images p179(cr), Camille Tokerud Photography Inc. p152(4), Melinda Chan p164(2), Clive Rees Photography p77(4), ColorBlind Images p92(3), Jason Colston p186(t), De Agostini/E. Lessing p140(5), Steve Debenport p6(2),Danita Delimont pp72,194(3),(1), Devrimb p116(1), Daniela Dirscherl p170(t), Dreamnikon p18(2), Marc Dufresne p77(2), Chad Ehlers p72(1), Cordelia Ewerth p44(t), EyeEm/Muslianshah Masrie p116(3), Michele Falzone p169(cr), Andrew Findlay pp50,51(t),(t), Mitchell Funk p86(b), Fuse p160(bl), Christopher Futcher p10(br), Martin Gray p169(tl), Gremlin p62(t), Guerilla p176(bl), Bartosz Hadyniak p153(b), Hero Images pp6,97,194(3),(br),(4), Highwaystarz-Photography p92(2), Seth K. Hughes p38(b), BAY ISMOYO p48(3), Jamesteohart p182(2), Karen Kasmauski p48(2), TARIK KIZILKAYA p15(t), Loop Images p89(t), Brianna May p122(r), Mediaphotos p94(c), Massimo Merlini p140(1), Momentimages p198(cl), Monkeybusinessimages pp53,101(t),(t), Jean Luc Morales p196(r), Gianluca D'Auri Muscelli p104(2), Liam Norris p140(3), Ignacio Palacios p164(1), Adrian Peacock p48(1), David Pedre p164(3), David Pickford p99(t), Robert Harding/Michael Runkel p194(3), Chad Slattery p35(tr), Bob Stefko p77(1), Keren Su p182(1), Manuel Sulzer p6(1), Superb Images p176(br), Tetra Images/Rob Lewine p152(3), Peter Unger p116(5), Betsie Van Der Meer p194(2), VCG/Corbis/Igor Emmerich p158(t), Klaus Vedfelt p34(tl), VisitBritain/Ben Selway p34(tr), Dougal Waters p140(4), AJ Watt p6(4), Thomas Winz p125(b), marco wong p189(bl), www.infinitahighway. com.br p116(4); **Macmillan Education Ltd** Corbis pp77,104(3),(3), Getty Images/Hemera/Thinkstock/Kwanjai Mueanyaem p108(b), Getty Images/iStock/ Thinkstock p72(2), Getty Images/iStock/Thinkstock/Brian Jackson p27, Getty Images/iStock/Thinkstock/Oleksiy Mark p18(4), Getty/iStock/Thinkstock/maki sasaki p169(tr), Getty Images/iStock/Thinkstock/ sunstock p25, Getty Images/ iStock/Thinkstock/Catherine Yeulet p160(br), PIXTAL p119(tr), STOCKBYTE p18(1); **National Gallery of Australia**/Fiona Hall p143; **Shutterstock** Amble Design p9(2), George Dolgikh p177(c), Sergio Gutierrez Getino p123(tr), Viktor Gladkov p18(3), risteski goce p73(c), goodluz p92(1), image Source Trading Ltd p201(bl), Dmitry Kalinovsky p180(c), Iurii p60(3), Monkey Business Images pp9,152(1),(2), Alta Oosthuizen p18(5), Scanrail p104(1), Artur Synenko p72(4).

The author and publishers are grateful for permission to reprint the following copyright material:
pp35–36 Abridged extract from 'Why exactly is this ride so thrilling?' by Roger Highfield, copyright © Telegraph Media Group Ltd 2006. First published in *The Daily Telegraph* 03.10.06. Reprinted by permission of the publisher; pp65–66 Abridged extract from 'Back to the Future Day: Six experts predict life in 2045' by James Titcomb and Madhumita Murgia, copyright © Telegraph Media Group Ltd 2015. First published in *The Daily Telegraph* 21.10.15. Reprinted by permission of the publisher; p38 Data from the table '3.4 Participants (a), Selected sports and physical recreation activities (b) – by sex – 2011-2012', Australian Bureau of Statistics, Participation in Sport and Physical Recreation, Australia, 2011-2012 (cat no. 4177.0), ABS. Licensed under the Creative Commons Licence, attribution 2.5 Australia (CC BY 2.5 AU) http://creativecommons.org/licenses/by/2.5/au/; pp52–53 Extract from 'Is there REALLY a skills shortage in the engineering industry, or are employers just not paying up' by Georgina Bloomfield 21.01.15., copyright © 2015-2016 The Institute of Engineering and Technology. Reprinted with permission of the publisher;

pp94–95 Adapted material from 'Why People Thrive in Coworking Spaces' by Gretchen Spreitzer, Peter Bacevice and Lyndon Garrett. Harvard Business Review, September 2015 (pp28, 30); pp11–12 Statistical data from 'Teens, Technology and Friendships' by Amanda Lenhart 06.08.16, copyright ©2016 Pew Research Center; p14 Statistical data from the graph '% of online adults who say they use the following social media platform, by year' in the article *'Pinterest and Instagram Usage Doubles Since 2012, Growth on Other Platforms is Slower'*, Pew Research Center Survey, March 17 – April 12, 2015, copyright ©2016 Pew Research Center; p206 Statistical data from 'Spring Tracking Survey, April 17-May 19 2003', *Internet & American Life Project Tracking Surveys 2010-2013*, copyright ©2016 Pew Research Center; p68 Data from 'Bloomberg New Energy Finance predicts renewable will be 55% of 2030's $7.7 trillion power investment' by HoundDog 08.08.14, copyright © Kos Media LLC; pp119–120 Abridged material from 'Giles Gilbert Scott: Architect (1880-1960).' Courtesy of the Design Museum © 2015. Reprinted with permission; p23 Material excerpted from 'Shang and Zhou Dynasties: The Bronze Age of China' in *Heilbrunn Timeline of Art History*, copyright © 2000-2016 by The Metropolitan Museum of Art, New York. Reprinted with permission; p237 Material from the article 'Social and Psychological Value of Money', www.mssresearch.org. Reprinted with permission of Mother's Service Society; pp143–144 Abridged material from 'Collections: Sculpture Garden: Fiona Hall fern garden' by Harijs Piekains. Essay published in the National Gallery of Australia's *Building the Collection* publication 2003 p337-337, and at http://nga.gov.au/sculpturegarden/fern.cfm, copyright © 2016 National Gallery of Australia, Canberra. All rights reserved. Reprinted by permission of the publisher; pp87–89 Extract from 'Earth in Our Hands – Coastal Erosion' by Cally Oldershaw, published by The Geological Society of London and available at www.geolsoc.org.uk. Copyright © The Geological Society of London. Reprinted with permission; pp73–74 Abridged material from *'Olea europaea (olive)'*, http://www.kew.org/science-conservation/plants-fungi/olea-europea-olive, copyright © Board of Trustees of the Royal Botanic Gardens, Kew. Reprinted with permission of Kew Royal Botanic Gardens; pp153–154 Material from 'Culture and Customs of Mozambique' by George O. Ndege (Greenwood Publishing Group, 2007), copyright © George O. Ndege 2007. Republished by permission of ABC CLIO Inc. Permission conveyed through Copyright Clearance Center, Inc; pp170–171 Excerpt from 'The Great Barrier Reef', www.environment.gov.au, copyright © Commonwealth of Australia. Licensed under the Creative Commons License, attribution 3.0 Australia (CC BY 3.0 Australia) https://creativecommons.org/licenses/by/3.0/au/deed.en; pp186–187 Adapted material from 'Bicycling for Transportation and Health: The Role of Infrastructure' by Jennifer Dill, *Journal of Public Health Policy* (2009) 30: S95, copyright © 2016 Springer International Publishing. Part of Springer Nature. Reprinted with permission of the publisher; p85 Extract from 'Xia Dynasty, Bronze Age China c2000-771 BCE' from *The Golden Age of Chinese Archaeology*, Part Two p12, by Brian Hogarth, Director of Education, Asian Art Museum of San Francisco, with Carla Benner, National Gallery of Art, Washington. http://www.nga.gov/content/dam/ngaweb/Education/learning-resources/teaching-packets/pdfs/Chinese-Archaeology-tp.pdf. Copyright© 1999 Board of Trustees, National Gallery of Art, Washington. Reprinted by permission of the National Gallery of Art; pp129, 130 Data from Figures 1.13 and 1.5 in the report 'Monitoring e-commerce, 2014', published by the Office for National Statistics 07.08.14, ©Crown copyright 2014. Contains public sector information licensed under the Open Government Licence v3.0. http://www.nationalarchives.gov.uk/doc/open-government-licence/version/3/; p131 Data from Figure 6 in the paper 'Characteristics of Home Workers, 2014', published by the Office for National Statistics 04.06.14, © Crown copyright 2014. Contains public sector information licensed under the Open Government Licence v3.0. http://www.nationalarchives.gov.uk/doc/open-government-licence/version/3/; pp190, 208 Adapted data from the article 'Travel Trends, 2013, published by the Office for National Statistics 08.05.14, © Crown copyright 2014. Contains public sector information licensed under the Open Government Licence v3.0. http://www.nationalarchives.gov.uk/doc/open-government-licence/version/3/; p206 Data from Table 8.1: *Sports participation by sex, 2005/06 to 2008/09* in the survey 'Adult participation in sport'. Commissioned by the Department for Culture, Media and Sport, and published on 26.09.13, ©Crown copyright 2013. Contains public sector information licensed under the Open Government Licence v3.0. http://www.nationalarchives.gov.uk/doc/open-government-licence/version/3/; pp198–199 Extract from 'Measuring Subjective Wellbeing in the UK', Working Paper, September 2010. Published by the Office for National Statistics, © Crown copyright 2010. Reprinted with the permission of the Office of Public Sector Information (OPSI). Contains public sector information licensed under the Open Government Licence v3.0. http://www.nationalarchives.gov.uk/doc/open-government-licence/version/3/; p206 Data from Table 1: *Production of cereals by country, 2014*, in the article 'Agricultural Production – crops', copyright © European Union 1995-2013 and published by 'Eurostat: Statistics Explained'. Reproduction is authorised under the Commission Decision of 12th December 2011 (2011/833/EU); pp202, 209 Data from Figure 19: *Frequency of being happy in the last 4 weeks, by age group, EU-28, 2013 (% of population)* and Figure 21: *Frequency of being happy in the last 4 weeks, by labour status, EU-28, 2013 (% of population)* in the article 'Quality of Life in Europe – facts and views – overall life satisfaction', copyright © European Union 1995-2013 and published by 'Eurostat: Statistics Explained'. Reproduction is authorised under the Commission Decision of 12th December 2011 (2011/833/EU); p207 Pie charts, whose data is generated from the International Futures (IFs) modelling system, version 7.00. IFs was initially developed by Barry B. Hughes and is based at the Frederick S. Pardee Center for International Futures, Josef Korbel School of International Studies, University of Denver, www.ifs.du.edu; Sample IELTS Listening and Reading Answer Sheet. Reproduced with permission of Cambridge English Language Assessment © UCLES 2016.
These materials may contain links for third party websites. We have no control over, and are not responsible for, the contents of such third party websites. Please use care when accessing them.

Printed and bound in Spain

2026 2025 2024 2023 2022
21 20 19 18 17 16 15 14 13